*Behavioral
Ecology*

Contemporary Thought in Ecological Science Series

Arthur S. Boughey/Editor

Lowell Adams	Population Ecology
Peter H. Klopfer	Behavioral Ecology
Herbert P. Riley	Evolutionary Ecology

Dickenson Series in Biology

Elof Axel Carlson/Consulting Editor

Donald J. Reish	Biology of the Oceans
Kenneth E. Maxwell	Chemicals and Life
Arthur S. Boughey	Contemporary Readings in Ecology

Contemporary Thought in Biological Science Series

Elof Axel Carlson/Consulting Editor

Bruce H. Carpenter	Molecular and Cell Biology
Edward Glassman	Molecular Approaches to Psychobiology
Elof A. Carlson	Gene Theory
J. Richard Whittaker	Cellular Differentiation
Arthur S. Boughey	Population and Environmental Biology
J. Eugene Fox	Molecular Control of Plant Growth
Rodolfo Ruibal	The Adaptations of Organisms

Peter H. Klopfer / Behavioral
DUKE UNIVERSITY Ecology

Dickenson Publishing Company, Inc., Belmont, California

Contents

Foreword

The science of ecology has vital implications for the many urgent problems which now beset us. Yet there is a dearth of readily accessible ecological information. While the ecosystem approach has provided a new direction and a new unity to the discipline, published information on the various aspects of ecology is still widely scattered through a great range of scientific publications.

Each volume in the series on CONTEMPORARY THOUGHT IN ECOLOGICAL SCIENCE gathers relevant material which presents current progress and contemporary ideas in some particular field of ecology. The various selections are carefully chosen to present to the teacher and student alike a deeper insight into both the problems and conclusions of recent research. Each collection of readings illustrates the direction of investigations and the modern concepts within the major interrelated fields which comprise the science of ecology.

The readings are intended for use in upper division and graduate courses in ecology. Collectively the series demonstrates the essential unity of modern ecology and establishes the fact that it is not an isolated discipline, but extends into all aspects of biology. Individual readings also illustrate the creative manner in which ecological advances are achieved and provide examples of how independent observations come to be incorporated in general concepts. The range of readings material emphasizes the growing realization that if we are to survive on this planet, our approach in the next millennium will have to be based on established ecological principles.

Arthur S. Boughey
Series Editor

Preface

Few tasks require so many compromises as that of assembling a book of readings. First of all, one must decide what purpose it is to serve. This is relatively simple, and my purpose in preparing this text can be easily stated: to make available within the confines of a single, slender volume studies representative of the field of behavioral ecology. Such a volume is expected to serve students whose opportunities for unrestricted browsing in well-stocked libraries are limited. But then come the problems: Where are the boundaries for so diffuse a field as behavioral ecology to be drawn? Are studies of hormonal mechanisms in population control to be included? The control mechanisms they discuss are behaviorally mediated. I have arbitrarily excluded them here, consigning them to a future volume on physiological ecology. Obviously, the editor of this later volume could as cogently argue that these studies belong here. My only defense will then be, "I assembled my volume before you did yours," and I freely admit to the weakness of the response.

Even with the field defined, other arbitrary decisions are demanded. For economic reasons, the size of this volume must be limited to about 50,000 words. Whose paper shall be chosen to represent studies of habitat selection? The "best" paper? Best by what criterion? Most conventional or representative? Most unique? The first major study (even though supplanted by others)? The most recent (though less complete than its predecessors)? And when some consistent, though arbitrary, rationale for selection is seized upon, how is this to be adjusted when the "sole satisfactory study" is copyrighted and the request for a waiver is denied? In this connection, let me give a prominent and grateful "thank you" to *The American Naturalist*, Arizona State University, Tempe, Arizona; *Animal Behaviour*, Baillière, Tindall & Cassell, Ltd., London, England; *Archives Néerlandaises de Zoologie*, Laboratoire de Zoologie, Pays-Bas, Netherlands; *The Auk*, The American Ornithologists' Union, Anchorage, Kentucky; *Behavior*, E. J. Brill, Leiden, Netherlands; *Ecological Monographs*, Duke University Press, Durham, N. C.; *Proceedings, XV International Congress of Zoology*, The Linnean Society of London, London, England; *Science*, American Association for the Advancement of Science, Washington, D. C.; *The Wilson Bulletin*, Wilson Ornithological Society, Morgantown, West Virginia; and *Zoologica*, New York Zoological Society, Bronx, N. Y., for having made this collection possible. Their specific contributions are acknowledged below.

This collection represents papers that I personally enjoyed, that my students have found profitable, and that illustrate the major themes I sought to trace in my first book, *Behavioral Aspects of Ecology* (Prentice-Hall, 1962; revised and translated in 1962 as *Ökologie und Verhalten*, Fischer-Verlag). I am certain it will prove enjoyable and profitable reading to others, just as I am certain that there are other articles equally as commendable as the ones presented here. (The authors represented in this volume will surely recognize this as in no way slighting their contributions.)

Finally, for a more complete and systematic bibliography than that presented here or in *Behavioral Aspects of Ecology*, I would refer you to Marler and Hamilton's *Physiological Mechanisms of Behavior* (John Wiley & Sons, 1967) or Klopfer and Hailman's *An Introduction to Animal Behavior: Ethology's First Century* (Prentice-Hall, 1967).

I am grateful to Diane Whitley and Catherine Dewey for their efforts in behalf of this volume; support for my research has been from the National Institutes of Health.

Durham, N. C.   PETER H. KLOPFER

1 / Individuals and Their Environments

There are two major questions that must be posed when one examines the reasons underlying the close association between particular animals and particular habitats: first, what is the ultimate, historical, or evolutionary cause of this association; and second, what is the proximate, immediate, or onto-genetic cause? For insights into the former, the classical papers of ecology are to be recommended; a recent summary and bibliography are available in P. H. Klopfer's *Habitats and Territories: A Discourse on the Use of Space by Animals* (1969, Basic Books). The latter problem is the one that concerns us here. What constrains the offspring in a particular lineage to continue to select the same habitat as their forbears?

The answer to this query, to be complete, requires some knowledge of the sensory and perceptual world, or *Umwelt*, of the animal in question. Such information is generally provided by the sensory physiologist. It also requires analytic studies of the response patterns of animals in simplified environments, only a few components of which are modified at a time. Finally, it requires longitudinal studies aimed at fixing the time course over which habitat preferences and their associated behavior are established. These will also provide information on the stability or rigidity of preferences, a matter of no small importance to ecology. (See P. H. Klopfer and J. P. Hailman, "Habitat Selection in Birds," in *Advances in the Study of Behavior*, Vol. 1, edited by D. S. Lehrman, R. A. Hinde, and E. Shaw, Academic Press, 1965.) The papers presented in this chapter illustrate studies directed, to one degree or another, to all of these requirements. The last paper in the section introduces the subject of migration, a pattern of behavior which can be viewed as providing an unchanged habitat in a changing world. The further question of the stimuli that initiate migration is not treated here. S. C. Kendeigh, G. C. West, and G. W. Cox, in their "Annual Stimulus for Spring Migration in Birds" (*Animal Behaviour 8:* 180–185, 1960), provide a review and bibliography of this topic.

The Role of Early Experience in Habitat Selection by the Prairie Deer Mouse, *Peromyscus maniculatus bairdi*

Stanley C. Wecker

Introduction

Despite the passage of time on a geologic scale, relatively few animal species have achieved a truly cosmopolitan distribution. Tolerance limits, evolutionary history, and geographic barriers have interacted to limit the majority to more or less well defined ranges.

Moreover, even within the confines of these geographic boundaries, random or uniform patterns of dispersion are the exception rather than the rule. Over a broad area, local populations of a species tend to be restricted in distribution by their behavioral and physiological responses to the environment. These reactions result in the occupation of suitable habitats, although not all of the potentially habitable areas occurring within the geographic range may be utilized at any given time. Both capacity for dispersal and internal population pressure are important factors in determining the extent to which a species occupies the more favorable portions of its environment.

It follows that animals with restricted ecological requirements must possess efficient mechanisms which enable them to locate their optimal habitat. The methods by which they accomplish this, however, are so numerous and varied that it is difficult to make meaningful generalizations concerning habitat selection.

On the one hand, many small organisms of otherwise low vagility have evolved the means to utilize natural agencies such as currents of air and water in promoting the dispersal of their species (Wolfenbarger, 1946). The ultimate result of this passive and essentially random dissemination of individuals is that a small percentage eventually reach environments conducive to continued survival and reproduction.

For the majority of animals, on the other hand, habitat selection is a more active process. This does not imply that individuals of most species make a critical evaluation of the entire constellation of factors confronting them. More probably, only an automatic reaction to certain key aspects of the environment is involved.

In some groups, habitat selection may be the result of a tactic or kinetic response to a particular physico-chemical gradient in the environment (Andrewartha and Birch, 1954: p. 220). While such stimuli may lead an animal

Reprinted by permission of the author and the publisher from *Ecological Monographs* **33**: 307–325, 1963.

to avoid the wrong habitat, these usually act as warning signals and are not in themselves injurious (Elton, 1927).

An apparently more complex form of stereotyped behavior is involved in the choice of oviposition sites by many insects. In certain beetles, butterflies, and wasps, the gravid female demonstrates an innate capacity to select plant or animal hosts that will satisfy the requirements of the developing larvae. This is carried out whether or not these requirements happen to coincide with her own (Andrewartha and Birch, *op. cit.*: p. 522).

Not all of the responses leading to selection of habitat appear to be entirely adaptive, however. The absence of certain specific environmental cues may account for the exclusion of a species from apparently suitable areas within its geographic range. Lack (1933) concluded that a bird's choice of habitat is frequently based on certain conspicuous features of the environment. These often showed little correlation with the essential physiological requirements of the species.

In shrub and forest dwelling birds, habitat occupation has been associated with the height, spacing, and life form of the vegetation, and with the presence of suitable song perches (Lack, 1933; Kendeigh, 1945; Gullion, 1960). Pitelka (1941) concluded that the distribution of birds in relation to certain biotic communities was influenced more by the structure of the dominant vegetation than by the species composition of the stands.

Apparently, a bird's behavioral response to various structural cues presented by its environment may provide the basis for the occupation of favorable habitats. This has been referred to as the "psychological factor" in habitat selection by Lack (*op. cit.*), and may be fully as important in explaining habitat preferences as stimuli more directly related to the physiological tolerance limits of the species. It is possible, however, that many apparently "psychological" factors could be explained in physiological terms if more precise information were available.

Other ecologists have been interested in the analysis of the physical and biotic factors which cause mammals to occupy certain habitats and avoid others (Grinnell, 1917; Dice, 1922; Johnson, 1926; Hooper, 1942; Odum, 1944; Harris, 1952; Pruitt, 1953; Brand, 1955; Getz, 1961). As in birds, high vagility, homoiothermism, and sociality make it unlikely that the distribution of these animals is limited solely by physico-chemical factors. There is little information, however, concerning the role of psychological factors in mammalian habitat selection.

Because they are widely distributed, readily trapped, and easily handled, rodents and lagomorphs have been the most frequent subjects for ecological investigation. Mice of the genus *Peromyscus* are especially well suited for study, as these small animals occupy a number of diverse environments throughout North and Central America. One or more of the 55 named species occurs in almost every part of this region (Blair, 1950). Within the more widely ranging groups, subspecific differences in habitat preference are common.

Peromyscus maniculatus, the deer mouse, is one of the most variable North American rodents, 66 subspecies having been described within its geographic range (Hall and Kelson, 1959). These are divided into two ecologically adapted types: the long-tailed, long-eared forest form, and the smaller, short-tailed, short-eared grassland form.

The prairie deer mouse, *Peromyscus maniculatus bairdi*, is a field-inhabiting subspecies that avoids forested areas—even those with a grassy herbaceous stratum (Dice, 1925; Blair, 1940; Howard, 1949). Moreover, the catch of these animals diminishes sharply as trap lines approach woody or brushy field borders (Harris, 1952).

Studies comparing food preferences (Cogshall, 1928; Williams, 1959) and temperature requirements (Stinson and Fischer, 1953) of grassland and forest forms of *Peromyscus* have not revealed differences of sufficient magnitude to account for the observed habitat restrictions. During an investigation of the factors influencing prairie deer mouse distribution, Dice (1922) found the animals fully able to tolerate simulated forest conditions in the laboratory. He concluded, therefore, that this subspecies' absence from forested areas within its range was primarily a behavioral response.

In an effort to evaluate some of the environmental cues involved in habitat selection by these small mammals, Harris (*op. cit.*) presented individual prairie deer mice, *Peromyscus maniculatus bairdi*, and woodland deer mice, *P. m. gracilis*, with a choice between an artificial "woods" and an artificial "field" in the laboratory. His data revealed that the animals exhibited a preference for the artificial habitat more closely resembling the natural environment of their own subspecies. Since the physical conditions were essentially uniform throughout the experimental room, Harris concluded that the mice were reacting to the form of the artificial vegetation. While *P. m. bairdi* was seemingly attracted to the "field", a negative reaction to the "woods" may also have been involved. The apparent avoidance of trees and shrubs by wild populations of this subspecies lends support to this hypothesis.

A question now arises concerning the underlying nature of the response which ultimately leads *bairdi* to select the field habitat. Since laboratory-reared animals with no outdoor experience chose the artificial "field" as readily as their wild counterparts, Harris concluded that this behavior had a genetic basis. But his experiment was not designed to investigate the possibility that learning might also be involved in habitat selection.

It has been established that early experience can play an important part in the development of adult behavioral characteristics (King, 1956, 1957; King and Eleftheriou, 1959; Scott, 1962). Moreover, there is often a critical period during which such experience must be realized if conditioning is to occur (Tinbergen, 1961). Lorenz (1937) discovered that the social behavior of young goslings was irreversibly determined during a critical period occurring shortly after hatching. He called this type of rapid and rigid conditioning "imprinting."

Thorpe (1945) extended these ideas in an attempt to explain the restriction of most animal species to specific habitats. Presumably, an individual's early experience in a particular environment will determine its subsequent preferences. Thorpe termed this phenomenon "habitat imprinting." The hypothesis has experimental support in both the changed habitat preference of adult *Drosophila melanogaster* and the modified host specificity of *Nemeritis canescens* after controlled conditioning of the larvae (Thorpe, 1939, 1940).

Since young prairie deer mice are normally born and reared under field conditions, one would expect their early experience to reinforce any hereditary response to habitat. If it could be demonstrated empirically that conditioning of this type actually plays a role in habitat selection, two interesting questions would arise:

(1) Is such experience, in itself, sufficient to bring about selection of the field habitat?

(2) Can the innate response normally resulting in a preference for field conditions be overridden if an animal is given early experience in a different environment?

The answers, if ascertained, could have considerable evolutionary significance, as they are directly related to the problem of ecological segregation.

I wish to express my deep appreciation to the many people who aided me in the course of this study. Paul Spradlin, Ronald Miscisin, Lawrence Camburn, and Lee R. Dice furnished invaluable technical assistance during the designing and construction of the experimental apparatus. David Rasmussen and Elizabeth Barto of the University of Michigan's Mammalian Genetics Center supplied most of the animals used.

The Edwin S. George Reserve Committee provided facilities for field work, living quarters, several grants-in-aid, and a stipend for the purchase of equipment and construction materials. The Department of Zoology also contributed funds to defray the cost of the latter. In addition, I wish to acknowledge the Horace H. Rackham School of Graduate Studies which furnished money for field travel, and the receipt of a National Science Foundation Cooperative Fellowship for the 1958–1959 academic year.

William H. Burt, Morris Foster, John A. King, Frederick E. Smith, and Warren H. Wagner read and criticized this manuscript in various stages of its preparation. Most of all, however, I am indebted to my doctoral chairman, Francis C. Evans, without whose advice, encouragement, and stimulating criticism this work would not have been successfully consummated.

Methods and Materials

The Study Area

The study was conducted on the Edwin S. George Reserve of the University of Michigan, located in southern Livingston County, three miles west of Pinckney, Michigan. The property, enclosed by a game fence, consisted of 1268 acres of rough, glaciated terrain. Oak-hickory woodlots cover about one-fourth of the area. These are flanked by abandoned fields, swamps, and marshes.

Before its establishment by Colonel Edwin S. George in 1927, the Reserve comprised several small farms. By the early years of the twentieth century, however, depletion of the soil had already rendered most of the fields unsuitable for cultivation. Following the decline in value of the farmland, there was some utilization of the woodlots and marshes for pasturage, with occasional cutting of timber and harvesting of marsh hay (Rogers, 1942).

Col. George presented the Reserve to the University of Michigan in 1930. It has remained relatively undisturbed since, although browsing by a controlled herd of 50–60 deer probably has retarded the extension of the forested tracts.

The area selected as the site for this study (K-9 on 1950 Reserve grid map) is characterized by a relatively sharp boundary between one of the woodlots and an adjacent field. The former is a relatively open stand of second growth oak-hickory forest, dominated by black oak (*Quercus velutina*), white oak (*Q. alba*), shagbark hickory (*Carya ovata*), and sweet pignut (*C. ovalis*). There is a well developed understory of wild cherry (*Prunus serotina*) and sassafras (*Sassafras albidum*), with the latter particularly concentrated at the woods' edges. Bracken (*Pteridium aquilinum*), a goldenrod (*Solidago juncea*), Kentucky bluegrass (*Poa pratensis*), a sedge (*Carex pensylvanica*) and various tree seedlings constitute the important components of the herbaceous stratum. A well developed accumulation of leaf litter is present.

The adjacent grassland is a typical sterile old field of a variety commonly found in southeastern Michigan. Detailed descriptions of this community type on the George Reserve have been published by Blair (1940) and Evans and Dahl (1955). In terms of both cover and abundance, Canada bluegrass (*Poa compressa*) and goldenrod (*Solidago juncea*) are the dominant species, although scattered clones of *Rubus flagellaris* cover a considerable area. An extremely dense growth of Kentucky bluegrass (*P. pratensis*) occupies most of the depressions. On the elevated portions dominated by *P. compressa* there are often small patches of bare soil.

Description of the Experimental Enclosure

To facilitate the study of habitat selection by prairie deer mice, I constructed a large rectangular pen (100 × 16 feet) with its long axis perpendicular to the woods-field boundary. The enclosure was situated so that half lay within the woods, half within the field (Fig. 1). It was assembled by stapling sheets of one-third inch hardware cloth to a previously erected wooden framework.

A series of partitions parallel to the habitat border subdivided the enclosure into ten equal compartments (Fig. 2). To determine the vegetational structure within, a complete list of the vascular plants was first compiled. The per cent cover contributed by each species was then estimated, using the following ten point scale (slightly modified from Evans and Dahl, 1955):

Fig. 1. The field (above) and woods (below) aspects of the experimental enclosure. The metal bands were attached to the trees to discourage climbing by the mice. Note the relatively sharp boundary between the two habitats (May, 1961. J. Alley).

+ = occurring as a single individual with reduced vigor; no measurable cover.
1 = occurring as one or two individuals; no measurable cover.
2 = occurring as several individuals; no measurable cover.
3 = cover less than 4 per cent of the total area.
4 = cover 4 to 10 per cent of the total area.
5 = cover 11 to 25 per cent of the total area.
6 = cover 26 to 33 per cent of the total area.
7 = cover 34 to 50 per cent of the total area.
8 = cover 51 to 75 per cent of the total area.
9 = cover 76 to 90 per cent of the total area.
10 = cover 91 per cent to complete.

Of the 48 species listed, only 11 were common to both the woods and the field (Table 1). Even in these cases, however, the cover values were usually considerably higher on one side of the boundary than on the other. The data, therefore, confirm the existence of two highly contrasting habitat types within

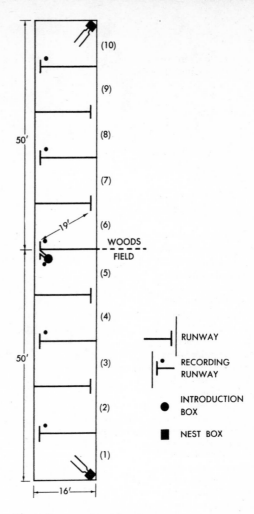

Fig. 2. The experimental enclosure.

the experimental enclosure. These will subsequently be referred to as "woods" and "field" respectively.

During the course of the study there was some tendency for leaf litter and small tree seedlings to accumulate in the field compartments bordering the woods. It was therefore necessary to maintain the sharpness of the habitat boundary by occasional raking and cutting.

Both the sides of the enclosure and the sub-dividing partitions were 28 inches high. An 18-inch strip of galvanized sheet metal nailed at right angles to the top of these walls precluded both escape and ingress of animals from this direction. Climbing by the mice was also discouraged by placing a wide

TABLE 1(a)

Cover estimates of plant species in compartments of the experimental enclosure. The scale (see text) is slightly modified from Evans and Dahl (1955).

Species	Compartments									
	(Field) 1 2 3 4 5					(Woods) 6 7 8 9 10				
Herbaceous stratum										
Anemone cylindrica Gray	3	3	.	.	.	.	.	.	.	.
Lactuca sp.	3	3	.	.	.	.	.	.	.	.
Rumex acetosella L.	.	3	3	.	.	.	.	.	.	.
Lespedeza capitata Michx.	.	3	3	.	.	.	.	.	.	.
Helianthemum sp.	.	2	1	.	.	.	.	.	.	.
Aster laevis L.	.	4	3	.	4	.	.	.	.	.
Antennaria neglecta Greene	.	4	3	.	3	.	.	.	.	.
Panicum oligosanthes Schultes	.	.	4	3	2	.	.	.	.	.
Erigeron strigosus Muhl	.	.	3	.	2	.	.	.	.	.
Ceanothus americanus L.	.	.	.	3	4	4	.	.	.	.
Polygala polygama Walt	4	3	4	4	2	.	.	.	.	.
Solidago nemoralis Ait	3	3	3	3	3	.	.	.	.	.
Poa compressa L.	8	8	8	8	8	5	.	.	.	.
Euphorbia corollata L.	4	4	4	4	3	2	.	.	.	.
Rubus flagellaris Willd	8	7	5	.	4	3	3	.	.	.
Solidago juncea Ait	4	8	8	8	9	5	4	3	3	3
Pterdium aquilinum (L.) Kuhn	.	.	.	3	3	7	5	5	5	3
Rosa carolina L.	.	.	.	.	4	6	6	3	.	3
Poa pratensis L.	.	.	.	.	2	4	4	4	4	.
Carya ovata (Mill.) Koch	.	.	.	.	.	6	5	4	4	5
Prunus serotina Ehrh	.	.	.	.	.	6	4	6	6	5
Carex pensylvanica Lam.	.	.	.	.	.	3	4	7	7	5
Sassafras albidum (Nutt.) Nees	.	.	.	.	.	3	3	5	4	3
Helianthus divaricatus L.	.	.	.	.	.	1	.	.	.	3
Quercus velutina Lam	.	.	.	.	.	6	4	3	3	.
Rubus occidentalis L.	.	.	.	.	.	3	.	.	3	.
Amphicarpa bracteata (L.) Fern	.	.	.	.	.	1	3	2	.	.
Acer rubrum L	.	.	.	.	.	1	3	3	.	.
Lysimachia quadrifolia L.	.	.	.	.	.	.	3	3	3	.
Geranium maculatum L.	.	.	.	.	.	.	3	3	3	3
Chenopodium album L.	.	.	.	.	.	.	+	.	3	2
Galium circaezans Michx.	.	.	.	.	.	.	.	2	4	3
G. boreale L.	.	.	.	.	.	.	.	.	4	3
Smilacina racemosa (L.) Desf.	.	.	.	.	.	.	.	.	3	3
Sanicula marilandica L.	.	.	.	.	.	.	.	.	3	3
Tree stratum										
Carya ovata (Mill.) Koch	.	.	.	.	1	.	5	.	4	9
Sassafras albidum (Nutt.) Nees	.	.	.	.	8	10	7	7	8	4
Quercus velutina Lam.	.	.	.	.	7	8	8	7	3	.
Prunus serotina Ehrh.	.	.	.	.	.	.	.	.	3	4

aluminum band around each of the trees included within the woods half of the enclosure (Fig. 1). In addition, to prevent the experimental animals from digging out, the wire mesh was extended beneath the surface of the ground to a depth of 4 inches, with a horizontal overturn of equal amount.

The above precautions proved adequate during the course of the study. Occasionally, a white-footed mouse (*P. leucopus*) or a chipmunk (*Tamias striatus*) managed to gain entrance from the surrounding area, but these were easily detected and removed.

Three underground nest boxes provided shelter for the experimental animals. One of these was located in each of the end compartments; the third, placed at the habitat boundary, served as an initial refuge from which an animal could enter the enclosure (Fig. 2). All of the nest boxes were constructed of $\frac{3}{4}$-inch pine and had outside dimensions of $9 \times 7 \times 8$ inches. After waterproofing the outer surfaces with roofing tar, I buried the boxes

TABLE 1(b)

Cover values of species occurring in only a single compartment.

Species	Compartment	Cover Value
Potentilla simplex Michx.	1	3
Desmodium illinoense Gray	2	4
Hieracium florentinum All.		3
Desmodium sessilifolium (Torr.) T. & G.	3	3
Ambrosia artemisiifolia L.	5	2
Monarda fistulosa L.	6	3
Quercus alba L.		3
Achillea millefolium L.		1
Parthenocissus quinquefolia (L.) Planch.	7	3
Corylus americana Walt	8	4
Cornus racemosa Lam.		3
Vitis riparia Michx.	9	3
Ulmus americana L.	10	3

until their upper edges just protruded above the surface of the ground. A low platform of hardware cloth set in the bottom of each prevented excessive contamination of the cotton nesting material by urine and feces.

When a cover was placed on the box, the surrounding earth provided sufficient insulation to keep the inside cool—even during the hot summer months. The mice gained access to the nesting chamber through a 3-foot length of $1\frac{1}{2}$-inch plastic pipe which led to the surface of the ground (Fig. 3).

Small metal runways ($3 \times 3 \times 10$ inches) traversing the sub-dividing partitions allowed the animals freedom of movement within the confines of the enclosure (Fig. 3). These passageways were covered with transparent plastic to prevent them from serving as darkened hiding places.

Five of the runways (Fig. 2) were equipped with an electrical device for

Fig. 3. Above: One of the subterranean nest boxes provided to shelter the experimental animals. The mice entered through a length of plastic pipe connected to the treadle seen on the right. The cover of the box was detachable to permit removal of the animals and changing of the nesting material. Below: One of the recording runways which traversed the partitions sub-dividing the enclosure (October, 1961).

recording the passage of a mouse. The mechanism consisted of a pair of mercury switches mounted on a treadle (Dice, 1961). When an animal traversed the runway it was compelled to trip the treadle, thereby momentarily closing the switches and permitting current to flow.

This action was recorded as a mark burned on an electrosensitive chart which rotated under a series of electrodes mounted on a 24-hour clock mechanism (Fig. 4). Since each electrode was connected to a different treadle, the time a mouse passed through a particular partition could readily be determined.

Fig. 4. The recording apparatus. Each of the 8 electrodes represented a different location with the enclosure. Note the record made
the previous night (spots burned on the rotating electrosensitive
chart) (May, 1961. J. Alley).

Eight electrically-operated counters served as a supplementary source of
data if one or more of the electrodes misfired. Moreover, they provided a
means for detecting repeated trippings of the same treadle, since it was not
ordinarily possible to resolve, as separate, spots burned on the chart less than
3 minutes apart. Power to operate the entire system was supplied by a 12-volt
automobile storage battery and induction coil.

The time an animal entered and left the nest boxes was also recorded, as
runways with switches were attached to the ends of the plastic tubes leading
to these subterranean chambers (Fig. 3). At the woods-field boundary, a
long runway containing two treadles was connected at right angles to the introduction box (Fig. 5). The mouse entered the runway at a point midway
between the treadles, and was then free to move into either of the two habitats.
This system, with each component connected to a different electrode, permitted
a more accurate determination of movements from one habitat to the other.

The battery, coil, and recording instruments were housed in a single shelter,
centrally located outside the enclosure. From this point wires led to each of
the mercury switches associated with the treadles.

Fig. 5. The introduction box. An underground plastic tube connected the nest chamber to the double runway at the habitat border (left). Note the sharp contrast between the substrates of the 2 habitats (May, 1961. J. Alley).

Experimental Procedure

Each of the animals was tested separately, and was initially introduced into the enclosure by being placed in the nest box at the woods-field boundary. Since a mouse could leave this chamber at will, a minimum of disturbance accompanied the procedure. Re-entry was prevented by a door, opening only from the inside, which closed behind the animal as it left.

Before it encountered another nest box, the mouse had to travel to either end of the enclosure (Fig. 2). Occasionally, some of the animals ignored these shelters, taking cover instead in natural hiding places within the compartments themselves.

Prairie deer mice are strictly nocturnal and normally pass the daylight hours in their burrows. Whenever possible, each individual was permitted to remain in the enclosure until it had nested in the same habitat on two consecutive days. Removal was effected sometime during the second such inactive interval. This procedure could not be followed in the few cases when either (a) animals disappeared, or (b) did not take refuge in the nest boxes. In the latter case the test period was extended and live traps were employed.

Because behavioral differences existed among individuals, there was considerable variation in the interval between the introduction of a mouse and its initial exploration of the enclosure. The starting point for any given trial was therefore taken at the time the animal first left the vicinity of the introduction box. The end point was considered to be the conclusion of the nesting period on the final day of testing. Because the removal of the animal from the enclosure usually interrupted this interval, the end point of the trial, as defined above, could not be determined directly. It could be estimated with reasonable assurance, however, since the mice normally did not leave the nest boxes of their own volition during the daylight hours. Both the observed time at which darkness set in and the animal's pattern of activity on its previous night in the enclosure were taken into consideration in making the necessary approximation. The test period thus extended from the initiation of the mouse's activity on its first night in the enclosure to the estimated termination of its nesting interval on the final day.

The experiments were conducted during the spring, summer, and fall months over a 2-year period (May 10–November 20, 1960; May 6–November 11, 1961). In the wintertime, when the vegetation was largely denuded and the substrate often blanketed by a uniform cover of snow, the physical and biotic differences between the two habitats were not so apparent. Moreover, the decrease in overall activity and sharp rise in mortality of the experimental animals during this season made year-round testing impractical.

Food was supplied to animals in the enclosure by the daily scattering of a small handful of pellets (Rockland Rabbit Ration) in each compartment. Higher concentrations, if provided, unduly attracted the mice and tended to restrict their natural movements. Moreover, the surplus was often stored in the nest boxes—an additional factor in lowering normal activity. No effort was made to remove uneaten pellets, as these soon disintegrated. The presence of sufficient moisture in the form of dew and rain made it unnecessary to furnish the animals with water.

Before each new individual was tested, I replaced any soiled nesting material and examined the treadles and switches to assure their continued functioning.

Methods of Determining Habitat Selection

The electrosensitive charts were replaced each day and taken to the laboratory for interpretation. This was achieved by superimposing a transparent replica of a standard 24-hour Hygrothermograph chart upon the record (Fig. 6). It was then possible to locate the spots burned by the electrodes in a network of vertical and horizontal lines. I used these as points of reference to denote the time each spot was made and the position of the electrode respectively. Since each electrode represented a specific location within the enclosure, the precise time the mouse passed through a particular runway could be ascertained. Moreover, a line drawn through and connecting all of the burned spots on the chart provided a continuous record of the animal's movements.

Because none of the mice maintained a constant level of activity throughout the trial, it was more meaningful to consider the extent of an animal's active

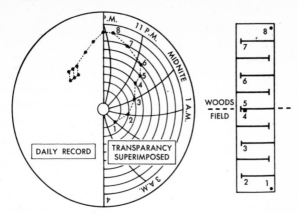

Fig. 6. Method of interpretation of the daily records. The relationship between the spots burned by the electrodes and the corresponding treadle locations within the enclosure is shown.

and inactive periods in each habitat as separate measures of habitat selection. In all, five different categories of measurement were employed. These were (A) the *per cent* of the total "*active time*" (i.e., time spent out of the nest boxes) in woods and field respectively, (B) the *per cent* of the total "*inactive time*" (i.e., time nesting) in woods and field respectively, (C) the *rate of travel*, or speed at which individuals moved about in each of the two habitats, (D) "*activity*" (expressed as the average time elapsed between counter records in woods and field respectively), and (E) the average "*penetration*" (in feet) into either of the two habitats whenever the woods-field boundary was crossed.

The extent of an animal's active and inactive periods in each habitat was determined directly from the daily records by subtracting the time the mouse spent in each of the nest boxes from its total time in the corresponding half of the enclosure. Since the overall length of the test periods was somewhat variable, these figures (Measurements A and B) were expressed as percentages to permit meaningful comparisons between individuals.

An animal's rate of travel in the woods and field respectively (Measurement C) was calculated by dividing the total distance it covered in moving about in each half of the enclosure by the total amount of time it was active in each habitat. Both of the variables involved were determined directly from the daily records.

The positioning of successive runways on opposite sides of the enclosure forced the mice to travel at least 95 feet (in a series of five 19-foot diagonals) before reaching the nest boxes at either end (Fig. 2). Since these shelters were actually located only 50 feet from the partition separating the two habitats, the distance traveled in either woods or field was always greater than the perpendicular penetration from the habitat boundary (Measurement E). Where the record indicated that an animal passed through a particular runway but did not trip the next recording treadle, it was assumed to have reached a point halfway between these.

The passage of a mouse through any of the electrified runways was recorded on both the appropriate 12-volt counter and the daily chart. Each count, therefore, represented the tripping of a particular treadle. Four of the counters operated from runways located in the field, the remaining four from runways in the woods. By considering these groups separately, the total number of counts originating in each habitat could be determined.

"Activity" or the average time elapsed between successive passages (Measurement D) was calculated by dividing the total number of counts recorded in each habitat into the total time the animal was active in that environment. Appropriate adjustments were made when the daily charts revealed that the number of counts might be too high (because of excessive treadle vibration) or too low (because of a mechanical failure in the recording system).

The distance a mouse penetrated into one habitat or the other each time it crossed the woods-field boundary was determined directly from the daily charts. Values ranged from zero, in cases where the animal returned immediately after crossing the border, to a maximum of 50 feet when it entered the nest box in either of the compartments. For purposes of comparison, the average penetration per crossing of the habitat boundary was calculated for both the woods and field (Measurement E).

Statistical Treatment of Data

Each of the five measures of habitat selection provided data which permitted comparison of an animal's response to the woods and field halves of the enclosure respectively. In three measures (rate of travel, activity, and average penetration) the woods and field values were independent (i.e., a mouse's activity in the woods was not affected by its activity in the field). This was not true of the two time measurements, where the number of minutes spent in one habitat varied inversely with the number spent in the other. Indeed, since they were both expressed as percentages, the woods-field values within each time category were actually proportional.

Habitat preference was indicated by the higher of the paired woods-field scores in all categories of measurement but one. The sole exception was rate of travel (Measurement C) in which the lower of the two values was taken to be indicative of habitat selection. It was assumed in this instance that a mouse would travel more slowly in the preferred habitat, since it presumably would be less subject to stresses in that environment.

Because an individual's woods-field scores for any given category of measurement could be paired, the Wilcoxon matched-pairs signed-ranks test was employed for comparison of group habitat means (Siegel, 1956). Statistically significant differences, when obtained, were taken to indicate the expression of a clearly defined habitat preference. Thus, in deciding whether a particular series of animals selected the woods or the field, I considered only the average response of the group as a whole.

In certain experiments, however, considerable variation was noted among the individuals tested. The coefficient of variation, C, provided a method for comparing variability in habitat response both within and between the groups of mice tested in the enclosure. This statistic was derived for each of the calculated means by dividing the mean into its standard deviation ($s/\bar{x}$). Since C is the ratio of two averages having the same unit of measurement, it is itself independent of the unit employed (Snedecor, 1956).

The Mann Whitney U test for two independent samples (Siegel, *op. cit.*) was used to compare the mean habitat scores attained by the different groups of animals tested in the experiments.

Experimental Animals

Both the forest and field adapted forms of *Peromyscus maniculatus* are represented in Michigan, where the range of the woodland deer mouse, *P. m. gracilis*, overlaps that of the prairie deer mouse, *P. m. bairdi* (Burt, 1954). The latter was formerly restricted to isolated grassy areas and forest openings in the southwest corner of the state, but extended its range in the mid-nineteenth century following clearing of the land for cultivation (Hooper, 1942). This eventually brought them into contact with local populations of *P. m. gracilis* in the northern counties of the Lower Peninsula.

Despite the ability of the two subspecies to interbreed in the laboratory, hybrids are not found in the field (Dice, 1931; Hooper, *op. cit.*). Since each exhibits a rather restricted habitat preference, it is assumed that ecological segregation has proven to be an effective barrier to interbreeding. Barbehenn and New (1957) reported what appeared to be *bairdi* × *gracilis* intergrades in New York State, but their evidence does not seem conclusive.

Because of its local availability and more narrowly defined habitat preference, the prairie deer mouse was selected to serve as the experimental animal. The original sources of mice for this study were the Mammalian Genetics Center of the University of Michigan and the old fields of the E. S. George Reserve. According to the records of the Mammalian Genetics Center, the laboratory animals used were 12–20 generations removed from actual experience in their natural environment. The original ancestors of this stock, designated *bairdi* Washtenaw, were ten pairs of mice live-trapped by Harris (1952) from two localities in the vicinity of Ann Arbor, Washtenaw County, Michigan in 1946 and 1947. Prior to 1958 the colony was maintained at a level of 300–600 individuals, but has since been reduced to 80–160.

During Harris's experiments, laboratory-reared offspring of the original twenty animals selected his artificial "field" habitat about as readily as field-caught individuals did. Since the former had had no prior field experience, Harris concluded that their behavior was genetically predetermined. The

present study afforded me a unique opportunity to test the effects of the *bairdi*
Washtenaw stock's long laboratory confinement on the innate habitat preference of subsequent generations.

Descriptions and Results of the Experiments

Experimental Design

During the course of the study the habitat responses of the following
groups of prairie deer mice were compared:

Control Series I   . . . . Field-caught animals.
Control Series II   . . . . Laboratory animals (*bairdi* Washtenaw
                                       stock).
Experimental Series I   . . . . . . Offspring of field-caught animals, reared in
                                       the laboratory.
Experimental Series II   . . . . . . Offspring of laboratory animals (*bairdi*
                                       Washtenaw stock), reared in the field.
Experimental Series III. . . . . . Offspring of field-caught animals, reared
                                       in the woods.
Experimental Series IV. . . . . . Offspring of laboratory animals (*bairdi*
                                       Washtenaw stock), reared in the woods.

Two principal variables existed in these experiments: (1) the experience
provided (rearing in field, woods, or lab) and (2) the hereditary background
(field or laboratory stocks) of the animals used. Each of the six series tested
in the enclosure was characterized by a different combination of these two
variables. The overall design of the experiments may be summarized as
follows:

Hereditary background	Experience provided		
	Field	*Laboratory*	*Woods*
Field stock	Control Series I	Experimental Series I	Experimental Series III
Laboratory stock (*bairdi* Washtenaw)	Experimental Series II	Control Series II	Experimental Series IV

Control Series I

Although the home range of *Peromyscus maniculatus bairdi* is often less
than one acre in extent (Burt, 1954), confinement in a 1600-square-foot pen

constituted an unnatural barrier to the movements of the experimental animals. It was therefore necessary to determine the extent to which the restrictive influence of the enclosure might interfere with normal habitat selection.

Accordingly, the first group of individuals to be tested was comprised entirely of individuals caught on old fields of the E. S. George Reserve, where both Blair (1940) and Howard (1949) had demonstrated the strong affinity of the prairie deer mouse for this environment. It was assumed, therefore, that the reactions of these animals to the experimental situation would form a basis for evaluating the effects of the enclosure. Moreover, their behavior provided a standard for comparison in all subsequent trials. The eight males and four females tested in this group were designated Control Series I.

The results are presented in the form of a bar graph (Fig. 7). In each of the five categories of measurement, a majority of the individuals tested selected the field half of the enclosure. As previously described, assignment of individual preference was simply based on the achievement of a higher score in

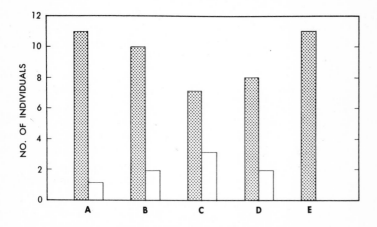

Fig. 7. Control Series I (12 animals). Number of prairie deer mice selecting the field (black columns) and woods (white columns) as determined for each of 5 measures of habitat selection: A. per cent active time; B. per cent inactive time; C. rate of travel (ft/min); D. activity (average time between treadle passages); E. average penetration from habitat boundary (ft).

one of the two habitats (for all measurements except rate of travel). This treatment, therefore, does not take degree of preference into consideration. The data from which Fig. 7 and subsequent graphs were derived are not included herein, but may be consulted in my original dissertation (Wecker, 1962).

Further inspection of Fig. 7 reveals a slight variation in the total number of individuals considered in each category of measurement. These differences arose from one or more of the following causes: (1) a mechanical failure in

part of the recording apparatus resulted in loss of data; (2) ties occurred—
i.e., an individual's score was the same for both woods and field; and (3)
the animal spent 100 per cent of its time (both active and inactive) in one
habitat or the other, making woods-field comparisons for the remaining three
measures (C-E) impossible.

As a group, the mice in Control Series I achieved higher total field scores
for each of the five measurements (Wecker, 1962: Appendix A). The clear
preference of these animals for the field environment was borne out by the
significant difference between the two habitat means in all categories but
rate of travel (Table 2).

Since field-caught *bairdi* exhibited a positive response to the field half of
the enclosure as anticipated, I concluded that the experimental situation
provided no marked interference with normal habitat selection.

TABLE 2

Mean value and coefficient of variation (s/x̄) for each of five measures of habitat selection
by 12 prairie deer mice in Control Series I.

	Mean and stand-ard deviation	Coefficient of variation
A. Per cent active time		
Field	**84.3 ± 16.8	19.9%
Woods	**15.7 ± 16.8	
B. Per cent inactive time		
Field	**85.5 ± 33.2	38.8%
Woods	**14.5 ± 33.2	
C. Rate of travel (ft/min)		
Field	2.0 ± 1.1	55.0%
Woods	3.2 ± 1.5	46.8%
D. Activity (min/count)		
Field	*15.1 ± 6.6	43.7%
Woods	*7.7 ± 5.2	67.5%
E. Average penetration (ft)		
Field	**41.5 ± 8.4	20.2%
Woods	**16.6 ± 13.0	78.3%

*Difference between habitat means significant at the 5 per cent level.
**Difference between habitat means significant at the 1 per cent level.

Control Series II

If, as Harris (1952) suggested, the habitat preference of prairie deer mice
has an innate basis, laboratory-reared animals should be expected to show the
same general response to the enclosure as the field-caught individuals of
Control Series I. To evaluate this hypothesis, seven males and six females,
obtained from the *bairdi* Washtenaw colony of the Mammalian Genetics
Center, were tested in the enclosure. These thirteen individuals constituted
Control Series II.

Since the original ancestors of this stock were tested by Harris (1952), it was hoped that the behavior of the generations ($F_{12}-F_{20}$) represented in the second control series would provide information relative to the hereditary determination of habitat selection. In addition, this group constituted a control for subsequent experiments in which laboratory-reared mice were used.

The data (Fig. 8) stand in sharp contrast to those obtained for Control Series I. In three of the five different categories of measurement (active time, inactive time, and rate of travel), more Series II individuals exhibited a preference for the woods than for the field. Moreover, the total woods scores were also higher in these cases (Wecker, 1962: Appendix B).

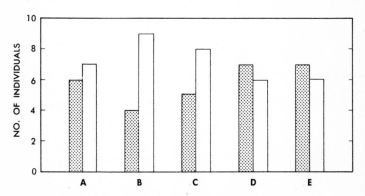

Fig. 8. Control Series II (13 animals). Number of mice selecting the field (black columns) and woods (white columns) as determined for each of 5 measures of habitat selection (A-E).

There is, however, little evidence that this group as a whole selected either half of the enclosure. The slight overall preference for the woods has been noted, but none of the differences between the paired habitat means was statistically significant at either level of rejection (Table 3). The bar graph, the original data, and the high coefficients of variation all reveal considerable heterogeneity in the behavior of the animals tested in Control Series II.

In the laboratory, the *bairdi* Washtenaw stock has been subjected to different selective pressures from those encountered in the field. Combinations of genes which are advantageous to prairie deer mice in nature (such as those determining response to habitat) would probably not be selected for, and might even be selected against, in the laboratory environment. While most wild mice will survive extended confinement in cages, not all will reproduce under these circumstances. Hence, selection for docility, operating through possible breeding limitations of this kind, may be at a premium.

Assuming the hereditary control of habitat selection to be polygenic, one might expect the frequency of the genes involved to differ in field and labora-

TABLE 3

Mean value and coefficient of variation $(s/\bar{x})$ for each of five measures of habitat selection by 13 prairie deer mice in Control Series II.

	Mean and standard deviation	Coefficient of variation
A. Per cent active time		
Field	47.8 ± 22.2	46.4%
Woods	52.2 ± 22.2	
B. Per cent inactive time		
Field	40.4 ± 38.5	
Woods	59.6 ± 38.5	94.3%
C. Rate of travel (ft/min)		
Field	2.8 ± 1.8	64.3%
Woods	3.1 ± 1.6	51.6%
D. Activity (min/count)		
Field	10.1 ± 4.9	48.5%
Woods	9.3 ± 3.9	41.9%
E. Average Penetration (ft)		
Field	24.8 ± 8.8	35.5%
Woods	29.4 ± 10.2	34.7%

None of the differences is significant at the 5 per cent level.

tory populations. It is suggested, therefore, that this has resulted in behavioral modifications which ultimately contributed to the high degree of variability manifest in the habitat response of the animals tested in Control Series II. Since both the original *bairdi* Washtenaw ancestors and their first-generation laboratory-reared offspring exhibited the normal affinity of the sub-species for the field environment (Harris, 1952), a loss (or reduction) of this capacity has occurred in only 12 to 20 generations. This in itself is of great interest.

In a situation that appears to be somewhat analogous to the present one, Rowland & Woods (1961) have found that relaxation of continuous selection for maze-brightness and maze-dullness in two inbred strains of rats has led to marked changes in maze performance. According to the authors, the animals apparently no longer possess the same differential genetic characteristics which were reflected by their behavioral differences in the original maze.

The data of Control Series II, therefore, neither support nor refute Harris's contention that the observed habitat preference of prairie deer mice is normally predetermined by heredity. A more rigorous evaluation was provided in the next experiment.

Experimental Series I

To obtain animals for testing, additional field-caught individuals were secured and brought into the laboratory for breeding. The litters were separated from their parents shortly after weaning, and were kept in laboratory cages for a period averaging about two months (58.5 days). Twelve of these offspring (eight males and four females) were tested in the enclosure as Experimental Series I. None had had any outdoor experience prior to this time.

Since these mice were directly descended from wild parents, there was no basis for assuming that hereditary modifications of the type postulated for Control Series II had had sufficient time to appear. Therefore, if habitat selection is genetically predetermined, the behavior of Experimental Series I should be expected to approximate the response of the first control group.

The graph derived from these data (Fig. 9) reveals that, as in Control Series I, a majority of the individuals tested selected the field half of the enclosure. Not only were the total field values higher for all categories of measurement except inactive time (Wecker, 1962: Appendix C), but all of the paired habitat means were significantly different also (Table 4).

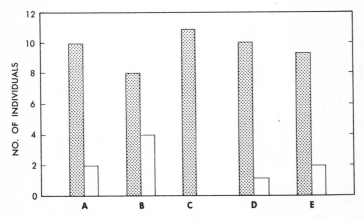

Fig. 9. Experimental Series I (12 animals). Number of mice selecting in the field (black columns) and woods (white columns) as determined for each of five measures of habitat selection (A-E).

These data clearly demonstrate the ability of first generation laboratory-born prairie deer mice to select the typical habitat of the subspecies without benefit of prior experience in the field. The animals involved were, however, raised by field-caught parents; it is possible, therefore, that some form of non-heritable social transference was operative in bringing about the observed results. If one accepts this viewpoint, the loss of the "innate" habitat response in older laboratory stocks becomes explainable in terms of a progressive dilution of information as transferred from generation to generation.

The ultimate resolution of this question must lie in data derived from cross-fostering experiments (wherein lactating laboratory females are allowed to rear litters born to field-caught parents). Such experiments are contemplated as this paper goes to press, but were not part of the original design.

Fortunately, however, relevant data are available from another source.

TABLE 4

Mean value and coefficient of variation (s/x̄) for each of five measures of habitat selection by 12 prairie deer mice in Experimental Series I.

	Mean and standard deviation	Coefficient of variation
A. Per cent active time		
Field	**71.5 ± 28.6	40.0%
Woods	**28.5 ± 28.6	
B. Per cent inactive time		
Field	60.7 ± 46.8	77.1%
Woods	39.3 ± 46.8	
C. Rate of travel (ft/min)		
Field	**2.7 ± 2.0	74.1%
Woods	**1.2 ± 0.5	41.7%
D. Activity (min/count)		
Field	**11.3 ± 6.8	60.2%
Woods	**23.5 ± 10.7	45.5%
E. Average Penetration (ft)		
Field	*21.9 ± 12.0	54.8%
Woods	*32.1 ± 9.1	28.4%

*Difference between habitat means significant at the 5 per cent level.
**Difference between habitat means significant at the 1 per cent level.

Foster (1959) selected animals from the *bairdi* Washtenaw stock (6th to 9th generation) in undertaking an intensive laboratory analysis of the behavior and temperament of *bairdi* and *gracilis*. Although the habitat selection response was not itself investigated, significant differences in the reactions of the 2 subspecies to a number of different experimental situations were readily apparent. Moreover, after reviewing data derived from cross-fostering, Foster failed to find any evidence to support a hypothesis of transfer of behavioral traits from generation to generation through learning. There was no consistent indication for maternal, paternal, or joint influence of both parents on the behavior of their offspring.

It seems likely, therefore, that the habitat preference of wild populations of prairie deer mice is actually predetermined by a hereditary pattern of behavior. This may be elicited by certain key environmental stimuli, but is apparently not dependent upon a prolonged period of habituation for its expression.

Experimental Series II

Harris was primarily interested in identifying the specific environmental cues which elicit selection of habitat in different subspecies of deer mice. While the use of first generation laboratory-reared animals enabled him to conclude (perhaps prematurely) that this behavior had a genetic basis, Harris's study was not designed to evaluate the role which early experience might play in the process of habitat selection.

To determine whether such experience actually influences subsequent selection of habitat, I allowed pairs of laboratory mice (*bairdi* Washtenaw stock) to raise litters in a 10 × 10 ft pen constructed in the field (Fig. 10). Located a short distance from the main enclosure, this structure was sub-divided into two compartments, each containing a number of nest boxes. Water and food to excess were supplied to the animals within.

Fig. 10. The field rearing pen used to condition animals tested in Experimental Series II (see text) (May, 1961. J. Alley).

Mice mated in the laboratory were moved into the nesting chambers after parturition had taken place. The age of the litters at the time was somewhat variable, but in all cases the transfer was accomplished before the eyes of the young had opened. After a mean period of 31 days of field experience, thirteen of these offspring were tested in the enclosure. The eight males and five females constituted Experimental Series II.

The results, presented in Fig. 11 and Table 5, reveal a well-defined preference for the field habitat. In terms of the two time measurements (A and B) this preference was expressed by all of the animals for which relevant data were obtained. Moreover, there were only four isolated instances arising from the remaining three categories (C, D, and E) in which the paired habitat values indicated that individuals selected the woods half of the enclosure. Irrespective of the type of measurement employed, the preference for the field (as revealed by the differences between the habitat means) was consistently significant at the one per cent level (Table 5). This clearcut selection of the habitat is also borne out by the higher total field scores attained by the ani-

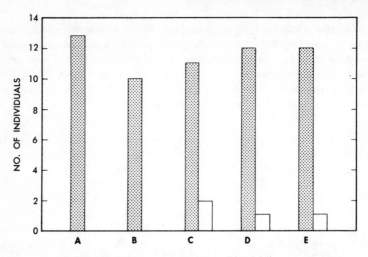

Fig. 11. Experimental Series II (13 animals). Number of mice selecting the field (black columns) and woods (white columns) as determined for each of five measures of habitat selection (A-E).

TABLE 5

Mean value and coefficient of variation (s/x̄) for each of five measures of habitat selection by 13 prairie deer mice in Experimental Series II.

	Mean and stand-ard deviation	Coefficient of variation
A. Per cent active time		
Field	**84.6 ± 10.7	12.6%
Woods	**15.4 ± 10.7	
B. Per cent inactive time		
Field	**97.3 ± 7.8	8.0%
Woods	**2.7 ± 7.8	
C. Rate of travel (ft/min)		
Field	**1.1 ± 0.5	45.5%
Woods	**2.4 ± 1.0	43.3%
D. Activity (min/count)		
Field	**24.4 ± 9.9	40.6%
Woods	**10.0 ± 5.6	56.0%
E. Average Penetration (ft)		
Field	**28.8 ± 12.1	42.0
Woods	**18.4 ± 15.2	82.6

**Difference between habitat means significant at the 1 per cent level.

mals in Experimental Series II in all five instances of measurement (Wecker, 1962: Appendix D).

Since the *bairdi* Washtenaw stock showed no tendency to select the field habitat when previously tested in the enclosure (Control Series II), the contrasting results of the present experiment can only be explained in terms of the experience provided. Thus, while laboratory animals have apparently lost the innate preference of the subspecies for the field habitat, they have retained a capacity for learning which enables them to achieve similar results if exposed to the field environment at an early age.

Experimental Series III

In nature, young prairie deer mice are reared in fields (Howard, 1959), an act which could reinforce any innate response to this habitat. Whether early experience in a different environment would be sufficient to reverse the normal environmental affinities of the subspecies remained to be determined.

In this experiment, field-caught *bairdi* were allowed to raise litters in a 10 × 10 ft pen constructed in the woods (Fig. 12). Seven of these offspring, six males and one female (designated Control Series III), were subsequently tested in the enclosure.

The results presented in Fig. 13 indicate that the two weeks of woods experience provided the young animals did not influence their subsequent selection of habitat. Irrespective of the type of measurement employed, a majority of the individuals tested exhibited the normal preference of the subspecies for field conditions. While the difference between the two habitat means was statistically significant in only two of the five cases (Table 6), this was not surprising in view of the small size of the test sample.

On the whole (although not borne out by the inactive time measurements),

Fig. 12. The woods rearing pen. This enclosure was used to condition animals tested in Experimental Series III and IV (see text) (October, 1961).

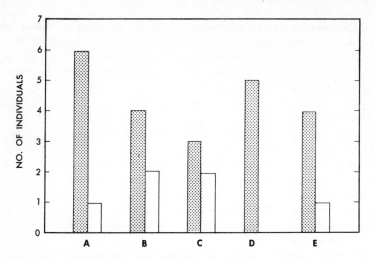

Fig. 13. Experimental Series III (7 animals). Number of mice selecting the field (black columns) and woods (white columns) as determined for each of five measures of habitat selection (A-E).

TABLE 6

Mean value and coefficient of variation (s/x) for each of five measures of habitat selection by seven prairie deer mice in Experimental Series III.

	Mean and standard deviation	Coefficient of variation
A. Per cent active time		
Field	*76.7 ± 22.1	28.8%
Woods	*23.3 ± 22.1	
B. Per cent inactive time		
Field	53.0 ± 45.1	85.1%
Woods	47.0 ± 45.1	
C. Rate of travel (ft/min)		
Field	1.3 ± 0.8	61.5%
Woods	2.5 ± 1.8	72.0%
D. Activity (min/count)		
Field	*21.4 ± 12.8	59.8%
Woods	*15.3 ± 14.1	92.2%
E. Average Penetration (ft)		
Field	29.0 ± 15.3	52.8%
Woods	12.4 ± 4.3	34.8%

*Difference between habitat means significant at the 5 per cent level.

the woods-reared individuals of Experimental Series III seem to have retained much of their innate ability to select the field habitat. In any event, no definite preference for the woods was demonstrated. This conclusion is supported by the original data, which show higher total field scores in all five categories (Wecker, 1962: Appendix E).

Experimental Series IV

Early experience in the "wrong" environment is apparently not sufficient to reverse the habitat preference of animals in which this response is normally genetically predetermined. Might not such experience, however, result in atypical habitat selection if young laboratory animals were so exposed?

In an attempt to answer this question, I transferred litters born to *bairdi* Washtenaw stock into the woods rearing pen. Nine of these offspring (six males and three females) were tested in the enclosure. This group (Experimental Series IV) averaged 24 days of woods experience.

The bar graph (Fig. 14) does not demonstrate a pronounced tendency for these mice to select the woods half of the enclosure. Unlike the results of the preceding experiment, however, no preference for the field environment is apparent either. (Only the activity measurement favored this habitat.) In two of the remaining four categories (inactive time and rate of travel) a majority of the animals tested preferred the woods, while both the active time and average penetration measurements resulted in ties.

The original data (Wecker, 1962: Appendix F) also show no consistent trend. Total values for active time, rate of travel, and average penetration favor the field, while higher woods scores were attained in the other two categories.

The failure of the animals in Experimental Series IV to select either habitat is borne out by the lack of statistically significant differences between the

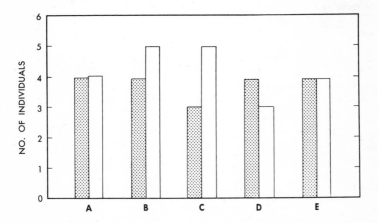

Fig. 14. Experimental Series IV (9 animals). Number of mice selecting the field (black columns) and woods (white columns) as determined for each of five measures of habitat selection (A-E).

TABLE 7

Mean value and coefficient of variation (s/$\bar{x}$) for each of five measures of habitat selection by nine prairie deer mice in Experimental Series IV.

	Mean and standard deviation	Coefficient of variation
A. Per cent active time		
Field	58.5 ± 39.1	66.8%
Woods	41.5 ± 39.1	
B. Per cent inactive time		
Field	44.4 ± 52.7	118.7%
Woods	55.6 ± 52.7	
C. Rate of travel (ft/min)		
Field	1.4 ± 0.8	57.1%
Woods	1.8 ± 1.4	77.8%
D. Activity (min/count)		
Field	27.2 ± 12.8	47.1%
Woods	28.4 ± 15.4	54.2%
E. Average Penetration (ft)		
Field	33.1 ± 16.7	50.5%
Woods	16.1 ± 5.5	34.2%

None of the values was significant at the 5 per cent level.

woods-field means in each of the five measurements employed (Table 7). With the possible exception of the average penetration values, these results do not appear to be directly attributable to the relatively small size of the test sample.

Discussion

General Conclusions

The results of the six experiments are summarized in Table 8. In each case, the preferred habitat was determined, as described, through a comparison of the paired mean scores in each of the five categories of measurement. Numerical values for these averages have already been presented (Tables 2–7).

Inspection of Table 8 reveals that the data fall into at least two major groups. The smaller of these (to be referred to as Group C) includes Control Series II and Experimental Series IV. The larger (designated Group AB) contains the remaining four series (Control Series I, and Experimental Series I, II, and III).

Each of the four series in Group AB exhibited a tendency to select the field environment in all categories of measurement. This preference was statistically significant 15 out of 20 times; in 12 of these, significance was at the one per cent level. On the other hand, the two series constituting Group C favored the field half of the enclosure in only four out of ten instances of measurement, and in no case was this preference statistically significant. The biological meaning of these results will now be considered.

TABLE 8

Summary of habitat selection by the control and experimental series of prairie deer mice tested in the enclosure.

Series	No. indiv.	Hereditary background	Experience provided	Categories of measurement				
				A	B	C	D	E
Control Series I	12	Field stock	Field	Field**	Field**	Field	Field*	Field**
Experimental Series II	13	Laboratory stock	Field	Field**	Field**	Field**	Field**	Field**
Experimental Series I	12	Field stock	Laboratory	Field**	Field	Field**	Field**	Field*
Experimental Series III	7	Field stock	Woods	Field*	Field	Field	Field**	Field
Control Series II	13	Laboratory stock	Laboratory	Woods	Woods	Woods	Woods	Field
Experimental Series IV	9	Laboratory stock	Woods	Field	Woods	Field	Woods	Field

** Difference between habitat means significant at the 1 per cent level.
* Difference between habitat means significant at the 5 per cent level.

One distinction between the two groups becomes obvious when the characteristics of the individuals constituting each are examined. Table 8 reveals that all of the field-selecting animals in Group AB either had field-caught parents, field experience, or both. The Group C individuals, on the other hand, were all offspring of laboratory animals and had no contact with the natural field environment prior to testing. Since the *bairdi* Washtenaw stock did not demonstrate any innate habitat preference, the failure of Group C to respond positively to the experimental situation is not surprising.

Further inspection of Table 8 leads one to surmise that mice with actual field experience (Control Series I and Experimental Series II) expressed a stronger preference for the field half of the enclosure than did animals merely having field-caught parents (Experimental Series I and III). This preliminary conclusion is based on the more highly significant habitat means attained by the animals in the first two series. But if Group AB is split along these lines, the differences between A and B tend to disappear when the data within each are pooled (Table 9).

TABLE 9

Summary of habitat selection by the three major groups of prairie deer mice tested in the enclosure.

Group	Series included	No. indiv.	Categories of measurement				
			A	B	C	D	E
A	Control I Experimental II	25	Field**	Field**	Field**	Field**	Field**
B	Experimental I Experimental III	19	Field**	Field	Field**	Field**	Field**
C	Control II Experimental IV	22	Field	Woods	Neither	Woods	Field

**Difference between habitat means significant at the 1 per cent level.

It is suggested, however, that the generally lower mean scores attained in the field habitat by the two series included in Group B can be taken as evidence that field experience tends to reinforce the innate response normally leading to selection of this habitat.

With a single exception (inactive time for B), both the A and B groups maintained a sharp contrast with Group C in all categories of measurement (Table 9). Even after combining the data from Control Series II and Experimental Series IV, I found no indication that the animals in Group C expressed a clearcut habitat preference. Higher mean values were obtained in the woods for two measures of habitat selection (inactive time and activity) and in the field for two others (active time and average penetration). In the remaining category (rate of travel) the two habitat means were equal (Wecker, 1962:

Appendix G). None of the differences which occurred was statistically significant at either the one or five per cent level of rejection.

The data derived from testing the two control and four experimental series of prairie deer mice in the enclosure warrant the following conclusions: (1) The choice of the field environment by *P. m. bairdi* is normally predetermined by heredity. (2) Early field experience can reinforce this innate preference but is not a necessary prerequisite for subsequent habitat selection. (3) Early experience in other environments (woods or laboratory) is not sufficient to reverse the normal affinity of this subspecies for the field habitat. (4) Confinement of the *bairdi* Washtenaw stock in the laboratory for 12–20 generations has resulted in an apparent reduction of the hereditary control over the habitat selection response. This has led to a marked increase in the variability of the behavior demonstrated by these animals when tested in the enclosure. (5) Laboratory mice did retain an innate capacity to utilize early field experience in learning to respond positively to stimuli associated with this environment. Experience in the woods or laboratory, however, did not have a corresponding effect. At no time did any group of mice so exposed exhibit a significant preference for the woods half of the enclosure. (6) Within either field or laboratory stocks the habitat response of woods-reared animals did not usually differ significantly from that of individuals raised in laboratory cages. It is concluded, therefore, that prairie deer mice can learn to respond to environmental cues only when the necessary stimuli are associated with the field habitat.

Utilizing a somewhat similar experimental design, Klopfer (1962: pp. 90–94) found that the chipping sparrow, *Spizella passerina*, is capable of a plastic habitat response. When placed in the test situation, both field-caught adults and their hand-reared young demonstrated a marked preference for the normal pine woods environment of the species. As in prairie deer mice, this behavior appeared to be independent of early experience. In contrast to the results obtained during the present study, however, the habitat preference of the chipping sparrow could be shifted to oak woods by hand-rearing young birds in the presence of oak foliage. Preliminary retesting has indicated considerable stability in the response of the individuals involved.

Habitat Imprinting

The results of the experiments described herein indicate that a prairie deer mouse's early exposure to the field environment can be a factor in determining its subsequent selection of habitat. While rearing in the field normally only reinforces an animal's innate preference for this environment, experience alone can apparently effect similar results. In its most rigid and stereotyped aspect, this behavior could involve some form of habitat imprinting (Thorpe, 1945).

If such a process is actually operative in *Peromyscus* habitat selection, one would expect the adult pattern of response to be determined during a critical period early in the life of the mouse. This would most likely occur shortly after a young individual leaves the nest for the first time. Linsdale (1957) agrees that the early stages of acquaintance with its habitat may be important in influencing an animal's subsequent reactions.

Although the present study was not designed to evaluate the role of imprinting in habitat selection, preliminary data derived from experiments now in progress lend some support to this hypothesis. The number of individuals involved is too small to substantiate any definite conclusions, but I have found that the limitation of early field experience to only ten days will not prevent young laboratory animals from responding positively to the field environment at a later date. Despite a 7–10 week interval of laboratory confinement prior to testing, there was no indication that these mice exhibited a weakened habitat response when subsequently placed in the enclosure. While habitat preference is, therefore, apparently determined early in the life of the individual, further study is obviously required before the precise nature of the learning process involved can be determined.

The Genetic Assimilation
of the Habitat Response

The results of the six experiments constituting the design for this study indicate that both heredity and experience play a role in determining the preference of *Peromyscus maniculatus bairdi* for the field habitat. This conclusion, however, raises an interesting question. Since the same effect can be directly produced in each generation through learning, why has natural selection operated to bring about a parallel, genetically predetermined response?

According to Waddington (1957) the genetic assimilation of an originally environmentally determined characteristic is advantageous, since it tends to produce a modally adapted phenotype. This provides the best possible adjustment to the ecological situation most commonly encountered by a particular population. One would expect, therefore, that so long as the environment remains relatively stable, the innate ability of prairie deer mice to select the field habitat constitutes a definite advantage.

If the innate and environmentally determined bases for habitat selection were completely unrelated, however, it would be difficult to account for the continued maintenance of both mechanisms in the wild population. For this reason, I feel that the two apparently contrasting patterns of behavior are probably interdependent, and may even represent the phenotypic consequences of quantitative differences in the number of "field" genes at various loci. Presumably, more of these factors are necessary to maintain a hereditarily predetermined habitat response than are needed to control the capacity of the animals to utilize early experience in responding in an adaptive manner to their environment.

This conclusion is supported by the data derived from Experimental Series II. Although laboratory mice did not demonstrate an innate habitat preference, they were able to select the field half of the enclosure when given field experience at an early age. If we are actually dealing with two independent mechanisms for habitat orientation, why should selection under laboratory conditions operate to remove one and not the other?

One can assume genetic drift, but I believe the question can better be resolved on the basis of the hypothesis set forth above: i.e., that given a certain number (X) of "field" loci, the animal attains a capacity for learning to respond to specific environmental cues. Given a greater number of such genes (X + Y), its habitat preference becomes genetically predetermined.

When the "field" character of enough of the loci was modified over the course of 12–20 generations, genotype X + Y reverted to X. Presumably, if the *bairdi* Washtenaw stock were kept in the laboratory for an even longer period of time, one might also expect a corresponding reduction in learning ability to occur. It is possible, however, that because genotype X was attained earlier in the evolutionary history of the subspecies than X + Y, the genetic determinants needed to maintain the capacity for learning are buffered by background modifiers. The phenotypic expression of X would, therefore, tend to be less subject to modification.

The genetic fixation of the habitat response may be correlated with a phenomenon which has been termed the "Baldwin effect." Originally called *"organic selection"* when postulated by J. M. Baldwin (1896), this hypothesis has been defined as the process by which "individually acquired changes may eventually, under the influence of natural selection, be reinforced or replaced in the population by similar hereditary characteristics" (Simpson, 1953).

Without resorting to either a teleological or Lamarckian interpretation, one can apply Baldwin's hypothesis to the present situation as follows:

(1) Within the geographic range of the prairie deer mouse, homing, imprinting, or other less rigid responses to habitat formed the basis for patterns of behavior which tended to restrict this species to the grassland community.
(2) Natural selection operating in this environment resulted in morphological and physiological modifications which further adapted the population for successful existence in the field habitat.
(3) If, at the periphery of their range, the animals had continued to interbreed with individuals evolving in ecologically distinct areas, these adaptive advantages would probably not have been maintained.
(4) Selection, therefore, favored the development of isolating mechanisms (such as behavior which tended to keep the two populations ecologically segregated). Chance mutations whose retention facilitated the formation of these patterns were selected for.
(5) Since there was presumably a selective advantage for the hereditary predetermination of habitat selection (i.e., animals born with an innate capacity to choose the field did not have to undergo a period of habituation), the original environmentally determined response was eventually reinforced

by an increase in the frequency of "field" genes. Thus a pattern of behavior which formerly depended upon experience for its expression was supplemented by a hereditary mechanism tending to produce a similar phenotypic effect.

This purely hypothetical scheme is based on Baldwin's original work (*op. cit.*) and on discussions of the Baldwin effect appearing in papers by Thorpe (1945), Simpson (*op. cit.*), and King (1961).

Waddington (1957; 1961) believes that the entire train of thought implicit in the old idea of "organic selection" is based on an oversimplification which ignores the fact that the environment is one of the determinants of the phenotype. He states that natural selection operates not in favor of genes whose effects happen, by chance, to parallel direct (acquired) adaptations, but for factors which control the capacity of an animal to respond to its environment. Environmental feedback has the effect of "canalizing" development along definite paths. This facilitates the expression of particular adaptive phenotypes. The more thorough the environmental remodelling of the epigenetic landscape, the more likely it will be that particular constellations of genes *already present in the population* in subthreshold frequency will find expression. These will then be able to take over the function of the original environmental stimulus. Waddington terms this process the "*genetic assimilation*" of an acquired character.

Habitat Selection and Evolution

According to Thorpe (1945), the occurrence of two ecologically restricted subspecies in the same area is a primary step in speciation. He believes two principal lines of evidence support the sympatric speciation hypothesis. These are: (1) the occurrence of sympatric monophagous (one food plant) and oligophagous genera of Microlepidoptera, which are comprised of more species than are polyphagous genera (Thorpe, 1945); and (2) experimentally modified habitat or host preference in certain insects as a direct result of larval conditioning (Thorpe, 1939; 1940).

The importance of habitat selection in initiating the division of bird populations into small groups was emphasized by Lack (1933), but he has since maintained that geographic isolation is normally the first step in speciation (Lack, 1940). Mayr (1947) holds, as does Thorpe, that establishment in a new environment may involve conditioning, but he does not believe that Thorpe's experiments with insects prove that this can result in the complete genetic isolation of two populations occupying the same area at the same time. Such conditioning may be important in the extension of the range of the species, but some form of spatial isolation, whether "macrogeographical" or "microgeographical," must occur in order for speciation to taken place (Mayr, *op. cit.*).

Blair (1950) cites the existence of woodland and grassland forms, the correlation between pelage color and soil color, and the direct relationship between the number of different races and the size and variability of the geographic range as evidence for the ecological nature of the subspecies of *Peromyscus*. This concurs with the opinion of Mayr (1947), who states that "all geographic races are also ecological and all ecological races are also geographic."

Rigid habitat restriction, however, may function in a conservative way in evolution. Lincoln's sparrow, *Melospiza lincolnii*, occurs in only three geographic forms despite the broad range of the species. On the other hand, the song sparrow, *Melospiza melodia*, a related but euryecious species, has 28 named races (Miller, 1942).

Geographic isolation at the periphery of the species range and on islands or mountain tops seems to have been a necessary prerequisite for speciation in the *Peromyscus maniculatus* complex (Blair, 1950). Blair further believes that ecological divergence favors the survival of a species by making it more adaptable to environmental change. It is not, however, important in the splitting off of new species unless some form of geographic discontinuity occurs.

In Michigan, the ranges of the prairie deer mouse and the woodland deer mouse overlap (Burt, 1954), but there is no evidence for intergradation between the two races (Hooper, 1942). Sympatric speciation was not involved in this situation, however, as *bairdi* and *gracilis* were formerly isolated geographically and have only recently come into secondary contact when clearing of the forests by man enabled the former to extent its range (Hooper, *op. cit.*).

Both Harris's work and the present study provide evidence that the observed difference in the habitat preference of these subspecies forms the basis for their continued segregation. As Mayr (1947) points out, ecological differences between two such sympatric forms are to be expected, since competition would otherwise prevent both from coexisting in the same area (Gause's hypothesis).

Summary

Despite an overlap of their ranges in Michigan, the restriction of the prairie and forest races of the deer mouse, *Peromyscus maniculatus*, to different environments has resulted in the ecological segregation of the two forms. This study was designed to evaluate the role of early experience in determining the observed habitat preference of the field-dwelling subspecies, *P. m. bairdi*. Mice tested in the experiments were either live-trapped or obtained from the *bairdi* Washtenaw stock of the University of Michigan's Mammalian Genetics Center.

A 1600-square-foot rectangular enclosure, constructed with its long axis lying halfway across a wood-field habitat boundary, provided opportunity for introduced animals to exercise habitat selection. Analysis of the vegetation within the enclosure revealed marked differences between the field and woods halves in terms of both species composition and the cover provided by the herbaceous stratum.

The movements of the experimental animals were recorded when the individuals tripped certain sensitized treadles located in runways at various positions in the pen. Habitat preference was ascertained for each mouse by measuring and comparing (1) the per cent *active time* (i.e., time spent out of nest boxes) in woods and field respectively; (2) the per cent *inactive time* (i.e., time nesting) in woods and field; (3) *rate of travel* (ft/min) in each habitat; (4) "*activity*" in woods and field (i.e., the average time elapsed between passages through successive recording runways); and (5) *average penetration* (i.e., the mean distance an animal moved into either the woods or the field from the habitat boundary). The data derived from these measurements were treated statistically.

Two variables existed in the experimental design: the hereditary background of the animals used and the experience (in field, woods, or laboratory) provided prior to testing. Six groups of mice were tested in the enclosure: (1) field-caught animals (Control Series I); (2) laboratory animals (Control Series II); (3) offspring of field-caught animals reared in the laboratory (Experimental Series I); (4) offspring of laboratory animals reared in the field (Experimental Series II); (5) offspring of field-caught animals reared in the woods (Experimental Series III); and (6) offspring of laboratory animals reared in the woods (Experimental Series IV).

Both field-caught animals and their offspring (Control Series I, Experimental Series I and III) selected the field half of the enclosure irrespective of previous experience. This preference was statistically significant for 10 of the 15 measurements involved. On the other hand, the laboratory animals and their offspring tested in Control Series II and Experimental Series IV did not exhibit a significant preference for either half of the enclosure. When laboratory mice (Experimental Series II) were reared in the field, however, they subsequently demonstrated a preference for that habitat which was significant at the one per cent level for all five categories. These data warrant the following conclusions: (1) The choice of the field environment by *P. m. bairdi* is normally predetermined by heredity. (2) Early field experience can reinforce this innate preference but is not a necessary prerequisite for subsequent habitat selection. (3) Early experience in other environments (woods or laboratory) is not sufficient to reverse the normal affinity of this subspecies for the field habitat. (4) Confinement of the *bairdi* Washtenaw stock in the laboratory for 12–20 generations has resulted in an apparent reduction of the hereditary control over the habitat selection response; this has led to marked increase in the variability of the behavior demonstrated by these animals when tested in the enclosure. (5) Laboratory mice retained an innate capacity to utilize early field experience in learning to respond positively to stimuli associated with this environment; experience in the woods or laboratory, however, did not have a corresponding effect.

Preliminary data derived from experiments now in progress indicate that some form of habitat imprinting may be operative in *Peromyscus*.

It is suggested that the genetic assimilation of originally learned responses provides a basis for interpreting the patterns of behavior which control habitat selection in these small mammals. Despite their marked ecological segregation, however, there is no evidence that the subspecies in the *Peromyscus maniculatus* complex have undergone sympatric speciation.

Literature Cited

Andrewartha, H. G. and L. C. Birch. 1954. *The Distribution and Abundance of Animals*. Univ. of Chicago Press, Chicago. 782 p.

Baldwin, J. M. 1896. A new factor in evolution. *Am. Naturalist* **30**: 441–451, 536–553.

Barbehenn, K. R. and J. G. New. 1957. Possible natural intergradation between prairie and forest deer mice. *J. Mammal.* **38**: 210–218.

Blair, W. F. 1940. A study of prairie deer mouse populations in southern Michigan. *Am. Midl. Nat.* **24**: 273–305.

———. 1950. Ecological factors in the speciation of Peromyscus. *Evolution* **4**: 253–275.

Brand, R. H. 1955. Abundance and activity of the wood mouse (*Peromyscus leucopus noveboracensis*) in relation to the character of its habitat. Ph. D. thesis. Univ. of Michigan, No. 3946.

Burt, W. H. 1954. *The Mammals of Michigan*. Univ. of Michigan Press, Ann Arbor, 288 p.

Cogshall, A. S. 1928. Food habits of deer mice of the genus *Peromyscus* in captivity. *J. Mammal.* **9**: 217–221.

Dice, L. R. 1922. Some factors affecting the distribution of the prairie vole, forest deermouse, and prairie deermouse. *Ecol.* **3**: 29–47.

———. 1925. The mammals of Marion Island, Grand Traverse County, Michigan. *Occ. Papers Mus. Zool. Univ: of Michigan*, No. **160**, 8 p.

———. 1931. The occurrence of two subspecies of the same species in the same area. *J. Mammal.* **12**: 210–13.

———. 1961. Laboratory instruments for measuring the behavior of shy or nocturnal small mammals. *J. Mammal.* **42**: 159–166.

Elton, C. 1927. *Animal Ecology*. Sidgwick and Jackson, London. 207 p.

Evans, F. C. & E. Dahl. 1955. The vegetational structure of an abandoned field in southeastern Michigan and its relation to environmental factors. *Ecol.* **36**: 685–706.

Foster, D. D. 1959. Differences in behavior and temperament between two races of the deer mouse. *J. Mammal.* **40**: 496–513.

Getz, L. L. 1961. Factors influencing the local distribution of *Microtus* and *Synaptomys* in southern Michigan. *Ecol.* **42**: 110–119.

Grinnell, J. 1917. Field tests of theories concerning distributional control. *Am. Nat.* **51**: 115–128.

Gullion, G. W. 1960. The ecology of Gambel's quail in Nevada and in the arid southwest. *Ecol.* **41**: 518–536.

Hall, E. R. and K. R. Kelson. 1950. *The Mammals of North America*. Ronald Press, New York. 1083 p.

Harris, V. T. 1952. An experimental study of habitat selection by prairie and forest races of the deer mouse, *Peromyscus maniculatus*. *Contrib. Lab. Vert. Biol., Univ. of Michigan* **56**, 53 p.

Hooper, E. T. 1942. An effect on the *Peromyscus maniculatus* rassenkreis of land utilization in Michigan. *J. Mammal.* **23**: 193–196.

Howard, W. E. 1949. Dispersal, amount of inbreeding, and longevity in a local population of prairie deer mice on The George Reserve, southern Michigan. *Contrib. Lab. Vert. Biol., Univ. of Michigan* **43**, 50 p.

Johnson, M. S. 1926. Activity and distribution of certain wild mice in relation to biotic communities. *J. Mammal.* **7**: 245–277.

Kendeigh, S. C. 1945. Community selection by birds on the Helderberg plateau of New York. *Auk* **62**: 418–436.

King, J. A. 1956. Sexual behavior of C57BL/10 mice and its relation to early social experience. *J. Genet. Psychol.* **88**: 223–229.

———. 1957. Relationships between early social experience and adult aggressive behavior in inbred mice. *J. Genet. Psychol.* **90**: 151–166.

———. 1961. Development and behavioral evolution in *Peromyscus*, p. 122–147. *In* W. F. Blair (ed.), *Vertebrate Speciation*. Univ. of Texas symposium.

King, J. A. and B. E. Eleftheriou. 1959. The effects of early handling upon adult behavior in two subspecies of deer mice, *Peromyscus maniculatus*. *J. Comp. and Physiol. Psychol.* **52**: 82–88.

Klopfer, P. H. 1962. *Behavioral Aspects of Ecology*. Prentice-Hall, New Jersey. 166 p.

Lack, D. 1933. Habitat selection in birds with special reference to the effects of afforestation on the Breckland avifauna. *J. Anim. Ecol.* **2**: 239–262.

———. 1940. Habitat selection and speciation in birds. *Brit. Birds* **34**: 80–84.

Linsdale, J. M. 1957. Ecological niches for warm-blooded vertebrate animals. *Wassman J. Biol.* **15**: 107–122.

Lorenz, K. 1937. The companion in the bird's world. *Auk* **54**: 245–273.

Mayr, E. 1947. Ecological factors in speciation. *Evolution* **1**: 263–288.

Miller, A. H. 1942. Habitat selection among higher vertebrates and its relation to intraspecific variation. *Am. Nat.* **76**: 25–35.

Odum, E. P. 1944. Water consumption of certain mice in relation to habitat selection. *J. Mammal.* **25**: 404–405.

Pitelka, F. A. 1941. Distribution of birds in relation to biotic communities. *Am. Midl. Nat.* **25**: 113–137.

Pruitt, W. O. 1953. An analysis of some physical factors affecting the local distribution of the shorttail shrew in the northern part of the lower peninsula of Michigan. *Misc. Publ. Mus. Zool., Univ. Michigan*, No. **79**, 39 p.

Rogers, J. S. 1942. The crane flies (Tipulidae) of the George Reserve, Michigan. *Misc. Publ. Mus. Zool., Univ. of Michigan*, No. **53**, 128 p.

Rowland, G. L. and P. J. Woods. 1961. Performance of the Tryon bright and dull strains under two conditions in a multiple T-maze. *Canad. J. Psychol.* **15**: 20–28.

Scott, J. P. 1962. Critical periods in behavioral development. *Science* **138**: 949–958.

Siegel, S. 1956. *Non-Parametric Statistics*. McGraw-Hill Book Co., New York. 312 p.

Simpson, G. G. 1953. The Baldwin effect. *Evolution* **7**: 110–117.

Stinson, R. H. and K. C. Fisher. 1953. Temperature selection in deer mice. *Canad. Zool.* **31**: 404–416.

Snedecor, G. 1956. *Statistical Methods*. Iowa St. Coll. Press, Ames, Iowa. 534 p.

Thorpe, W. H. 1939. Further experiments on preimaginal conditioning in insects. *Proc. Roy. Soc.* **127**: 471–82.

———. 1940. Ecology and the future of systematics, p. 341–364. In J. S. Huxley (ed.), *The New Systematics*, Clarendon Press, Oxford.

———. 1945. The evolutionary significance of habitat selection. *J. Anim. Ecol.* **14**: 67–70.

Tinbergen, N. 1951. *The Study of Instinct*. Oxford Univ. Press, London. 288 p.

Waddington, C. H. 1957. *The Strategy of the Genes*. Macmillan Co., New York. 211 p.

———. 1961. Genetic assimilation. *Adv. in Genet.* **10**: 257–293.

Wecker, S. C. 1962. The role of early experience in habitat selection by the prairie deer mouse, *Peromyscus maniculatus bairdi*. Ph.D. thesis No. 6143, Univ. of Michigan.

Williams, O. 1959. Food habits of the deer mouse. *J. Mammal.* **40**: 415–420.

Wolfenbarger, P. O. 1946. Dispersion of small organisms. *Am. Midl. Nat.* **35**: 1–152.

Cliff-Nesting Adaptations of the Galápagos Swallow-Tailed Gull[1]

Jack P. Hailman

E. Cullen (1957) showed that the cliff-nesting Black-legged Kittiwake [*Larus* (*Rissa*) *tridactylus*] differs from "typical" (i.e., ground-nesting) gulls in many respects. The species' unique morphological and behavioral characters, Cullen cogently argued, have resulted from adaptation (either directly or indirectly) to cliff-breeding. Epistemologically, the correlation between cliff-nesting and unusual characters constitutes a hypothesis that must be "tested" independently on a relatively unrelated cliff-nesting gull. Therefore, while I was studying the chick-feeding behavior of the cliff-nesting Galápagos Swallow-tailed Gull [*Larus* (*Creagrus*) *furcatus*] I noted the general habits of this species for comparison with the Kittiwake.

Methods

The results of observations of the colony on southern Plazas Island off Santa Cruz (Indefatigable) Island and of several colonies on Tower Island, made during November, 1962, are presented in tabular form with explanatory comments in the text. The observations are compared with characteristics of the Kittiwake and "typical" ground-nesting gulls.

The horizontal distance from the outer edge of the nest to the edge of the nesting ledge was measured with a tape measure in the beginning, and later estimated by eye; the vertical height of the nest above the sea was estimated by eye. Behavioral observations were made with binoculars and in some cases recorded photographically with still and motion pictures. Notes on the nocturnal habits, breeding cycle, and displays of *furcatus* are presented elsewhere (Hailman, 1964c, 1964a, and in prep., respectively).

In this and other publications on gulls I have followed the latest family revision (Moynihan, 1959), which assigns all species of gulls to the genus *Larus*. Except where noted, all information on the Kittiwake's adaptations has been taken from Cullen (1957). Information for comparisons with "typical, ground-nesting gulls" has come primarily from Cullen (1957), my unpublished notes on *Larus atricilla*, Tinbergen (1953), and accounts in Bent (1921).

In the "visual cliff" experiment reported below, a standard, albeit make-

[1] To Ernst Mayr (on the occasion of his 60th birthday), who taught me that the study of whole animals is not only an intellectually respectable pursuit but moreover an exciting life's devotion.

Reprinted by permission of the publisher from *The Wilson Bulletin* 77: 346–362, 1965.

shift, visual cliff apparatus (Fig. 3) was made from a wooden box 16.5 inches long, 11 inches wide, and 9 inches deep. Across the glass top ran a center strip of black tape (3.5 inches wide) upon which the chick stood. To one side of the strip was the plain glass ("deep" side), under which the inside of the box lined with square-ruled paper (0.9-mm squares) could be seen. On the other ("shallow") side, ruled paper lined the underside of the glass. Each chick was placed in the center of the strip under a small translucent box for a 30-second habituation period, after which the box was lifted and timing with a stopwatch begun. Ten newly hatched *furcatus* chicks raised from the egg in a dark incubator were tested. The chick was scored as having chosen a side (i.e., deep or shallow) if it placed one foot on that side so that the foot did not touch the center strip. If no choice was made within 10 minutes, the chick was scored as "no choice" and was gently pushed toward the deep side or pinched in order to force a choice.

Cliff-Nesting of the Swallow-Tailed Gull

The Actual Cliff Habitat

There are certain important differences between the "cliff" habitat of the Swallow-tailed Gull and the Kittiwakes. (1) The Swallow-tail nests on lava ledges or barancas whose angle varies from vertical to nearly horizontal, while the Kittiwake nests almost exclusively on vertical cliffs. (2) The two gulls nest at different heights, the Kittiwake sometimes very high (130 meters), the Swallow-tail at variable heights (1 to 25 meters), rarely higher than 8 meters (Fig. 1). (3) The Kittiwake's cliff almost always overlooks the sea, while that of the Swallow-tailed Gull may overlook land near the water (e.g., the colony in NW corner of Darwin Bay on Tower Island). (4) Similarly, flat land at the top or foot of the nesting cliff, or at least near it, is available to Swallow-tails for display activities; this is usually not so true for Kitti-wakes. (5) Finally, the distance from the nest to the edge of the cliff gives some idea of the restriction of living space and of the likelihood of eggs or chicks falling off the cliff. Minimum distances from the center of the nest to the edge are shown in Figure 1 for a sample of 41 nests of the colony at Plazas. Apparently all Kittiwakes nest on ledges which just barely hold a nest and two standing adults, so each nest is placed at about the shortest distance found for the Swallow-tailed Gull (25–50 cm). (Recently, however, Kitti-wakes have begun nesting on flat ground; see Paludan, 1955; Coulson, 1963).

Possible Selective Pressures
Producing Cliff-Nesting Habits

Cullen (1957) believes that the Kittiwake's cliff-nesting is an adaptation to avoid predation on the eggs and chicks, and even upon the adults. Predation is probably unimportant in the Swallow-tailed Gull (see below), since its nest

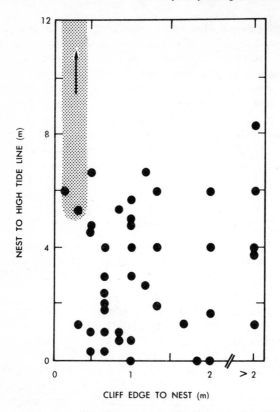

Fig. 1. Sites of 41 active nests of *Larus furcatus* on South Plazas Island, November 1962. The median height is 4 meters above the sea. The stippled portion indicates nest sites of *Larus tridactylus*, which go to above 130 meters, with median values of 15–35 meters above the sea (Coulson, 1963).

predators would be primarily aerial (and thus would have access to the nest) no matter where the gulls nested in the Galapagos (Hailman, 1964c). However, even aerial predators, such as Frigatebirds (*Fregata* spp.) may have difficulty landing on narrow ledges; aerial predators also have difficulty landing on the Kittiwake's ledges. The Swallow-tailed Gull's cliff-nesting might be linked in some way with pelagic habits; such an idea, if correct, would probably also apply to the Kittiwake. Also, the *furcatus* population may merely have exploited an unoccupied niche. The number of "typical" nesting sites for gulls (high grass in sand dunes or marshy area) is severely restricted in the Galápagos, which may account for the small population of the endemic Lava Gull (*L. fuliginosus*), a "typical species." (Food may also limit *fuliginosus* due to competition with other species for refuse; Hailman, 1963.)

Environmental Conditions and Correlated Characteristics

"Selective Pressures" Accompanying Cliff-Nesting

The multiple differences from typical gulls shown by the Kittiwake are presumably the results of several separate selective pressures. Probably only some of these selective pressures act on *furcatus*, partly because of the habitat differences (above). Thus, if Cullen's hypothesis be correct, the relatively unrelated Swallow-tailed Gull should prove convergent with the Kittiwake in those characters presumably related to situations that both species experience; in other respects the Swallow-tail should resemble typical gulls.

Specifically, the special environmental conditions experienced by the Kittiwake as a result of its cliff-nesting habits are: (1) reduced room for nesting; (2) scarcity of nesting sites; (3) scarcity of nest materials; (4) relaxation of predation on nest eggs; and (5) danger of eggs rolling off cliff and chicks falling off cliff. (I have altered this classification somewhat from Cullen's presentation.)

(1) Reduced room for nesting.—The nesting space of individual pairs of cliff-nesting birds is limited to small ledges, particularly if all possible nest-sites are utilized by the species. To hold as large a territory around its nest as does a ground-nesting gull, the ancestral cliff-nesting gull would have had to defend many separate ledges. Deviant individuals psychologically "satisfied" with defending merely the nesting ledge might have left more offspring because parental care improved with lessening of territorial disputes (see discussion of "aggressive neglect" in Hutchinson and MacArthur, 1959). The converse holds for ground-nester, which gain an antipredator advantage by spacing-out.

Some problems arising from this reduced living-space are: (a) reduced space for territorial "fighting" and display; (b) reduced room for display and copulation between mates; (c) undue hostility aroused between mates because of continual propinquity; and (d) fouling of the nest. Some adaptations to these problems are summarized in Table 1, and further explained by the following notes.

In the early part of the nesting season, Kittiwakes display on the water at the foot of the cliff (Tinbergen, 1958). That Swallow-tailed Gulls do not appear to do this might be explained by the fact that they have available other areas for display (see above). Twice I observed copulation on flat land near the nesting-cliffs but never saw it on the cliffs (which were watched for much longer periods of time). E. Curio (personal communication) also observed copulation once on the flat surface of a large rock. Allo-preening within the pair (J. M. Cullen, 1962) is probably a "display" evolved to reduce hostility.

TABLE 1

Characteristics presumably related to amount of nesting space

Species	Typical gulls	Swallow-tailed gull	Kittiwake
Living Space:	*Large*	*Reduced*	*Small*
1. Fighting			
a. frequency	frequent	infrequent (?)	frequent
2. Displays			
*a. chasing and moving displays	several	none (?)	a few
*b. long distance displays	several	none (?)	a few
*c. upright threat	common	absent (?)	absent
d. Long Call ceremony	loud	silent (?)	"Kittiwaking" (?)
*e. pairing displays	on pairing territory	occasionally on flat land	occasionally at base of cliff (and top of)
3. Copulation			
*a. where	on ground	on ground	on ledge
*b. female	stands	stands	sits on tarsi
4. Hostility Reduction			
*a. allo-preening (pairs)	absent (?)	present	present
*b. Head-flagging (adults)	uncommon	uncommon (?)	common (in certain situations)
*c. Head-flagging (chicks)	absent	(never seen)	present
*d. dark neck band	absent	immatures	chicks
5. Prevention of Fouling			
a. older chick defecates (cf. Table 4 : 2e)	off nest	over ledge	off nest or over ledge
b. eggshells (cf. Table 4 : 1d)	parents remove or eat	parents remove	not removed

*See Table 6.

(This characteristic was not commented upon by E. Cullen, 1957, but was discovered in the cliff-nesting tern *Anous tenuirostris* by J. M. Cullen and Ashmole: see Postscript to this paper.)

Appeasement Head-flagging exhibited between Kittiwake chicks is absent in *furcatus*, which has only one chick per clutch. (I saw Head-flagging, or something like it, only twice in adult birds.) I do not know whether or not strange Swallow-tail adults landing on a nest tend to peck the chick; in this situation the Kittiwake chick Head-flags. The very dark neck band of *tridactylus* chicks used in appeasement ("Bill hiding"—Cullen, 1957: Fig. 1) is likewise absent in *furcatus* chicks. However, such a neck band is found in white-plumaged (prefledged) immature birds, which interact with their parents and possibly birds on other territories. (This band is shown in Hailman, 1964c: Fig. 2.)

(2) *Scarcity of nesting sites.*—The Swallow-tailed Gull may breed at any time of the year (Hailman, 1964a; Leveque, 1964: 87), although Snow (Hatch, personal communication) has found recent evidence that individual pairs breed

on a 10-month cycle. Furthermore, synchrony of breeding is pronounced only in local areas, not on whole islands or between islands (Hailman, 1964*a*), although Snow's recent observations and also those of E. Curio indicate a general synchrony within whole colonies as well (Curio, personal communication). Therefore the competition for nesting sites might be less acute than in the seasonally breeding Kittiwake. Furthermore, on Tower Island I noticed many unused areas that seemed to me capable of supporting *furcatus* nests. However, this situation seems to be true of Kittiwakes as well. The real competition for nest sites may be for nest sites *near other pairs*. Probably as a result of a reduced competition for nest sites, the territory of the ledge is not guarded (at night) before the egg is laid as strongly as after this time. Adaptations to nesting space are summarized in Table 2.

TABLE 2

Characteristics presumably related to availability of nesting sites

Species:	Typical gulls	Swallow-tailed	Kittiwake
Nesting sites:	*Abundant*	*Ample (?)*	*Scarce*
1. Reduction of Competition			
a. breeding	seasonal	probably a 10-month cycle, with islands not in phase	seasonal
b. site	stereotyped	varied	stereotyped
2. Territory			
*a. when assumed	after pairing	probably after pairing	before pairing
b. guarding before first egg laid (cf. Table 3 : 3b)	rare	sometimes	always, but not necessarily continuously

*See Table 6.

(*3*) *Scarcity of nest materials.*—Kittiwakes compete for nesting material because vegetation does not grow on the breeding cliffs. For such materials, the birds must go to flatter land, which they "fear" (Cullen, 1957). The Swallow-tailed Gull solves the vegetation shortage by using lava stones (Fig. 2), and sometimes coral fragments and sea urchin spines, all of which I found abundantly near the nests in which they occurred. This difference in abundance of materials correlates well with the multiple differences between the two species (Table 3).

There is some local synchrony of the general breeding cycle among *furcatus* pairs within sight and sound of one another. However, this synchrony may be an "accidental" extension of the normal responses to displays of the mate (i.e., a sort of "behavioral pleiotropism") and may not have been specifically

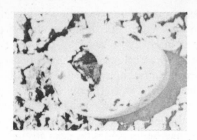

Fig. 2. Nests of *Larus furcatus*. a. (above) A typical nest of lava stones. The white egg tooth on the chick's bill is visible in the pipped hole. b. (below) A less structured nest placed under overhanging rocks, presumably for protection from the hot sun. In some areas, nests contain sea urchin spines and shells, as well as lava stones.

TABLE 3

Characteristics presumably related to availability of nesting materials

Species:	Typical gulls	Swallow-tailed	Kittiwake
Materials:	*Abound*	*Abound*	*Scarce*
1. Nest Materials			
a. materials used	vegetation	lava stones	mud and vegetation
*b. place	near nest	near nest	distant areas
*c. collecting	individual	individual	social
2. Building Nest			
*a. timing	individual	individual	synchronized
*b. technique	simple	simple	elaborate
3. Stealing from Other Nests			
*a. frequency	seldom	seldom	often
b. guarding before first egg laid (cf. Table 2:2b)	rare	sometimes	always

*See Table 6.

selected for (Hailman, 1964a). The Swallow-tailed Gull's synchrony is certainly not as remarkable as the specific synchrony of building found in Kittiwakes. The latter's unique building synchrony was thought to be due to the availability of mud on rainy days and to the social process of inland collecting (Cullen, 1957).

(*4*) *Predation at the nest.*—In Kittiwakes, nest predation (e.g., by foxes) is virtually eliminated because of the inaccessibility of the nest. However, in the Galapagos there are relatively few potential predators that cannot fly (e.g., two species of native rats which, however, climb readily) so the cliff-nesting habit of *furcatus* has not completely eliminated nest predation. Frigatebirds (*Fregata magnificens* and *F. minor*), which abound in the Galapagos, regularly patrol the nesting-cliffs. Furthermore, the native owl *Asio galapagoensis* (which hunts both by day and night) and the hawk *Buteo galapagoensis* probably prey on *furcatus* nests (Murphy, 1936). In fact, one of the primary selective advantages of nocturnal habits of *furcatus* may be to allow the parents to stand guard at the nest through all the daylight hours when the aerial predators abound (see Hailman, 1964c for a discussion of other possible factors). However, it is not known whether the parent's merely being at the nest actually reduces predation or not.

Table 4 compares antipredator adaptations in typical gulls, in *furcatus* and in *tridactylus*. Reduction of the clutch size might make a nest less conspicuous to predators, thereby decreasing the probability of destruction of all the eggs (also see below). However, this possible reduction of predation would not seem, *a priori*, to be of such magnitude as to offset the approximately 66 per cent reduction in productivity caused by fewer eggs. Table 4 indicates that not only *furcatus* (Fig. 2) but also *tridactylus* have cryptically colored eggs. Cullen (1957) considers this crypticity to be ancestral, and, although of no benefit to the Kittiwake, retained because it is of no disadvantage.

TABLE 4

Characteristics presumably related to amount of nest predation

Species:	Typical gulls	Swallow-tailed	Kittiwake
Nest predators:	*Aerial and ground*	*Aerial*	*(none)*
1. *Parental Protection*			
*a. alarm call	frequent	frequent	rare
*b. flight distance	far	variable (far to very near)	near
*c. attacks	vigorous	variable (vigorous to very weak)	very weak
d. eggshells (cf. Table 1 : 5b)	parents remove or eat	parents remove or eat	not dispersed
2. *Eggs and Chicks*			
a. egg coloration	cryptic	cryptic	cryptic
b. clutch size (cf. Table 5 : 2a)	three	one	two
*c. plumage	cryptic brown	cryptic gray	not cryptic
*d. behavior	hides in vegatation	hides in cracks	does not hide

*See Table 6.

Fig. 3. A one-day-old chick of *Larus furcatus* on the visual-cliff apparatus. The chick is facing the "deep side" of the cliff. The ruled squares on the paper lining the deep and shallow sides do not show well in the photograph partly because the film used is less sensitive to blue than is the eye.

(5) *Danger of falling off the cliff.*—Most Kittiwakes nest at the very edge of a real precipice; Swallow-tailed Gulls do not, on the average, nest in such a dangerous situation, although certain individuals may (see Fig. 1). Kittiwakes prevent eggs from rolling out of the nest by making an extra deep nest cup, whereas Swallow-tails use lava stones (Fig. 2). I tried rolling eggs out of several *furcatus* nests and found it very difficult (much more so than from the nest of *L. atricilla,* the American Laughing Gull, for instance). Gulls themselves might accidentally dislodge the egg from the nest, though possibly other natural causes do too. Curio (personal communication) recorded one incidence of sea breakers washing an egg from its nest. Possibly the reduction of crowding due to the small clutch size also helps prevent eggs from rolling over the ledge.

One trait not appearing in Table 5 requires comment. Cullen (1957: 300) notes that the Kittiwake has "strongly developed claws and toe-musculature" compared with ground-nesting gulls. The Swallow-tailed Gull appeared to me to have strong claws as well, but no stronger than those of the Lava Gull, *L. fuliginosus.* I attributed this similarity to the fact that the latter species, although not a cliff-nester, spends its life on the rock substrate of Galápagos shores. However, I later compared a long series of specimens at the U. S. National Museum and could find no consistent differences between species

TABLE 5

Characteristics presumably related to danger of falling off cliff

Species:	Typical gulls	Swallow-tailed	Kittiwake
Cliff danger:	*(None)*	*Some*	*Great*
1. Eggs and Chicks			
a. clutch (cf. Table 4 : 2b)	three	one	two
*b. nest	shallow cup of vegetation	shallow cup of stones	deep cup of vegetation
2. Chicks			
*a. stay in nest	a few days	long period	long period
*b. face toward	any direction	cliff wall	cliff wall
*c. locomotion	frequent	immobile	immobile
*d. when attacked	run	do not run	do not run
*e. flight movements	vigorous	intermediate	weak
f. "visual cliff" behavior	random choice (?)	avoid deep side	?
*g. feed from	ground and parent's bill	parent's bill	parent's throat
*h. parental feeding call	present	present	absent

*See Table 6.

of gulls, adults or chicks. Perhaps important differences are obscured in dried skins, so further checking of claws and musculature in the field is desirable.

Emlen (personal communication) is attempting to do "visual-cliff" experiments (Walk and Gibson, 1961) on the Kittiwake. Emlen (1963) has already shown that newly hatched chicks of the ground-nesting Herring Gull (*L. argentatus*) may avoid the deep side of an artificial "cliff." However, his apparatus and experimental procedures are sufficiently different from the standard visual-cliff situation that a direct comparison with the usual experiments cannot be made. Cullen (1957) reports that chicks of the ground-nesting Black-headed Gull (*L. ridibundus*) placed in *tridactylus* nests wandered "blindly" off the cliff. However, Shinkman (1963) showed that newly hatched domestic chicks (*Gallus gallus*) do recognize and avoid the deep side of a visual cliff apparatus; this shows that such perceptual organization is possible in a newly hatched precocial bird.

Of the ten newly hatched chicks I tested, six chose the shallow side, one the deep, and three made no choice during the 10-minute test period. The probability that this choice is due to chance is small (binomial of $\frac{1}{7}$ is $p = 0.062$). Of the three immobile chicks, one turned and stepped onto the shallow side when pushed toward the deep; the other two refused to take a step in any direction. It is further of interest that the single "deep-choosing" chick scampered ("without looking") onto the deep side immediately upon removal of the translucent box. Thus, it seems quite likely that *furcatus* chicks (like those of *Gallus gallus*) possess depth perception at hatching.

Cullen (1957) considers that the feeding of Kittiwake chicks is adaptive to cliff-nesting. Most gull species (including *furcatus*) regurgitate food upon the ground or hold it in the bill in response to the chick's pecking at red markings on the parental bill. (The marking is a white tip in *furcatus*, presumably an adaptation to nocturnal feeding: Hailman 1964b, 1964c.) However, Kittiwake chicks take food from the throat of the parent. Lacking red markings on the bill, the parent Kittiwake has a bright red throat, to which the chicks direct pecking-like movements when it is open (although they also peck at the yellow beak; J. M. Cullen, personal communication). It could be that the releaser has been moved inside the bill so that Kittiwake chicks will not be tempted to approach adults and topple over the edge of the cliff. At any rate, chicks do not need a "long distance signal" in order to find the parent, nor does the parent require a Pumping display of the chick in order to find its offspring (Cullen, 1957). Since the Swallow-tailed Gull's feeding is additionally influenced by its nocturnal timing, it is not reasonable to expect this species' throat to become white, since this would probably reflect very little light indeed. However, the *furcatus* parent does have a "feeding call" that releases the approach of the chick, as has *atricilla* (Hailman, 1964b) and other ground-nesting species. The Kittiwake lacks this call, presumably to prevent accidentally calling chicks over the cliff.

Since in all other adaptations relating to prevention of falling over the cliff, *furcatus* resembles *tridactylus* (see Table 5), the chick-feeding differences seem to be anomalous. I suggest that in all species bill and throat colors are also under selective pressures relating to displays between adults. I have argued elsewhere, for instance, that the position of the white bill-tip of *furcatus* in relation to the white feathers at the base of the bill indicates the displaying bird's head position in very low light intensities (Hailman, 1964c). Surely the throat color of all gull species is evident during displays in which the mouth is held wide open during vocalizations. It is possible, then, that the chick-feeding method is influenced by display-methods and vice versa.

Discussion and Conclusions

Multiple Selective Pressures

Few characteristics are governed by only one selective pressure during evolution. Thus, the removal or eating of eggshells and the young chick's droppings might serve both to prevent fouling of the nest and to prevent discovery of the nest by predators. Tinbergen and co-workers (1962) have demonstrated by field experiments that nests with broken eggshells are found and destroyed by predators more readily than nests without shells. Fouling has not been studied experimentally. Older chicks of all species defecate out of the nest. However, Kittiwakes with little nest predation defecate on the nesting ledge, while Swallow-tailed Gulls with more predation defecate over the ledge. This difference suggests that predation is important as a selective agent in defecation habits. Also, guarding of the nesting ledge prior to laying may serve to protect both the site and the nesting materials from being usurped by conspecifics in Kittiwakes (see above).

The clutch size of *furcatus* might be explained by Lack's (1954) proposal that clutch size in birds is determined by the number of young that can be fed successfully, although there seem to be other factors acting as well. The essence of Cullen's (1957: 289 ff) interpretation of the reduction of clutch size from three to two in the Kittiwake seems to be a special case of Lack's hypothesis: if a pair of gulls can feed only two young successfully, Kittiwakes need lay only two eggs to have the maximum clutch, while "typical" gulls must lay three since there is a high probability that at least one will die from causes other than starvation (e.g., predation) that do not affect Kittiwake chicks.

Cullen's suggestion probably could not apply to the Swallow-tailed Gull, which has many potential nest predators. Instead, two additional hypotheses were advanced for *furcatus* (above). The first, that clutch reduction makes the nest less conspicious to predators, is presumably not effective in Kittiwakes because of the lack of predation. However, I think it is unlikely as the major force in reducing clutch size in *furcatus*. The other explanation, lessening of crowding of eggs and chicks to prevent their accidental falling over the cliff, might operate in Kittiwakes as well, although Cullen does not specify this possibility.

However, still a fourth factor may be acting in the Swallow-tailed Gull, one that is a corollary of Lack's hypothesis. The breeding period of seasonally breeding gulls coincides with the abundance of food available for the young and clutch size is expanded to utilize the food maximally. In tropical species for which food is available in moderate supply the year around, the long nocturnal trek at sea for food may severely restrict the number of chicks that can be fed successfully. Although laying but one egg, *furcatus* pairs may actually rear more than one chick per year by breeding more often than annually (Snow's recent evidence, mentioned above, indicates a 10-month cycle).

Test of Cullen's Hypothesis

With the data at hand, we are now in a position to test E. Cullen's (1957) hypothesis that the peculiarities shown by Kittiwakes are indirectly the result of selective pressures accompanying cliff-nesting habits. Given the degree of environmental similarity in Kittiwakes and Swallow-tails, we can see how closely their characters match. (The following comparison omits (a) characters that cannot be evaluated as being either like Kittiwakes or ground-nesting gulls and (b) characters that cannot be assigned, *a priori*, to a single presumed selective pressure.)

Table 6 divides 30 characters of *L. furcatus* into a matrix of the degree of similarity with *tridactylus* versus the degree of similarity of the environmental conditions presumably related to the characters. It is evident that in those respects in which the environmental conditions (i.e., presumed selective pressures) are similar, the morphological and behavioral characters

TABLE 6

Summary of the Swallow-tailed Gull's morphological and behavioral characteristics

Environmental conditions	Like ground-nesting gull species		Intermediate		Like or equivalent to Kittiwakes	
Like Kittiwake						
reduced nesting space	4⎱	6	0⎱	1	6⎱	11
cliff danger	2⎰	6	1⎰	1	5⎰	11
Intermediate						
nest sites scarce	1⎱	5	0⎱	2	0⎱	0
nest predation	4⎰	5	2⎰	2	0⎰	0
Like Ground-Nesters						
nest materials scarce	5		0		0	

Morphological/behavioral characteristics*

*Those relatively unambiguous characters marked with an asterisk (*) in Tables 1–5. See text.

are also similar. Taken as a whole, the data constitute a clear vindication of Cullen's (1957) hypothesis that peculiarities of the Kittiwake are the result of special selective pressures that accompany cliff-nesting.

Why does the Swallow-tailed Gull in some respects resemble ground-nesting gulls when the environmental characteristics are similar to those of Kittiwakes? Several answers are possible. (a) First, *furcatus* does not experience as extreme an environment as does *tridactylus*, even in those respects where the environment is designated as "like Kittiwake" in Table 6. (For instance, Figure 1 shows that the danger of falling over the cliff is not as great.) (b) Secondly, the independent adaptation of *furcatus* to cliff-dwelling may not yet have proceeded far enough to evolve the full complement of characters possessed by *tridactylus*. That is, in evolutionary time *furcatus* may be a more recent cliff-nesting species; or *furcatus* may have some kind of genetical limitations which have not produced the variation for natural selection to work upon. (c) Lastly, other selective pressures which have escaped the notice of Cullen and me might be acting upon these characters in different ways in the two species. Very probably all of these reasons have some validity. The important thing is, I think, that *furcatus* completely lacks Kittiwake-like traits where its environment resembles that of ground-nesting gulls.

Epistemological Status of Comparative Data Concerning Natural Selection

The most satisfactory method of demonstrating that a morphological or behavioral character is under the influence of a specific selective pressure is to measure that pressure within a population of organisms; deviants from the norm of the character should be more strongly selected against. For instance, Kruuk (1964) has shown that the farther a pair of Black-headed Gulls (*Larus ridibundus*) nests from the center of a colony, the heavier the nest predation by foxes.

Another method, setting up an artificial situation closely resembling the natural one, is often necessary because of the rarity of natural deviants or the difficulty of measuring deviants and differential selection in natural populations. Thus, Tinbergen et al. (1962) have shown that Black-headed Gull nests artificially set up and placed near a nesting colony will be preyed upon by both aerial and ground predators. Aerial predators find and destroy such nests more readily when broken shells are placed in or near a nest with chicks or eggs. This demonstrates rather satisfactorily at least one of the selection pressures that maintain the eggshell removal behavior of nesting adults.

Least cogent among methods of demonstrating selective pressures on specific characters is the method of this paper. A population (which may be a species, as in this case) is discovered which shows differences in morphology or behavior from other, presumably genetically related, populations. This discovery, in and of itself, is not a valid demonstration that the characters are under selective pressures due to observed environmental differences between the populations. However, this correlation does function as a *prediction* as to what characters will be found in another population with the same environment as either the deviant or the "normal" populations already known. This third population, for which the prediction was made, constitutes a valid test of the hypothesis (i.e., environment–character causation) *only* if its characters were unknown at the time of conception of the hypothesis. (Conversely, if the new population's characters were known—say from museum skins—but its environment was not, prediction of the conditions of its environment would constitute a valid method of approach.)

This indirect, "comparative" method is, however, full of methodological pitfalls. The gene pools of all populations concerned must be similar enough that the same variations would be produced for natural selection to act upon. The populations should have been isolated and living in their present environments for sufficient time for natural selection to work. Furthermore, multiple selective pressures will usually be involved, as well as selective pressures of which the investigator is unaware. There are certainly other problems as well.

In conclusion, the present method for studying natural selection has a rather low reliability. It is, however, a vast improvement over glibly assigning a "selective advantage" to a particular morphological or behavioral character just because to do so seems "reasonable" *a priori*.

A Postscript

Shortly after the manuscript of this paper was finished, there appeared a study of the cliff-nesting tern, *Anous tenuirostris* (the Black Noddy). J. M.

Cullen and N. P. Ashmole (1963) found many differences between this species and other terns, and these unique characters closely resemble those of the Kittiwake and the Swallow-tailed Gull. The one "new" possible cliff-nesting adaptation reported for *furcatus* (allo-preening), Cullen and Ashmole discovered in the Black Noddy as well. Their study adds a further confirmation of E. Cullen's (1957) hypothesis.

Summary

The Galápagos Swallow-tailed Gull (*Larus* (*Creagrus*) *furcatus*) nests on shallow to steep cliffs. In some respects (i.e., reduced nesting space, danger of falling over cliff) its environmental conditions resemble those of the cliff-nesting Kittiwake (*L.* (*Rissa*) *tridactylus*). Unlike *tridactylus*, *furcatus* has abundant nesting materials available, as do ground-nesting gulls such as *L. argentatus* and *atricilla*. In some aspects of its ecology (availability of nest sites, amount of nest predation) *furcatus* is intermediate between the *tridactylus* and ground-nesting gulls.

Many behavioral and morphological characteristics of *furcatus* were noted in field study and experiments. Thirty of these are unambiguous enough for comparison with the other species. Of those characters presumably adaptive to the environmental conditions shared with ground-nesting gulls, all five resembled the characters of the ground-nesting species. Of seven characters presumably related to the "intermediate" ecological conditions, five resembled characters of ground-nesters and two were intermediate. Finally, of 17 characters presumably adaptive to conditions shared with Kittiwake, 11 resembled those of the Kittiwake, one was intermediate, and 6 resembled those of ground-nesting species.

Thus, Cullen's (1957) hypothesis that the Kittiwake's unusual characters are adaptive to special ecological conditions accompanying cliff-nesting is, in general, confirmed.

Acknowledgments

The research trip to the Galápagos was sponsored by NSF Grant No. GB98 to Dr. Peter H. Klopfer. I was accompanied in the field by Jeremy J. Hatch and Robert Risebrough, who were helpful in many ways. Dr. A. Brosset, then director of the Darwin Station, was instrumental in arranging field trips in the Galápagos. Dr. George Watson of the U.S. National Museum made available the gull collections there for study of claws and toe musculature. The manuscript was improved greatly through the critical comments of J. J. Hatch, Dr. E. Curio, Dr. P. H. Klopfer, and especially Drs. J. M. and E. Cullen.

Literature Cited

Bent, A. C. 1921 Life histories of North American gulls and terns. *U.S. Natl. Mus. Bull.* **113**: 1–345.

Coulson, J. C. 1963 The status of the Kittiwake in the British Isles. *Bird Study* **10**: 147–179.

Cullen, E. 1957 Adaptations in the Kittiwake to cliff-nesting. *Ibis* **99**: 275–302.

Cullen, J. M. 1962 Allo-, auto- and hetero-preening. *Ibis* **105**: 121.

Cullen, J. M., and N. P. Ashmole 1963 The Black Noddy *Anous tenuirostris* on Ascension Island. II. Behaviour. *Ibis* **103b**: 423–446.

Emlen, J. T. 1963 Determinants of cliff edge and escape responses in Herring Gull chicks in nature. *Behaviour* **22**: 1–15.

Hailman, J. P. 1963 Why is the Galápagos Lava Gull the color of lava? *Condor* **65**: 528. 1964a Breeding synchrony in the equatorial Swallow-tailed Gull. *Amer. Nat.* **98**: 79–83. 1964b The ontogeny of an instinct: the pecking response in chicks of the Laughing Gull (*Larus atricilla* L.) and related species. Unpublished Ph.D. thesis, Duke University. Durham, North Carolina. 1964c The Galápagos Swallow-tailed Gull is nocturnal. *Wilson Bull.* **76**: 347–354.

Hutchinson, G. E., and R. H. MacArthur 1959 On the theoretical significance of aggressive neglect in inter-specific competition. *Amer. Nat.* **93**: 133–134.

Kruuk, H. Predators and anti-predator behaviour of the Black-headed Gull. (*Larus ridibundus* L.) *Behaviour Suppl.* XXI, 196.

Lack, D. 1954 *The Natural Regulation of Animal Numbers*. Oxford Univ. Press, London.

Leveque, R. 1964 Notes sur la reproduction des oiseaux aux Iles Galapagos. *Alauda* **32**: 5–44.

Moynihan, M. 1959 A revision of the family Laridae (Aves). *Amer. Mus. Novitates* **1928**: 1–42.

Murphy, R. C. 1936 *Oceanic Birds of South America*. Amer. Mus. Nat. Hist., New York.

Paludan, K. 1955 Some behavior patterns of *Rissa tridactyla*. *Vidensk. Medd. Dansk. Naturh. Foren.* **117**: 1–21.

Shinkman, P. G. 1963 Visual depth discrimination in day-old chicks. *J. Comp. Physiol. Psychol.* **56**: 410–414.

Tinbergen, N. 1953 *The Herring Gull's World*. Collins, London. 1958 *Curious Naturalists*. Basic Books, New York.

Tinbergen, N., G. J. Broekhuysen, F. Feeks, J. C. W. Houghton, H. Kruuk, and E. Szulc 1962 Egg shell removal by the Black-headed Gull, *Larus ridibundus* L.; A behaviour component of camouflage. *Behaviour* **19**: 74–117.

Walk, R. D., and E. Gibson 1961 A comparative and analytical study of visual depth discrimination. *Psychol. Monogr.* **75** (no. 519).

Determinants of Cliff Edge and Escape Responses in Herring Gull Chicks in Nature

John T. Emlen, Jr.

Cullen (1957) and others have noted that chicks of the cliff-nesting kittiwake gull, *Rissa tridactyla*, characteristically "freeze" in position when approached by a human observer while those of plateau nesting gull species run for cover. Observations on chicks of the herring gull, *Larus argentatus*, at Kent Island, New Brunswick, suggest that both of these distinct types of escape behavior occur within this single species according to the nature of the substrate on which the birds are hatched and reared. Accordingly, a series of tests and experiments was made during the summers of 1960 and 1961 designed to analyze the natural determinants of escape and cliff edge responses in chicks from the two situations.

A majority of the herring gulls on Kent Island nest on the gently rolling, turf-covered interior of the island where their nests are hidden in dense low stands of forbs irregularly broken by small rock outcroppings, barren trails, muskrat foraging areas and hillocks trampled by the gulls. Peripherally, the colony extends over the rim and down onto the rocky cliffs which border the island's south and south-east shores. Here the birds nest on narrow rocky ledges essentially devoid of vegetative cover. Chicks resting in or near their nests in these two contrasting situations provided the subjects for the study.

The plan of procedure was to test all birds on site using an elevated translucent platform on which behavior could be observed from concealment below. The drop from the platform edge constituted a psychological barrier restricting the subject's freedom to escape. Separate tests were devised for evaluating edge withdrawal reactions and escape reactions.

I am indebted to Dr. C. E. Huntington and Mr. T. Skaling for assistance in the field, and to Drs. Huntington, J. Neess, and W. Welker for reading and criticizing this report.

Methods and Procedures

The apparatus used in all the tests described in this report consisted of a 16 × 17 inch platform fixed to the top of a tripod at a height of 78 inches above ground (Fig. 1). The apparatus was carried into the field and was set up for each bird at a convenient point on level ground as close as possible to the nest or capture site. Subjects were tested only once.

The platform was made of $\frac{1}{8}$ inch plexiglass which retained the protective gummed-paper covering on its upper surface. This provided a translucent

Reprinted by permission of the author and the publisher from *Behaviour* 22: 1–15, 1963. The study was supported in part by a grant (No. G–13064) from the National Science Foundation.

Fig. 1. The portable elevated platform used in all ledge response and jump tests summarized in this report. The bird here being tested came from a precipitous (type 5) nest site a few yards to the right of the platform.

"one way" film through which the activities of the test bird could be watched against the sky while the observer remained invisible below (Fig. 2). Portions of the gummed paper covering were removed to provide "visual cliff" conditions for certain of the tests.

Birds to be tested were approached quietly as they rested in their nests or in the vegetation or rocks. All birds of appropriate size were used as they were encountered in order to minimize bias in the selection of test subjects. Very few potential subjects escaped. A hood, generally a tin can, was quietly slipped over the head and the bird quickly and gently lifted to the platform above the observer's head. After placing the bird in the first test position on the translucent platform the hood was carefully removed and observations started. In the 1960 observations responses were recorded for three "edge tests" followed by a graded series of six "jump tests" as described below.

Edge Test A (visual cliff)—The bird was placed with its head directly over and parallel with the line dividing the paper-covered portion and the transparent (visual cliff) portion of the platform (Fig. 3). The tendency for the bird to turn its head or its body toward the opaque side was evaluated at four levels: no response (o),—slight (1),—moderate (2),—strong (3) in three repeated tests, the bird being replaced in the test position each time by the

Fig. 2. A gull chick as observed from below through the translucent platform. The opaque vertical pusher used in edge tests 2 and 3 is in place and appears as a dark band across the platform. The transparent portion of the platform used in the visual cliff test lies at the near side.

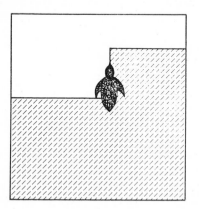

Fig. 3. Position of chick on test platform during the visual cliff edge test. The shaded area indicates the opaque, paper-covered part of the platform.

observer's hand reaching up from below as soon as it had made a recordable response.

Edge Test B (push resistance)—Immediately after the completion of test A the bird was slowly pushed by a vertical shield of dark opaque pressboard (see Fig. 2) to the edge of the platform and its resistance to being pushed evaluated at four levels as above. Again the test was repeated three times for each bird.

Edge Test C (edge withdrawal)—The tendency of the bird to withdraw from the platform edge to the vertical wall of the pusher as it was moved back or after it had been moved back about six inches was evaluated at four levels (as above) following each of the three pushing tests.

These edge tests were effective only in birds less than about 14 to 16 days of age. In older birds the edge responses were masked by developing escape responses to the experimenter's hand and the pusher. No objective procedure was devised for avoiding bias in the observer's evaluation of edge responses other than the postponement of data analysis. It should be noted, however, that no hypothesis on the nature of the results had been formulated at the time of testing.

Jump Tests.—Following the edge response tests, the birds, still on the platform and unable to see the observer below, were watched in their tendencies to escape by jumping to the ground during six stages of increasing provocation as described below:

Stage 1. The pusher was quietly removed and the bird permitted an adjustment period of 10 seconds.

Stage 2. The bird was allowed to explore the platform and its edges undisturbed for 30 seconds.

Stage 3. The observer quietly reached up with his hand and repeatedly placed the bird with its toes at the edge of the platform during a period of 30 seconds.

Stage 4. The observer handled the bird roughly for 10 seconds, then stepped back to make himself visible for an additional 30 seconds.

Stage 5. The observer walked away to a distance of 30 to 50 feet where he sat quietly for 30 seconds in full view of the subject.

Stage 6. The observer remained seated for an additional two minutes, then ran noisily back to the platform with arms waving.

If the bird jumped from the platform during the first stage (or during the edge tests) it was graded with a score of 0. If it remained during the sequence of tests it was rated with progressively higher scores, the highest score of 5 being given to birds which were still on the platform at the end of the series. The ratings used in 1961 were based on a slightly modified and supposedly more sensitive test sequence involving eight stages.

These testing and scoring procedures were, of course, arbitrarily designed, and the stages must not be interpreted as equal increments along a single continuum. The values derived are useful only for comparing birds of different origin by nonparametric techniques.

Fig. 4. A gull chick atop the test platform in the flat vegetated plateau of the island's interior (type of nesting habitat).

Fig. 5. Three gull nests in rocky cliff situations (type 5 nesting habitat).

Data recorded with each test included: (1) subjective categorization of the topography of the nesting substrate into 5 classes from level (Fig. 4) to precipitous (Fig. 5); (2) estimated distances to the nearest significant drop or rise in topography, the nearest beach or coastline and the nearest vegetated area; (3) an indication of substrate texture, whether loam, peat, sand, gravel or rocks; (4) a formula description of the vegetation at the nest site giving height, density and foliage type; (5) distance of the test chick from its nest at time of capture; (6) distance from nest or capture site to the test site (where pertinent, the texture and topography of the substrate at the site of testing was noted and the direction selected by the jumping bird with respect to these features); (7) a subjective rating of the "temperament" of the bird based on responses to being captured and handled; (8) records of the occurrence of regurgitation or defecation on the platform; (9) a crude evaluation into three categories of the clamor and general excitement of local adult gulls during the test; (10) a record of the time of day, the sky cover, wind and temperature conditions at the time of testing, and (11) an age index—the tarsal length measured at the conclusion of each test and subsequently translated to absolute age (Fig. 6).

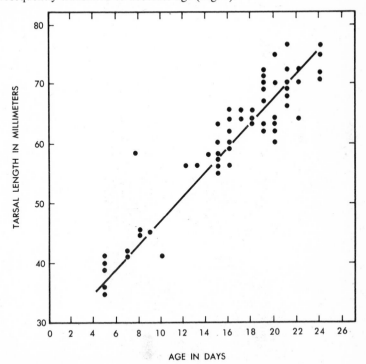

Fig. 6. Correlation of tarsal length and absolute age in 56 free-living gull chicks marked during the first few days of life for subsequent capture and measurement. The line for the mean, drawn by eye, indicates a fairly even growth rate of approximately two millimeters per day.

Results

Edge Response

A negative edge response apparently develops during the first day post-hatching in all gull chicks. In six incubator-hatched chicks in which the age was known to within an hour, the withdrawal response to the platform edge was detected shortly after the birds could stand and walk at ages varying from 3 to 18 hours. By the second day the response was universal and readily detectable in the edge tests.

In edge tests with chicks hatched in nature (Fig. 7) the level of responsiveness declined with advancing age, a decline which coincided with and was presumably related to the development of locomotor skills and of the escape response. In the visual cliff and edge withdrawal tests, the two considered most valid as indicators of edge response, the declining trend was more pronounced in the birds from cliff nests than in those from plateau sites. The difference was significant (chi square test) in the visual cliff tests but not in the others.

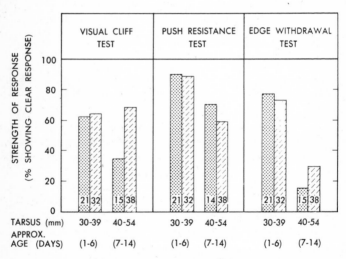

Fig. 7. Visual cliff, push resistance and edge withdrawal responses of chicks from cliff nests (stippled bars) and plateau nests (hatched bars) at two stages of development. The height of the bars indicates the percent of birds in each size (age) category which showed moderate or strong responses. The numbers in the bars indicate sample size.

Escape Response

In the jump tests all gull chicks old enough to stand and walk but with tarsi less than 35 mm. ((ca 1–3) days of age) remained on the platform through at least five of the six successive stages (Fig. 8). A marked drop in

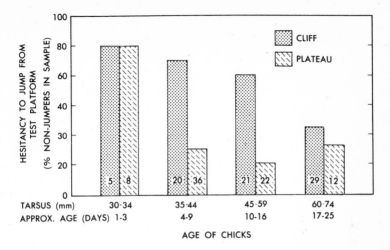

Fig. 8. Decline in reluctance to jump from the test platform with advancing age in chicks from cliff nests (stippled bars) and from plateau nests (hatched bars). The height of the bars indicates the percent of birds in each size (age) category which were non-jumpers, i.e., remained on the test platform through stage 5 of the test series. The numbers in the bars indicate sample size.

this hesitancy to jump occurred about the fourth or fifth day in chicks from plateau nests with less than a third of them remaining on the platform through stage five of the testing. Chicks from nests in cliff situations showed no comparable change of response, and, except for a few individuals, continued in their refusal to jump until about 17 days of age. The difference between the two groups during the intermediate stages (4th to 17th day) was highly significant by the chi square test.

Examination of the recorded data on the condition of the birds and the nature of the habitat and weather at the time of testing failed to reveal any correlations of interest other than those described above for topography at the nest or capture site. Test birds were deliberately selected from the extreme types of topography. No correlations of edge or escape behavior with topography and substrate texture at the testing site, as opposed to nesting site, could be detected, and no consistant tendencies to select a jumping direction towards or away from a cliff or plateau situation were found.

Egg Transplant Experiments

An experiment was conducted in the summer of 1961 in which eggs from cliff nests and plateau nests were inter-changed during the early incubation stage of nesting, and the chicks allowed to develop in the environment of their foster parents. All eggs from each of the designated cliff nests were removed shortly after the clutch had been completed and immediately replaced by an equal number of eggs of plateau origin. Experimental nests were visited at frequent intervals during the period of hatching and the chicks marked for subsequent identification when one or two days of age by punching a diagnostic pattern of holes in the toe webs. The birds were then left undisturbed with their foster parents until they had reached an appropriate age for testing. At that time 53 toe-clipped chicks were recovered and tested on the jump platform, 28 of them from the plateau and 25 of them from the cliff area. Without exception these chicks were found in and had presumably been reared entirely within the habitat type and topographic situation in which they had hatched.

Chicks hatched on the plateau from eggs laid in cliff nests showed the free jumping characteristics of native plateau birds, while birds hatched and reared on cliff sites from eggs of plateau origin behaved like their cliff-dwelling neighbors (Table 1).

TABLE 1

Comparison of platform jump scores of chicks from eggs transplanted between cliff and plateau nest sites and their controls*

Site of origin	Site of rearing	Non-jumpers (6–8)	Inter-mediates (4–5)	Jumpers (1–3)
Cliff	Plateau	4(14%)	4(14%)	20(72%)
Plateau	Plateau (control)	3(13%)	6(25%)	15(62%)
Plateau	Cliff	8(32%)	10(40%)	7(28%)
Cliff	Cliff (control)	14(31%)	20(44%)	11(24%)

*Because of different scoring techniques used in the 1961 tests, these figures are not directly comparable to those shown in Figs. 7 and 8.

Experiment with Experience Deprivation

In the summer of 1961 an experiment was performed to test the hypothesis that the hesitancy to jump in cliff-reared chicks is related to restrictions on movement imposed by narrow ledge situations during early stages of behavioral development. Circles of poultry netting, 4 feet in diameter were placed around 30 plateau nests during the early stages of incubation.

In 15 of these all vegetation within the fence was cleared away so that the chicks were hatched into a spatially restricted environment without sheltering foliage (Fig. 9). In the other 15 the vegetation was left intact and the chicks, on hatching, had the natural cover of the plateau but were restricted in their freedom to move more than two feet from the nest (Fig. 10). Standard jump tests were made after the chicks had reached an appropriate age. Chicks from unfenced nests in the same area served as local controls.

The number of penned chicks available for testing at the appropriate age was small, and the results are quite inconclusive (Table 2). If we adopt the questionable procedure of adding the data from the plateau controls

Fig. 9. Fenced nest enclosure stripped of vegetative cover as used in the experiments with experience deprivation. The shingle on the left provided shade.

Fig. 10. Fenced nest enclosure with vegetation left undisturbed as used in the experiments with experience deprivation.

TABLE 2

Comparison of platform jump scores of plateau chicks restricted to the close vicinity of their nests with controls not so restricted

	Non-Jumpers (6–8)	Inter-mediates (4–5)	Jumpers (1-3)
a–Restricted in cleared pens	5(33%)	3(20%)	7(47%)
b–Restricted in vegetated pens	3(30%)	5(50%)	2(20%)
c–Unrestricted on vegetated plateau (local control)	3(23%)	7(54%)	3(23%)
d–Unrestricted on vegetated plateau (total controlled)	6(16%)	13(35%)	18(49%)

of the transplant experiment to those of the local controls, there is a slightly higher refractoriness in the penned birds comparable to that of cliff birds. No difference is detectable in the scores of penned birds from cleared as opposed to vegetated pens.

Discussion

Habitat-Response Correlations

Avoidance of cliff edges and reluctance to jump are behavior traits with obvious survival value for chicks of any species living in precipitous nesting situations. Herring gulls examined in this study all showed such negative responses in elevated platform tests during the first few days of life regardless of their site of origin. After that, however, responses changed variously according to the topography of the substrate on which the bird had its home. These changes may be summarized as follows:

(1) Negative responses declined with advancing age in all platform tests.
(2) Cliff chicks dropped their withdrawal responses at the platform edge more rapidly than plateau chicks.
(3) Cliff chicks retained their reluctance to escape by jumping longer than plateau chicks.

The decline in the withdrawal response in the platform edge tests indicates a growing refractoriness or insensibility to edge situations with advancing age. It suggests an adaptive adjustment of behavior to conditions to which a cliff-resident bird is continuously exposed, an habituation to a stimulus situation consistently presented without negative reinforcement. The visual cliff and edge withdrawal tests (A and C in Fig. 7) would seem to be the best indicators of this changing response; the failure of the push resistance test (B in Fig. 7) to show the same differential decline may be due to complications introduced with the direct disturbance of the subject during testing.

The results of the jump tests graphically shown in Fig. 8 indicate that after the first few days of life chicks from cliff nests were more reluctant to jump than chicks from plateau nests. Thus, the birds which showed the greatest boldness in the platform edge tests were the most hesitant in the jump tests. This apparent contradiction, if real, can only be resolved by attributing invalidity to the weaker set of data—the edge test data. A more satisfactory explanation is that there is no contradiction, and that the two tests in fact measure two different response categories. Support for this latter interpretation is found when we consider that the suggested habituation to edge situations in chicks from cliff nests could be highly destructive if it increased the probability of hasty escape responses under provocation. Under these circumstances natural selection would strongly favor a dissociation of the escape response from the edge response.

Available information on mortality factors operating in the two nesting situations under consideration suggest survival values for each of the escape resposes according to the situation in which it occurs. Predation by adult gulls is the principal factor among plateau nesting herring gulls where from 50 to 88 % of all chicks may succumb before fledging (Paynter, 1949; Paludan, 1951; Darling, 1938). The causes of mortality in herring gull chicks on cliff sites is not known, but studies by Cullen (1957) on ledge nesting kittiwake gulls suggest that accidents associated with the hazard of the physical situation are more important. Insofar as these observations apply to the nesting situations of Kent Island, a chick situated on an exposed ledge overlooking a precipice would do well to stay put, while another perched in the center of a clearing on the plateau would be exposed to danger until it had moved to cover.

The differences between plateau and cliff-reared chicks as observed could conceivably be based upon genetically determined behavioral characteristics fostered by an intense natural selection of adapted phenotypes. On the other hand it is possible that the differences in escape response are acquired through learning processes operating at different levels or in different ways in the two nesting situations. Each of these possibilities is considered below.

Genetic Considerations

A study of the visual cliff responses of a variety of neonate animals led Walk and Gibson (1961) to conclude that "an animal's response to the lack of visual support is unlearned, a reflex that is characteristic of the species." If this is true for species it could also be true for genetic varieties, and the response difference between gull chicks from the two nesting sites examined in this study could have its basis in a behavioral dimorphism of origin. Such a possibility gains plausibility when one considers the divergent selective pressures operating in the two nesting situations. Under the conditions described above, natural selection would favor cliff clinging variants in cliff situations and more mobile wanderers and shelter seekers in the vegetated plateau areas of the colony.

The maintenance of two genetic types in a gull colony would depend on one of two mechanisms: 1) *reproductive isolation* or polytypy—a segregation of breeding adults of the two genotypes in the appropriate rearing situations; or 2) *stable polymorphism*—a broad range of genetic variation in each successive generation spanning the phenotypes required for survival in the two rearing situations.

Reproductive isolation of the genotypes responsible for a phenotypic dimorphism in juvenile behavior would require that the birds on maturing return to nest on the same type of site on which they were reared several years before. A tendency to return to the rearing locality for nesting has been demonstrated for a number of bird species and a predilection for a similar nesting situation has been indicated for several (Miller, 1942; Thorpe, 1945; Hochbaum, 1958). There is no evidence, however, for a tendency to return to site sufficiently developed to provide the level of inbreeding necessary to maintain effective genetic segregation as here postulated. The results of the egg transplant experiments (Table 1), furthermore, provide rather convincing evidence against the existence of distinct breeding genotypes in the two nesting situations.

Stable polymorphism requires that enough individuals be produced at the extremes of variation to insure survival of an adequate breeding stock in each of the environmental situations to which these extreme variants are adapted. No segregation of breeding types is required, only the repetitive production of appropriately adapted phenotypes in each generation of chicks. Such stable polymorphism has been demonstrated in nature in the snail (*Cepea nemoralis*) by Cain and Sheppard (1950) and in various moths by Kettlewell (1956). Its occurrence in the Kent Island herring gull colony is problematical, but the high levels of overproduction and juvenile mortality which characterize gull colonies could conceivably be a reflection of the expensive selection process inherent in this mechanism. Evidence against the occurrence of stable polymorphism is seen in the recorded increased number of birds in the median score categories with advancing age (Table 3). In a stabilized polymorphism based on selective juvenile mortality one would expect a decrease rather than an increase in the numbers of intermediate performers.

The alternative to a genetic explanation of the observed behavioral differences between cliff and plateau chicks is that the respective characteristics of the two groups are acquired as a result of divergent individual experience in the two contrasting habitats during the early days of life. We have seen that the hesitance to jump declined during the first week in plateau birds while it remained high in cliff birds (Fig. 8). Insofar as learning is involved, this difference must have been associated with provocative factors in the

TABLE 3

Percent representation of birds in the low score, median score and high score categories of the 1960 jump tests at four age (tarsal length) levels

	Tarsal length (age)			
	30–39	40–49	50–59	60–74
High score birds	70	52	45	39
Median score birds	15	25	32	41
Low score birds	15	23	23	20
Sample size	40	39	34	39

plateau situation, inhibitory factors in the cliff situation, or a combination of the two. Since there is no way to determine which of the two courses, if either, is "normal," we can do no more than compare and evaluate the relative significance of distinctive environmental factors in the two situations as possible determinants of the respective behavioral characteristics. Modern learning theories suggest three processes which may have been operating on the birds under study:

(1) A negative conditioning process in birds from cliff sites in which injuries received in falls reinforce the reluctance to jump.
(2) A negative conditioning process in birds from vegetated plateau sites in which attacks from adult gulls in the nesting area reinforce tendencies to flee from exposed situations.
(3) An increase in general adaptability and boldness in chicks from vegetated plateau situation as a result of wider experience in a varied and relatively unrestricted environment.

The first process, a simple learning to refrain from jumping in edge situations as a result of negatively reinforcing experience loses its initial logical appeal when one considers that in the precipitous situations of this study most trial jumps or falls would be lethal either directly through injuries or indirectly through difficulties in returning to the home ledge to which the parent birds bring food. The possibility that negative reinforcement is generated by simple visual exposure to cliff edges seems to be refuted by the results of the edge and visual cliff tests discussed above. It is also interesting and perhaps pertinent that of six birds which jumped when the test platform was set up near the brink of a precipice, three selected the outward direction.

The proposition that chicks from vegetated plateau sites learn through experience the value of protecting shelter and hence tend to flee from exposed situations such as the test platform, was examined directly in the cleared pen experiment in which chicks were reared on small plots at the nest from which all vegetation had been removed (Table 2, groups a and b). The evidence provided by this experiment is weakened by the fact that the encircling fences incidentally excluded marauding gulls and thus may have lowered the incentive value of vegetative cover. The results, depreciated by this consideration and by the small sample size, fail to provide evidence for the proposition.

The possibility that jumps from the platform were motivated by attraction to sheltering cover rather than escape from exposure was tested unsystematically by deliberately placing the platform in contrasting situations during many of the tests and by noting the directions selected for jumping by the test birds. No useful correlations were detected. In the twenty instances where the platform was placed over the boundary line between a vegetated and a barren, rocky surface, the birds jumped without regard to the nature of the substrate even in those cases where the bird spent a minute or more circling the platform edges and peering down before jumping.

The third proposition links the dropping of the initial reluctance to jump in plateau birds with a general adaptability or boldness acquired through rearing in a relatively complex environment. Chicks from plateau nests characteristically venture many yards from their nests sites within a few days of hatching and in so doing inevitably encounter a wide variety of objects and situations including hostile attacks from neighboring birds. Chicks reared on a narrow cliff ledge are, by comparison, closely restricted. Schaller and I (1962) have presented experimental data showing that visual exposure to a relatively rich environment during the first few days of life reduces the level of escape responses to strange objects and situations in chicks of the domestic fowl. The varied background of experience acquired by gull chicks from plateau situations may, in a similar way, increase the boldness with which they respond to unfamiliar situations such as that presented by the elevated jump platform; the lack of it may underlie the hesitancy of cliff birds on the platform.

Data obtained by experimentally restricting the environmental experience of plateau chicks by confining them within a small area near the nest (Table 2, lines b, c, and d) are disappointingly meagre. The results suggest, however, that such restrictions may influence the birds to respond conservatively as proposed in this hypothesis.

General Conclusions

Where all or essentially all members of a species living in nature respond to a given stimulus situation in a more or less stereotyped way, the response is referred to as a *natural* or *species-characteristic* response. The role of environmental factors in the ontogenetic development of such responses has been difficult to assess, and two more or less opposing schools of interpretation are generally recognized. One group follows the nativist approach and holds that the uniformity and ubiquity of species-characteristic pattern are due primarily to genetic homogeneity, and that the form of the pattern is the inevitable result of an innately determined maturational process. Environmental factors are regarded as secondary modifiers rather than determinants of the natural pattern. The other group emphasizes the importance of environmental factors throughout development and attributes the uniformity and ubiquity of the natural response to the uniformity of the natural environment of development as much as to genetic homogeneity. The natural pattern is thought to be natural mainly because it was developed in, and hence molded by factors of the natural environment.

Experimental approaches to the resolution of this disagreement have been thwarted by semantic problems. The simple procedure of rearing birds in the presence of experimental (unnatural) environmental factors fails to provide an answer so long as one group interprets these factors as secondary modifiers of a genetically predetermined pattern and the other regards them as essential determinants of the pattern.

The occurrence of two behavioral phenotypes in a single population provides a situation in which the matter of unnatural, secondary factors is bypassed and in which environmental influences during development can be analysed and compared on equal terms. On this basis the two distinct response patterns found in the present study of herring gull chicks are interpreted as ontogenetic equivalents, and the concept of natural or species-characteristic response patterns is considered inapplicable except as it incorporates recognition of the role of environmental determinants.

Summary

Herring gull chicks from nests on (a) cliff ledges and (b) vegetated plateaus showed different types of escape and edge response when tested on an elevated platform. The birds from cliff sites, though bolder at the platform edge, were more reluctant to jump. Those from the plateau nests leapt to the ground with relatively little hesitation. Chicks from cliff eggs, hatched and reared in the plateau by foster parents, resembled native plateau chicks in their escape responses while chicks of plateau origin reciprocally transplanted to and reared on cliff sites showed the reluctance typical of cliff chicks. The possibility of two genetic types reproductively isolated on the two breeding situations is thus essentially eliminated. The likelihood of a stable genetic polymorphism is considered and tentatively discarded as less plausible than an explanation based on learning. Although conditions favorable for simple instrumental conditioning along divergent lines are present in the two rearing situations, a theory is favored which attributes the divergence to major differences in the amount and variety of experience afforded by the two environments. Modest support for this theory is provided by experiments in which plateau chicks confined by fencing to the immediate nest vicinity tended to resemble the naturally deprived cliff chicks in their reluctance to jump.

In conclusion the concept of species-characteristic responses is considered inapplicable to the cliff edge and escape patterns of herring gull chicks except as it incorporates recognition of a determining role in factors of the rearing environment.

Bibliography

Cain, A. J. and Sheppard, P. M. (1950). Selection in the polymorphic land snail, *Cepaea nemoralis. Heredity* **4**: 275–294.

Cullen, E. (1957). Adaptations in the kittiwake to cliff nesting. Ibis **99**: 275–302.

Darling, F. F. (1938). *Bird Flocks and the Breeding Cycle.*—Cambridge University Press.

Hochbaum, H. A. *Travels and Traditions of Waterfowl.* University of Minneapolis Press, Minneapolis.

Miller, A. H. (1942). Habitat selection among higher vertebrates and its relation to intraspecific variation. *Amer. Nat.* 76, p. 25–35.

Paludan, K. (1951). Contributions to the breeding biology of *Larus argentatus* and *Larus fuscus. Vidensk. Medd. Dansk. Naturh. Foren.* 114, p. 1–128.

Paynter, R. A. (1949). Clutch size and the egg and chick mortality of Kent Island herring gulls. *Ecology* 30, p. 146–166.

Schaller, G. B. and Emlen, J. T. (1962). Ontogeny of avoidance responses in various precocial birds. *Animal Behaviour* 10, p. 370–381.

Thorpe, W. H. (1945). The evolutionary significance of habitat selection. *J. Animal Ecology* 14, p. 67–70.

Walk, R. D. and Gibson, E. J. (1961). A comparative and analytical study of visual depth perception. *Psychological Monographs* 75 (15), p. 1–44.

On the Breeding Distribution Pattern of North American Migrant Birds

Robert H. MacArthur

The first review of the Palearctic migration system as a whole "in its essential aspect as a seasonal ecological adjustment on a gigantic scale" was provided by Moreau (1952). The Nearctic, too, has a migration system and certain aspects of this system can be studied much more thoroughly than is possible at present for the Palearctic, for there is more accurate census data from undisturbed North American areas. It is the purpose of this paper to present information about the pattern of breeding distribution of Nearctic birds which migrate into the Neotropical region.

For present purposes, a Nearctic species will be called a "migrant" if most of the area of its winter range as outlined in the A.O.U. Checklist (1957) lies within the Neotropical Region as outlined by Darlington (1957). (Roughly, as here defined, the Neotropical Region covers all the American continent south of the United States, including the West Indies, but excepting the Mexican highlands; the Nearctic Region is the area north of the Mexican border, plus the Mexican highlands.) The species treated should properly be called "Neotropical migrants," but for brevity the term "migrant" will be used with this meaning throughout this paper.

Although this definition of migrant neglects the many species which move shorter distances within the Nearctic, it is relatively objective, and provides a basis for drawing some general conclusions. Water birds present a rather separate problem from other birds and so are excluded. Game birds and birds of prey constitute such a small proportion of the total number of species or individuals that the question of whether to include them will have little bearing; for consistency they have been included.

It is rewarding to consider an individual about to start its northward migration. Since its destination is presumably a result of natural selection (at least in part), it may be postulated that the individual will tend to breed in the area which permits it the greatest output of reproducing progeny. Figure 1 shows, in black, the proportion of migrant individuals in the breeding populations of various relatively undisturbed vegetation communities in North America. The underlying data are in more detail in Table 1. The extent of the forest biomes (Pitelka, 1941) is shaded in the figure. The proportion of migrant individuals is taken from breeding bird censuses from the areas listed on Table 1. The census species regarded as neotropical migrants are listed in the Appendix. Censuses from obviously man-modified habitats have been omitted, the censuses used being of essentially "virgin" (or at least climax) areas. These undisturbed areas have changed sufficiently slowly and have

Reprinted by permission of the publisher from *The Auk* 76: 318–325, 1959.

TABLE 1

Breeding Bird Census Data of Habitats Representing Undisturbed Conditions

Habitat	Location	Reference	% Migrant† individuals	% Migrant† species	Ratio migr. ind. to migr. sp.
Desert					
	California	Hutchinson, 1942	0	0	
	Utah	Fautin, 1946	0	0	
	Arizona	Hensley, 1954	3(−14)*	7(−13)	.43
Prairie					
	Oklahoma	Howell, 1941	0	0	
	Wyoming	Mickey, 1939	0	0	
	Iowa	Kendeigh, 1941	0	0	
	Texas	Allan & Sime, 1939	8	12.5	.67
Chaparral					
	California	Cogswell, 1948	0.5	6	.083
Oak Savanna					
	Texas	Dixon, 1957	5	10	.5
Dry Pine					
	Colorado	Thatcher, 1956 Hering, 1956 Snyder, 1950	5,10,19,20	20.5,20,7,30	(.7)**
	S. Dakota	Whitney, 1956	13	30	.43
	Georgia	Fleetwood, 1948	0	0	
Redwood					
	California	Pugh & Pugh, 1957	16	11	1.43
Sitka Spruce					
	Oregon	Fables & Fables, 1957	27.5	17	1.62
Northern Coniferous					
	N.W.T.	Stewart, 1955	37	25	1.48
	Ontario	Kendeigh, 1947	74	40	1.85
	Idaho	Longley, 1944	63	50	1.26
	Maine	Stewart & Aldrich, 1952	72	48	1.50
	Maine	Cadbury & Cruick- shank, 1941	62	33	1.88
Oak-Gum					
	Alabama	Imhof, 1948	43	53	.81
	Illinois	Snyder et al., 1948	62	59	1.05
Hammock					
	S. Carolina	Mellinger, 1948	63	65	.97
Oak-Pine					
	Arkansas	Hoiberg, 1957	59	47	1.23
Hemlock					
	N. Carolina	Odum, 1947	75	59	1.27
Northeastern Deciduous					
	New York	Kendeigh, 1946	82	61	1.34
	Ohio	Williams, 1947	87	50	1.74
	Maryland	Stewart & Robbins, 1947	82	60	1.37
	Tennessee	Aldrich & Goodrum, 1946	84	67	1.25
	W. Virginia	DeGarmo, 1948	89	71	1.25

†See Appendix for species regarded as "migrants," *i.e.*, neotropical migrants.
*The figures in parentheses hold if Wied's (Arizona) Crested Flycatcher (*Myiarchus tyrannulus*) is considered a migrant.
**Refers to a mean of the ratios of the four habitats.

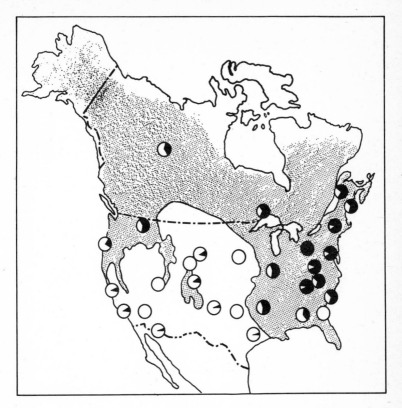

Fig. 1. Proportion of Neotropical Migrant Individuals. The black sectors of the circles represent the proportion of breeding bird individuals in undisturbed vegetation communities at that locality which will migrate out of the Nearctic region in the winter. The stippled zone is roughly the forested region. The species regarded as neotropical migrants are listed in the Appendix.

been present sufficiently long to have their own characteristic bird fauna; this is in contrast to cultivated areas whose fauna has usually come from other habitats such as prairies, shores, and tundra. Thus the censuses from undisturbed areas are more likely to represent the conditions for which the pattern of migration gradually evolved.

Effect of Climate

The first thing to note is that nearby censuses usually show similar proportions of migrants, except when the habitat changes rapidly; so the distribution is not chaotic. It is also important to notice that there is no simple correlation between climate and the proportion of migrants. Thus, the prairies with severe winters and warm summers have a lower proportion of neotropical migrants than the west coast forests with mild winters and cool summers.

The east coast region is intermediate in climate but has a much higher proportion of such migrants than either. Furthermore, at the edge of the prairie the gross aspects of climate such as temperature and rainfall do not show sudden changes, yet the proportion of migrants does. (The proportion of migrants in the avifauna was also compared with the more complicated climate-vegetation classification of Holdridge (1946) with no more success.)

Correlation with Differences in Vegetation

Roughly speaking, the proportion of neotropical migrants is highest in the deciduous forest of the northeast. At the periphery of this region where the amount of conifers increases, the amount of evergreen, oak, etc. increases, or the amount of grass and general aridity increases, the proportion of neotropical migrants falls off. In the northern coniferous forests, where most needles are shed when between two and three years old, the proportion of such migrants drops. It is still lower in the west coast coniferous forests which, with their mild wet winter, are much less seasonal in aspect than the boreal coniferous forest. The dry open coniferous forest of the Colorado Rockies and Black Hills has a still lower proportion of migrants, and chaparral, desert, and prairie habitats have virtually none.

On the available evidence, the most reasonable explanation of the pattern shown in Figure 1 is that where change between winter and summer in the supply of food suitable for migrants is greatest, the proportion of migrants is greatest. Since direct measurements of food supply are not available, the following rough indication must suffice. Although some of the suggested explanation seem slightly *ad hoc* or at least tenuous, there is little doubt about their validity for the major effects. There is little doubt that the northeastern forests which are 100% deciduous have great summer outbreaks of defoliating insects, and, on the other hand, that there is much less seasonal change in supply of insects in the western habitats which have virtually no migrants.

A more detailed analysis is as follows. The food increase which governs the proportion of migrants must be moderately predictable. Thus, a summer increase in food depending upon a desert bloom which may take place at various seasons or not at all for several years is of little use to a migratory bird population. The summer food must also last a sufficient length of time to supply the migrant population during its stay in the breeding area. The grasshopper population of the prairies may fail in this respect. Prairie and desert may also provide a large seed crop which the more omnivorous resident species can utilize in the winter. This makes possible a high population of residents, which in turn permits them to use much of what summer insect increase does occur. For these reasons, desert and prairie areas would be expected to provide little summer increase or else little winter decrease in food for migratory bird species. By contrast, the most obvious seasonal change in wooded areas of severe cold or drought is the loss and renewal of leaves. A host of species of defoliating insects and their parasites are an obvious source of food for insectivorous birds, and they do in fact provide the major portion of the food of migrants (Mitchell, 1952; McAtee, 1932). With this in mind it is not difficult to provide tentative explanations of the varying percentages of migrants in the remaining regions of Figure 1. Coniferous trees retain their needles for two or three years and may thus be considered about 40% deciduous, compared with 100% in the angiosperm forests of the northeast. Therefore, the high proportion of migrants in the northeast and the lower proportion in all coniferous forests are to be expected.

Within the coniferous forest, there is a variation in the proportion of migrant individuals, northern spruce-fir forest having more migrants than the pine and redwood forests farther south. A tentative explanation is as follows. Spruce and pine have about equal densities of insects per unit volume of compressed foliage (Kuusisto, 1941), but the ratio of foliage to wood in spruce is 1.5–2 times that for pine (Baker, 1950, page 284). Thus the insect-eating bird might be expected to comprise only half to two-thirds as large a percentage in pine as in spruce. (This explanation is only partly correct; the relative importance of spruce and pine cones and of the under story surely complicate the exact answer.) A difference in shade tolerance is the most likely explanation of the greater foliage/wood ratio in spruce than in pine. Trees, such as various spruce species, that are quite shade tolerant can maintain a thicker layer of foliage before the inside leaves suffer from the lack of light. If this is correct, it may, along with simple food preferences, explain the low numbers of migrants in oak-gum communities of the south and oak forests of the midwest. Oaks are quite intolerant of shade (Baker, 1950) and probably have a small foliage/wood ratio. It is also true that the season when the leaves are on the trees is much longer in the south, at least, which may make less probable a seasonal insect bloom of the type utilized by migrants. Thus, the information supports the suggestion that migrating birds tend to breed in the areas with the greatest available food supply during the nesting season.

Correlation with Latitude

There is another interesting feature summarized in the table of censuses. For the more northern undisturbed vegetation types censused, the proportion of individuals which migrate to the neotropics is greater than the proportion of species which do not so migrate, as evidenced by ratios greater than one of migrant individuals to migrant species (see Table 1). That is, migrants constitute a greater proportion of the total individuals than of the total species. This means that, in the northern areas censused, the average abundance of the neotropical migrant species is greater than that of the residents and species which move short distances, which are in the table called "non-migrant." (This is not to say that no migrant is rare or no nonmigrant abundant; it refers only to averages.) In southern areas, on the other hand, the tendency is reversed, as evidenced by ratios less than one, meaning that, on the average, "non-migrant" species are commoner. The trend with latitude seems quite consistent and appears to be nearly independent of the nature of the particular undisturbed habitats censused. No one explanation of this pattern is obviously correct; a proper weighing of the possibilities will probably have to wait until a better understanding has been achieved of the factors controlling relative abundance of species.

Acknowledgments

The author wishes to thank David Lack, Director of the Edward Grey Institute, for encouraging this work and for providing very useful criticisms of the manuscript. W. R. Henson, P. H. Klopfer, M. Lloyd, R. E. Moreau, and F. Pitelka made valuable comments. Finally, the author is very indebted to Miss Helen MacArthur for preparing the illustrations.

This work was done when the author was at the Edward Grey Institute of Field Ornithology at Oxford, England, as a regular postdoctoral fellow of the National Science Foundation.

Summary

1. Over a variety of undisturbed habitats throughout the continent, the density of breeding individuals of species migrating to the Neotropics seems to correlate with the contrast between winter and summer food supply in the given habitat.

2. In the undisturbed northern habitats considered, the average migrant to the Neotropics is commoner than the average species which fails to make this journey. The reverse is true in the southern habitats.

Appendix: Nearctic Land Birds, Occurring in the Censuses, Here Considered Neotropical Migrants

Accipitridae: *Buteo platypterus.* Pandionidae: *Pandion haliaetus.* Cuculidae: *Coccyzus americanus, C. erythropthalmus.* Caprimulgidae: *Caprimulgus carolinensis, Chordeiles minor.* Apodidae: *Chaetura pelagica.* Trochilidae: *Archilochus colubris, Selasphorus platycercus.* Tyrannidae: *Tyrannus tyrannus, Myiarchus crinitus, M. tyrannulus, M. cinerascens, Empidonax flaviventris, E. virescens, E. traillii, E. minimus, E. difficilis, Contopus virens, C. sordidulus, Nuttalornis borealis.* Turdidae: *Hylocichla mustelina, H. ustulata, H. fuscescens.* Vireonidae: *Vireo griseus noveboracensis, V. flavifrons, V. s. solitarius, V. olivaceus, V. philadelphicus, V. gilvus.* Parulidae: *Mniotilta varia, Protonotaria citrea, Helmitheros vermivorus,*

Vermivora peregrina, V. r. ruficapilla, Parula americana, Dendroica petechia, D. magnolia, D. tigrina, D. caerulescens, D. coronata, D. virens, D. occidentalis, D. cerulea, D. fusca, D. dominica, D. pensylvanica, D. castanea, D. striata, D. discolor, Seiurus aurocapillus, S. noveboracensis, S. motacilla, Oporornis formosus, O. philadelphia, O. tolmiei, Geothlypis trichas brachydactylus, Wilsonia citrina, W. p. pusilla, W. canadensis, Setophaga ruticilla. Thraupidae: *Piranga ludoviciana, P. olivacea.* Fringillidae: *Pheucticus ludovicianus, Passerina cyanea, P. ciris.*

When not all North American subspecies of a listed species are neotropical migrants, the particular subspecies considered a migrant is listed; otherwise, only the species name is given. Some species included (*e.g., Dendroica coronata*) are possibly doubtful; however, their numerical abundance is sufficiently small that their inclusion makes little difference to the data. Many highly migratory species (*e.g.,* most orioles and swallows) are not included, because they did not occur in any of the censuses considered.

Literature Cited

Aldrich, J. W., and P. Goodrum. 1946. Census 26. *Aud. Field Notes Suppl. Aud. Mag.* **146**: 144–145.

Allan, P. F., and P. R. Sime. 1939. Census 10. *The Season Suppl. to Bird Lore* **129**: 18.

Baker, F. S. 1950. *Principles of Silviculture.* New York: McGraw-Hill.

Cadbury, J., and A. D. Cruickshank. 1941. Census 27. *The Season Suppl. Aud. Mag.* **139**: 493.

Cogswell, H. L. 1948. Census 3. *Aud. Field Notes* **2**(6): 226.

Darlington, P. J. 1957. *Zoogeography.* New York: John Wiley & Sons.

Davis, L. I. 1955. Census 27. *Aud. Field Notes* **9**: 425–426.

De Garmo, W. R. 1948. Breeding-bird population studies in Pocohontas and Randolph Counties, West Virginia. *Aud. Field Notes* **2**(6): 219–222.

Dixon, K. L. 1957. Census 21. *Aud. Field Notes* **11**(6): 450.

Fables, S., and D. Fables. 1957. Census 9. *Aud. Field Notes* **11**(6): 440.

Fautin, R. W. 1946. Biotic communities of the northern desert shrub biome in western Utah. *Ecol. Mon.* **16**: 252–310.

Fleetwood, R. J. 1948. Census 18. *Aud. Field Notes* **2**(6): 238–239.

Hensley, M. M. 1954. Ecological relations of the breeding bird population of the desert biome of Arizona. *Ecol. Mon.* **24**: 185–207.

Hering, L. M. 1956. Census 9. *Aud. Field Notes* **10**(6): 423.

Hoiberg, A. J. 1956. Census 17. *Aud. Field Notes* **10**(6): 426.

Holdridge, L. R. 1946. Determination of world plant formations from simple climatic data. *Science* **105**: 367–368.

Howell, J. C. 1941. Census 7. *The Season Suppl. Aud. Mag.* **139**: 484.

Hutchinson, A. E., and M. C. Hutchinson. 1942. Census 7. *The Season Suppl. Aud. Mag.* **142**: 19–21.

Imhof, T. A. 1948. Census 17. *Aud. Field Notes* **2**(6): 238.

Kendeigh, S. C. 1941. Birds of a prairie community. *Condor* **43**: 165–174.

Kendeigh, S. C. 1946. Breeding birds of the beech-maple-hemlock community. *Ecol.* **27**: 226–244.

Kendeigh, S. C. 1947. Bird population studies in the coniferous forest biome during a spruce budworm outbreak. Ontario Dept. Lands and Forests, Div. Res., *Biol. Bull.* 1.

Kuusisto, P. 1941. Studien über die Ökologie und tagesrytmik von *Phylloscopus trochilus acredula* (L.). *Acta Zool. Fenn.* **31**: 1–120.

Lack, D. 1954. *The Natural Regulation of Animal Numbers.* Oxford: Clarendon Press.

Longley, W. H. 1944. Census 27. *The Season Suppl. Aud. Mag.* **151**: 24.

McAtee, W. F. 1932. Effectiveness in nature of the so-called protective adaptations. *Smithsonian Misc. Coll.* 85, No. 7.

Mellinger, E. O. 1948. Census 20. *Aud. Field Notes* **2**(6): 240.

Mickey, F. W. 1939. Census 7. *The Season Suppl. Bird Lore* **129**: 17.

Mitchell, R. T. 1952. Consumption of spruce budworms by birds in a Maine spruce forest. *J. For.* **50**: 387–389.

Moreau, R. E. 1952. The place of Africa in the Palearctic migration system. *J. Anim. Ecol.* **21**: 250–271.

Odum, E. P. 1947. Census 18. Aud. Field Notes **1**(6): 203–204.

Pitelka, F. 1941. Distribution of birds in relation to major biotic communities. *Amer. Mid. Nat.* **25**: 113–135.

Pugh, E., and R. Pugh. 1957. Census 10. *Aud. Field Notes* **11**(6): 440–441.

Snyder, D. P. 1950. Bird Communities in the coniferous forest biome. *Condor* **52**: 17–27.

Snyder, D., C. Bonney, and W. B. Robertson. 1948. Census 15. *Aud. Field Notes* **2**(6): 237.

Stewart, R. W. 1955. Censuses 9, 10. *Aud. Field Notes* **9**(6): 415–416.

Stewart, R. E., and J. W. Aldrich. 1952. Ecological studies of bird populations in northern Maine. *Ecol.* **33**: 226–238.

Stewart, R. E., and C. S. Robbins. 1947. Census 22. *Aud. Field Notes* **1**(6): 211–212.

Thatcher, D. M. 1956. Census 8. *Aud. Field Notes* **10**(6): 421–423.

Williams, A. B. 1947. Climax beech-maple forest with some hemlock (15 year summary). *Aud. Field Notes* **1**(6): 205–210.

Whitney, N. R. 1956. Census 9. *Aud. Field Notes* **10**(6): 423.

2 / Individuals and Others of Their Kind

The character of inter-individual responses, their significance, evolution, and control, is a topic as varied as any in the field of behavior. Nor is any area of more immediate relevance to problems of human behavior. The sample of papers presented here must, therefore, be regarded as little more than an indication of the range of problems that our rubric includes. It should be noted that studies relating social behavior and hormonal function are not included. Reviews of this vital subject will be found in J. J. Christian's "Endocrine Adaptive Mechanisms and the Physiologic Regulation of Population Growth," in *Physiological Mammalogy* (edited by W. V. Mayer & R. G. van Gelder, Academic Press, 1963), and D. S. Lehrman's "Interaction Between Internal and External Environments in the Regulation of the Reproductive Cycle of the Ring Dove," in *Sex and Behavior* (edited by F. A. Beach, Wiley, 1965).

Collective Territories in Galápagos Mockingbirds, with Notes on Other Behavior

Jeremy J. Hatch

Collective territories do not fit easily into the more usual categories of territoriality (e.g., Hinde, 1956) and the few cases described for birds demonstrate a variety of forms. In the evolution of social behavior in the Crotophaginae, one of the six subfamilies of cuckoos, the defense of colonial territories coincides with the reduction or disappearance of territorial defense by the pair, which has permitted communal nesting (Davis, 1942). In contrast, the Jackdaw (*Corvus monedula*) and Rook (*C. frugilegus*) both defend, albeit not very rigorously, colonial territories within which they feed, but also maintain pair territories around the nest. Coveys of quail (*Lophortyx californica*) outside the breeding season do not defend a particular area but familiarity with the area is important in determining the initial dominance of aliens by resident birds (Howard and Emlen, 1942). Carrick (1963) describes a particularly interesting situation in the Australian Magpie (*Cymnorhina tibicen*) in which territorialism and associated social and sexual interactions limit breeding to about one-quarter of the adult population, these breeding birds being among those in small social groups (each of two to ten birds) that live permanently within territories of five to 20 acres. In no other species has the nature of the reserve of nonbreeding birds been distinguished so clearly (cf. Hensley and Cope, 1951, who found a large but usually invisible reserve). The mockingbirds described below defend collective territories within which they feed and roost but intensive observations were not made during the breeding season.

Apart from the ubiquitous finches the mockingbirds are among the most obvious of the small land birds of the ímpoverished Galápagos avifauna. They have been considered sufficiently distinct from other mockingbirds (*Mimus,* spp.) to be placed in a separate genus, *Nesomimus*. Within the archipelago this genus shows considerable variation; no island has more than one form but the forms on Chatham (San Cristóbal), Hood, and the islets near Charles (Floreana) are so different from each other that they are described as separate species, and Swarth (1932) divides the fourth species into seven races that occur on most of the other islands.

The behavior of the Galápagos mockingbirds was first studied by Venables (1940) who found *N. melanotis* on Chatham Island to be strongly territorial while breeding. In particular he describes a form of aggressive territorial display which he calls "posture dancing" and a "branch chase" which may be sexually motivated. Both of these displays are considered again below.

Reprinted by permission of the publisher from *The Wilson Bulletin* **78**: 198–207, 1966.

Methods

During 1962–63 I spent about three months on the Galápagos Islands and had occasion to watch the mockingbirds on several islands. Most of the observations reported here were made from 12-28 December 1962, on Hood Island where *N. macdonaldi* is numerous and particularly tame. Shorter visits were made to Tower Island (22–24 November, 4–8 January) and Champion Islet (near Charles) 11-15 January. Intervening periods were spent at Indefatigable Island (Santa Cruz). In many cases the birds were caught, usually in mist nets, and marked with colored plastic legbands. On some occasions identifications were based on plumage characters.

On Hood Island our camp was about two miles east of Punta Cevallos on the north shore at the eastern end of the island on a small triangular patch of sand between the bank of rounded lava boulders that fringes the sea and the thorny shrub characteristic of the island. Immediately upon our arrival we were "taken over" by the resident "band" of mockingbirds that were a constant source of delight to us with their boundless curiosity. Their tameness meant that it was little trouble to catch them in mist nets (or by hand in the cooking pots) and I marked a total of 21 birds at various places near the camp. Most of the observations were made on these birds, in the course of other work. In addition I watched some of the mockingbirds on the south coast for short periods and marked four of these.

Results of Marking

On Hood Island the mockingbirds on the north shore characteristically occurred in groups that I have called "bands." Of the 21 birds marked near our camp, six comprised the band that occupied the campsite (called RW's band after the color combination of the dominant member). Eight formed RR's band to the east of the camp. Of seven marked birds not in these two bands, three were rarely or never seen again, two were in a band of seven to the west and two formed the band to the south of the campsite.

None of these mockingbirds showed the spotted breast characteristic of young ones (Swarth, 1931), nor did they have the yellow gape and buffcolored rump that I saw on young *N. parvulus* on Indefatigable Island. Every bird was in worn plumage; the tails were so worn that measurements were difficult to evaluate but the 20 wing measurements fall clearly into two groups which fit well with Swarth's (*op. cit.*) nonoverlapping measurements for males and females. In the two bands there were eight males (of which six were heard to sing) and six females.

Observations of Behavior

Each of the two bands of mockingbirds (RW,RR) studied closely occupied a restricted area within which they fed and roosted; this situation seemed to apply elsewhere near the coast, but in the more arid interior of the island the mockingbirds occurred in twos, or less often threes or fours, and during my brief visits I saw little territorial behavior. On the windswept treeless southern coast of the island amongst the nests of boobies (*Sula nebouxii* and *S. dactylatra*), frigatebirds (*Fregata minor*), and albatrosses (*Diomedea irrorata*) the mockingbirds appeared not to form discrete bands and to lack the obvious dominance hierarchy of RW's band. For much of the time the members of a band moved around together in a widely scattered group. Occasionally (six or more observations) a single alien bird furtively crossed a territorial boundary only to be driven off by one or more of the residents (nos. 1, 2, 4, and 6 were observed chasing intruders). The structure of these bands and the relations between bands are described below.

Intragroup Behavior

On Hood Island the mockingbirds are particularly noisy and the most noticeable behavior within the band is a display which resembles the begging of young birds. It is given by both males and females to dominant members of either sex. The crouched posture is accompanied by a raucous squeak (Fig. 1) and is apparently a sign of submission. Very frequently the submissive bird turns its back on the dominant individual. Occasionally this submis-

Fig. 1. Begging display. The bird on the right has just arrived and is dominant to the bird on the left. (Photo by R. W. Risebrough.)

sive posture is given in response to the call of a dominant bird up to 20 yards away. In feeding situations there was a linear dominance hierarchy, demonstrated by "Begging" to all higher birds, except that in RW's band (at least) no. 2 did not beg to RW (no. 1) but gave a faint rattle call instead; between nos. 2 and 3 there was no begging and it was as if they were equal. I never saw a Begging bird being fed, but at least twice the dominant bird pecked in a slow, hesitant manner at the open beak. Bryan Nelson writes (*in litt.*), ". . . if a dominant individual is trying to dispel another bird from, say, a source of food it uses (or may use) a *quite distinct* form of pecking, which is essentially that used to hoist heavy twigs or stones aside, when feeding." I never recorded this kind of pecking, possibly because it only occurs commonly amongst larger, probably unstable, groups of mockingbirds. A silent running chase in which the wings were slightly drooped occurred frequently, and occasionally ended with the chaser (male) attempting to peck the nape of the chased (female?). This is Venables's "branch chase" except that I usually saw it on the ground. This type of chasing was mostly seen between 1, 3 and 5, 6, suggesting that they were pairs, but I saw no copulation. Dominant birds also chase squawking subordinates. I could detect no differences in the dominance of individuals in different parts of the group territory, but I did not set up feeding stations or watch extensively at distant sites. Some of the interactions within RW's band during 0600–1200 hours on 15 December 1962 are recorded in Table 1.

Of the members of RW's band, RW and no. 3 sang each day in occasional short bursts, preferring different song posts. Song was twice heard briefly from no. 5, the only other male in the band. On five occasions mockers (two then unmarked, once RW, twice no. 5) were seen to carry a twig to two uncompleted nests in bushes. Three of RR's band sang (two birds with the measurements of males were not heard to sing).

TABLE 1

Interactions of Members of RW Band

Subordinate individual	Sex	Dominant individual					
		RW	RBk	PM	OB	BY	OG
RW	♂	—					
RBk	♂	B, (C)	—				
PM	♀	(R)	(R?)	—			
OB	♀	—	B, C	B, C	—		
BY	♂	B	4B, C	2B, 2C	2B, (C)	—	
OG	♀	B	B	C	(C)	C, 2R	—

The majority of interactions that occurred between dawn and 1200h on 15 December 1962 are included. Parentheses indicate interactions observed on other days. B = Begging-squawk. C = Chase and squawk. R = Silent running-chase.

J. B. Nelson (*in litt.*) considers that the mockingbirds at Punta Suarez recognized each other by their facial patterns; frequently "before attacking, a bird would run round or stretch round and peer into the face of the other as though it was uncertain of the other's identity." In this region the bands apparently number up to 40 individuals which may account for this uncertainty, for I saw little behavior that could be explained in this way amongst the bands of six and eight that I watched closely near Punta Cevallos.

Intergroup Behavior

On Hood Island Dancing occurred whenever two bands met, but this was infrequent. Usually it was initiated by the dominant members of the bands and often spread to all the others nearby so that ten birds might be posturing at each other. I never saw two lone individuals Dancing (except once on Tower Island). It seemed to me that one hand was opposing the other and it was not merely "other birds attracted by the spreading excitement and by their natural curiosity," as suggested by Venables (1940) for *N. melanotis*. The Dancing occurred at the boundary of the collective territory (Fig. 2) and

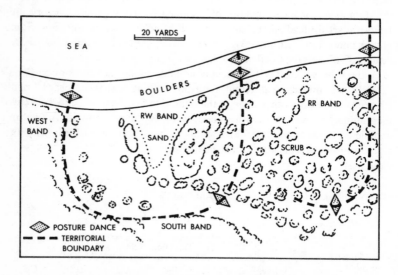

Fig. 2. Sketch map of territories of mockingbirds on the north coast of Hood Island, showing approximate boundaries (from observations of feeding, chasing, etc.) and sites of observed Dances.

presumably the display serves to delimit this boundary. The form of the dance is rather similar to the Dancing of *Mimus polyglottos* which is described in detail by Hailman (1960) except that flicks of the tail and wings are more pronounced. Ranged on either side of an imaginary line the birds make a series of forward, backward, or lateral steps following and keeping within about three feet of each other and often almost touching. Each jerky step is accompanied by a flick of the wings and followed by an exaggerated upward flip of the unspread tail. The tail-flip sometimes included some lateral movement also. The characteristic posture during this display is an upright one with the body tall and thin, but this is usually alternated with a head-forward position sometimes with feathers fluffed (presumably betokening a more aggressive tendency). The head-up posture is more often accompanied by a step back or sideways and the head-forward posture by a step forward. Dancing is often accompanied by various calls, some are squawks probably given by non-dancers in response to the other calls. On the few occasions I saw single birds chased from a territory, these were never the dominant members of a foreign band.

The mockingbirds in the seabird colonies on the south coast were often in groups but I found no evidence of territorial behavior and I never saw a Dance. However, the Nelsons saw two Dances and other territorial behavior in the seabird colonies on Punta Suarez. Of about 20 mockingbirds that clustered at my feet to drink from a small can of water, I marked four and subsequently saw some of these up to half a mile from the marking site.

On Tower Island Dancing by *N. parvulus* was seen on several occasions, once between two birds (one, at least, a songster) immediately following a fight (the only fight that I saw). Four bands, of two to four individuals each, could be distinguished in the area near our camp at Darwin Bay.

On Indefatigable Island the mockingbirds (*N. parvulus*) are less numerous and less tame than on Hood; some of them were nesting during the period November 1962–April 1963. Dances were apparently limited to pairs and I never saw other birds attracted to the dancers as described by Venables for breeding mockingbirds on Chatham Island. Once I saw a recently fledged bird beg (unrewarded), sing briefly, and feed the next brood of its parents in the nest.

On Champion Islet there were few *N. trifasciatus*; I saw Dances on four occasions, but noted no clear differences from the Dances of *macdonaldi*.

Other Behavior

Not only are the mockingbirds of Hood fearless of man but they also showed no fear of a hawk (*Buteo galapagoensis*) while it perched in the camp. They neither mobbed the hawk nor fled from it, but did show interest in it and approached within about ten yards while it fed on a lizard (*Tropidurus*). At first sight this lack of fear seems remarkable since D. W. Snow found a hawk's nest with young near Punta Suarez (Hood) at which the food remains were mainly mockingbirds. J. B. Nelson (*in litt.*) observed that the mockingbirds "have a special 'chirrup' alarm call which immediately elicits a striking fleeing response from every mockingbird within hearing. We saw it several times *when a hawk flew over*." (Italics added.) I heard a few "chirrups" when the hawk flew short distances but saw no directed fleeing. At no time did the hawk fly overhead. Finches (*Geospiza conirostris* and *G. fuliginosa*) watched the perched hawk intently and made "tink" calls when it was on the ground amongst bushed. The doves (*Nesopelia*) appeared more alarmed. Several snakes (*Dromicus*) appeared in the camp and elicited immediate interest from the mockingbirds, which followed them and usually made a characteristic churring, chattering note.

Sunbathing occurred quite frequently, especially among the lower members of the band. Sometimes the bird would bend forward and fluff its back feathers but more usually it would lean to one side, raise the upper wing, and fluff the flank and back feathers while twisting the head and closing the nictitating membrane. Apparently identical movements were seen during three light misty showers.

Discussion

Territory and Dancing in Two
Other Mockingbird Species

Mimus polyglottos of North America defends a pair territory in the spring and summer and both sexes may defend individual or joint winter territories (Laskey, 1962) but the pattern of exclusive breeding territories is distorted by the presence of a rich source of food (e.g., a feeding station at a house) to which territorial birds come from up to $\frac{1}{4}$ mile but show no lasting territorial behavior near the feeding place (Michener, 1951). Dancing usually involves only two birds but Michener and Michener (1935) watched pairs opposing a new bird on several occasions. The Micheners' observations suggest that Dancing occurs during the establishment of the territories; my limited observations support this. Even when territories are being established, Dancing is a rarer display than the Dancing of *Nesomimus*, which occurs through a longer period.

In the arid coastal region of Ecuador the mockingbird, *Mimus longicaudatus*, is locally numerous and was breeding during my stay at Palmar during February and March 1963. They are markedly less aggressively territorial than *M. polyglottos* and respond less noisily to humans approaching nests with eggs or young. Marchant (1960) agrees that the territories may be less strongly held than *M. polyglottos*, and suggests that there may be a tendency to polygamy. "Amicable associations of more than two birds were often noted in the breeding season, apart from the normal dry-season parties, and pairs forage for food for the young or building material far from their own territories, across intervening ones." I saw a few groups of three or four adult individuals but did not elucidate their breeding status; on one occasion I had a distant view of a Dance in which four of seven birds were involved.

The Significance of Collective
Territories in Nesomimus

It is difficult to evaluate the ecological significance of the collective territories without a series of observations of marked birds extending through the breeding season. The clutch size of *parvulus* and *melanotis* is two or three (Venables, 1940), and *macdonaldi* is unlikely to differ markedly from this, so if the bands represent family parties they must be derived from several broods and have existed since the previous breeding season and subsequent postjuvenal molt. Breeding and molting may be dependent upon increased food, and thus upon rainfall, which occurs irregularly from December to March. The peak of breeding is probably about February; two broods per season are well known (Venables, 1940) and there might be more. Swarth (1931) suggests on the basis of 78 specimens, that the annual and postjuvenal molts are "accomplished by different individuals over a long period of time." But to explain the smaller bands inland it would be necessary to postulate a lower breeding success there. Alternatively the young birds from inland might move to the coast and form the large southern groups. Perhaps these southern birds are nonterritorial nonbreeders (with no nest-sites nearby) taking advantage of the rich food supply in the littoral zone or from the seabirds (cracked eggs, food scraps, etc.; Hatch, 1965), and are thus akin to Carrick's nonbreeding magpies (Carrick, 1963). If this is true, then the holding of collective territories may be linked with the control of population in the absence of many predators. It would be interesting to discover the fate of the different birds during the breeding season: do the bands split to form exclusive breeding territories and do the birds at the south coast move inland to breed although continuing to feed among the seabirds? These observations, admittedly scant, are reported in the hope of encouraging others to take advantage of the avifauna peculiar to the Galápagos Islands.

Summary

Mockingbirds (*Nesomimus macdonaldi*) on part of Hood Island in the Galápagos were found in December 1962 to occupy collective territories within which they fed and roosted, which they defended against neighboring bands with a characteristic "Dance" similar to that of *Mimus polyglottos*. Within the band of four to ten birds there is an approximately linear hierarchy and up to three individuals were heard to sing. Elsewhere on the island, amongst seabird colonies where there were no nesting sites, the band structure was apparently absent and it is suggested that these may be nonbreeding birds. Behavior of mockingbirds on other islands was not markedly different. Some observations are presented of other behavior patterns including responses to potential predators, and recognition of individual mockingbirds.

Acknowledgments

This paper is a result of a visit to mainland Ecuador and the Galápagos Islands from November 1962 to April 1963, supported by the National Science Foundation and the National Institutes of Health (Grants GB98 and 04453 to Dr. Peter H. Klopfer, to whom I am indebted for much help). I am most grateful to the Charles Darwin Foundation and the Directors of the Station on Santa Cruz, successively

Dr. Andre Brosset and Dr. D. W. Snow for assistance, and especially to Drs. Jack
P. Hailman, R. W. Risebrough, and J. B. Nelson for fruitful comments and memor-
able companionship in the field. Sr. and Sra. Zeller of Guayaquil offered me the
hospitality of their cottage at Palmar.

Literature Cited

Carrick, R. 1963 Ecological significance of territory in the Australian Magpie
(*Gymnorhina tibicen*). *Proc. XIII Internatl. Ornith. Congr.* 740–753.

Davis, D. E. 1942 The phylogeny of social nesting habits in the Crotophaginae.
Quart. Rev. Biol. **17**: 115–134.

Hailman, J. P. 1960 Hostile dancing and fall territory of a color-banded Mockingbird. *Condor* **62**: 464–468.

Hatch, J. J. 1965 Only one species of Galápagos Mockingbird feeds on eggs. *Condor*
67: 354–355.

Hensley, M. M., and J. B. Cope 1951 Further data on removal and repopulation
of the breeding birds in a sprucefir forest community. *Auk* **68**: 483–493.

Hinde, R. A. 1956 The biological significance of the territories of birds. *Ibis* **98**:
340–369.

Howard, W. E., and J. T. Emlen 1942 Intercovey social relationships in the Valley
Quail. *Wilson Bull.* **54**: 162–170.

Laskey, A. R. 1962 Breeding biology of mockingbirds. *Auk* **79**: 596–606.

Marchant, S. 1960 The breeding of some S. W. Ecuadorian birds. *Ibis* **102**: 349–382.

Michener, J. R. 1951 Territorial behavior and age composition in a population of
mockingbirds at a feeding station. *Condor* **53**: 276–283.

Michener, H., and J. R. Michener 1935 Mockingbirds, their territories and indi-
vidualities. *Condor* **37**: 97–140.

The Role of Juvenile Elk and Moose in the Social Dynamics of Their Species

Margaret Altmann

Analysis of the social behavior patterns in wild, free-ranging ungulates has led to the recognition of definite periods of stress and readjustment in some animals. Among the age groups studied under a long-range plan (Altmann, 1958, 1959), the juveniles in elk and moose were quite obviously such a problem group. This study aims to point out the role of these "in-between-agers" and their interactions with the social order of their species.

As juveniles we designated the one-year-old elk and the one- and two-year-old moose of both sexes. They are no longer accepted as calves, but do not rate as yet as adults. The two particular species under investigation were the wapiti, or Wyoming elk (*Cervus canadensis nelsoni*), and the Wyoming moose (*Alces alces shirasi*). The behavior observations were carried out in the Teton Wilderness area of Wyoming and in Grand Teton National Park, respectively, mainly over a period of three years (1956–58), but supplemented by additional notes from a nine-year period in the same area. The work was supported by grants in aid from the National Science Foundation and the New York Zoological Society. Our appreciation of the grants in aid and of the kind encouragement by Dr. L. F. Clarke, Research Station Director at Moran, Wyoming, headquarters of the investigation, is herewith expressed.

Observations of juvenile elk and moose over the three-year (1956–58) period were made on 1,663 animals in 931 observation periods, varying in duration from 14 minutes to 4 hours.

Dawn and dusk hours provided the majority of the observational material, but moonlight and daytime records were also included in order to get a balanced ethological picture.

The distance from the observed animal varied from 12 feet (in hiding) to one and a half miles (from lookout). The use of 7×50 light-weight binoculars and of a 15- or 27-power B. & L. spotting scope on a tripod provided the means of accurate wide-field observation. In the study of social situations involving "marginal" activity of the juveniles, such equipment permitted long-range observations and yielded discoveries not possible by a close-up stalk.

A graduate student assistant, Mr. James R. Ruos, participated in some phases of the observations with great efficiency.

The two big game species selected for this study have been previously shown to have striking differences in their social organization and in their calf-raising patterns (Altmann, 1959).

Reprinted by permission of the publisher from *Zoologica* **45**: 35–39, 1960, published by New York Zoological Society.

The general dynamics of the elk and moose groups have been presented elsewhere (Altmann, 1952, 1956, 1959; Denniston, 1956; Dodds, 1958).

This paper deals with the changes which the individual animal, in particular the juvenile, has to undergo in adaptation or in resistance to group formation and dissolution.

As a rule, it appears at first to an observer that there is great uniformity of expressions and behavior reaction in all group individuals. With more intense observation and effort, however, one discovers more and more individual differences in morphology as well as in behavioral detail. At the same time definite patterns of behavior become more apparent and allow the recognition of trends. We are, even after twelve years of work on such problems, still quite absorbed in finding species-specific and group-specific behavior. But we are also fully aware of many cases of "marginal behavior" and of non-conformity and deviation in some animals.

Keeping careful tab on the non-conforming individuals, we intend to investigate their occurrence and fate in individual case histories against the background of their respective groups.

So far, it appears that the juvenile age class exhibits more non-conforming behavior, but it remains to be seen[1] whether the aging or aged wild ungulates equal or exceed them in this respect.

An examination of juvenile behavior in moose and elk must take into consideration the social background and the typical calfhood experiences in the development pattern of each species.

Moose Juveniles

In the moose, emergence from the calfhood pattern has its beginning during the fall rutting season. The calf's dam comes in heat and joins a bull moose, and the calf by her side is integrated into the mating group. At this time, weaning of the calf is in progress and its complete isolation from other members of its own kind is relaxed by its dam. The hardships of the first winter follow and leave their mark on most moose calves. Leadership and protection by the cow appear to be still an essential requirement for the survival of the calf, even after weaning is completed. The daily routine, feeding, rest. shelter selection, defense and evasion activities are determined by the cow moose for the weaned calf all through the winter.

Then at the climax of the period of scarcity and hardship in early spring, the heavily pregnant cow moose becomes gradually more and more hostile toward her growing yearling, when at close range. About 10 to 15 days before the birth of the new calf the cow chases the yearling from her side. Confusion is the first reaction of the yearling to this new situation. Circling and aimless drifting and irregular feeding are characteristic, and it makes numerous

[1] Our current research phase, on an N.I.M.H. grant, deals with the role of aging and aged wild ungulates.

attempts over many days to rejoin its dam, by approach and by following her footsteps again. When the yearling eventually, after 12 to 25 frustrated attempts, learns to stay at the "safe distance" from the dam (200–300 feet), it continues nevertheless to participate in her general movements and routine activities. This is often done barely within sight; at times beyond the visible distance, by scenting and listening. This life "in the margin" is endured by the majority of yearlings. Some juvenile moose of both sexes, however, do not remain "in the margin" for long. They leave and stay solitary or try to find an association with other unattached moose, usually with older bulls. Such a partnership with one or more elder moose is frequently established by juvenile bulls—in rare instances also by female yearlings. This association is called a "satellite attachment" in our study, since direction and type of activity are determined by the older partner. Remarkable tolerance and nonaggression characterize this relationship in general. The satellite condition appears to substitute for the dam-yearling attachment and usually lasts all summer long, up to the rutting time in September, when another critical period arises for the juveniles.

During the prerutting period in August this satellite moose relationship gradually undergoes changes which lead to its deterioration. First sign of tension between the older bulls and their satellite partners is a tendency to mock fight and tussle more intensively. This accompanies the velvet-rubbing time, which in mature moose bulls begins earlier (late August), in juveniles later. Satellite groups running in single file over extended areas (3–6 miles per day) were observed at this stage of the prerut. Periods of over-activity alternate with quiet browsing and grazing in peaceful unity. The number of animals in such satellite groups is variable. Two and three are found most frequently, but some groups may contain five and up to nine members on occasion. In the larger groups there is a changing leadership role and no longtime group cohesion, but the juveniles—the yearlings and two-year-olds—do not play leading roles in such groups. The tolerance of the bull moose toward their satellites diminishes, and the spacing within the still-persisting groups widens. On narrow trails, passages or salt licks the juvenile stays cautiously out of reach of mature bulls or waits in cover until they have passed.

The end stage of the satellite relationship occurs when the actual rut begins. The rutting bull moose threatens or fights off all satellite attachments. If former satellites are met, the rutting bull moose will threaten them as if they were strangers.

Another less frequently occurring form of attachment in juvenile moose is the banding together of two to several immature animals, designated as "clubs" in this paper. "Clubs" differ from the satellites in mode of violent, erratic travel and in lack of steadiness and become most conspicuous during the prerut.

By the end of August, with feeding conditions at their best, the juveniles as well as the mature moose are in supreme physical condition. It is in those few weeks, preceding the actual rutting period (September and October) that the special behavior patterns of the prerut are evident in the juvenile moose. There is, no doubt, a partial activation of the sex drive in both sexes, but it is more intense in the juvenile males. The young moose bulls are excitable, feed only intermittently and drive their club partners, irrespective of their sex. Much tussling, kicking and running in circles takes place. It is apparent that an expression of the rutting drive at this time is present in most well-developed juvenile moose, as well as in those attached as satellites, or in solitary and marginal positions. Increased restlessness and irritability are indicators of this condition but its manifestation is more or less suppressed or kept under control by the presence of dominant, mature members of the species. Remnants of this prerutting behavior, however, can be found in various degrees of strength or suppression.

The juvenile moose, living in "the margin," succeeds at times, after a number of weeks, in reapproaching its dam and being tolerated for a while. But the prerut and the onset of the rutting period bring increased difficulties for the immature moose of both sexes. If the juvenile is a male, the threat of the bull moose will keep him under stress and dislodge him again. If the juvenile is a female, its own dam chases it from the proximity of the bull and from the wallow which is usually the focus of the cows' attention (Altmann, 1959). It was noticed in our observations that occasionally moose juveniles were tolerated near the mating group, but this always involved poorly developed yearlings, individuals of quiet and submissive behavior.

Elk Juveniles

The social situation of juvenile elk is also characterized by critical periods of adjustment, in which existing bonds are loosened and dissolved and new associations become necessary. But the social organization of elk, with their definite herd formation, modifies and reduces the impact of such changes, at least for the female juvenile.

The elk cow-calf relationship is from the very beginning, the day of birth, built upon a "spacing basis." For several weeks the calf is left hidden for hours at a time, while the dam rejoins the herd groups for grazing. Later, at about 20 days of age, when the calf is following the cow, it does so in a hard-integrated manner, not "heeling" as closely as the moose calf follows its dam. When a disturbance of the herd occurs, the cow often leaves the calf with other group members, covering their retreat by a special shielding maneuvre (Altmann, 1956) which is also based on a spacing, not on a closeness, reaction.

In this way each elk yearling is from calfhood on integrated as a member of a group (band) or herd. As such it is not quite so dependent upon the close association with its own dam. Nevertheless, the elk yearling attempts to gradually weaken the barrier of distance established and rigidly enforced by the cow at the birth of a new calf. The opportunity to do this arises for the yearling at times during the resumption of the migration, as soon as the stationary pause for calving is terminated. In most of the observed cases the yearlings were not tolerated in the close vicinity of the dam and the young calf. Two exceptional cases were noted in different years and locations, when a yearling elk knelt down and nursed an elk cow, who apparently had lost her young calf. No obvious resistance to this nursing procedure was noticeable. One yearling was a female (1951), the other a spike bull (1954).

As the high summer ranges get gradually dryer and the big nursery herds of elk begin to break into smaller groups grazing in the secondary valley slopes and meadows toward the end of August, the prerut of elk gets under way.

Distinctive changes in individual activity and group structure become apparent. The big mature elk bulls are dispersed in the timbered areas in order to rub the velvet off their antlers in preparation for the rut. The yearling spike bulls suddenly show greater activity and display overt sexual behavior.

Driving, "tending,"[2] mounting elk cows and mock fighting among each other characterize this "prerut pattern." Actual mating does not take place, since the cows are not yet in heat. They are, in fact, most refractory to the advances of the yearling bulls. Squealing, kicking and bugling with a high-pitched, juvenile voice, the yearling bulls create a veritable upheaval in the small herds and by their behavior obviously break up the routine of daily activities. Erratic and incomplete as it appears, the sex behavior of the juvenile elk has a number of characteristics of the adult rutting pattern—the tending, mounting, bugling, reduced feeding and increased locomotion. The prerut lasts about three weeks and then, with the reappearance of the mature bulls from their timber hideouts, the role of the spikes suddenly changes. In the most emphatic manner the spikes are driven away from the cow-calf groups by the harem-owning bull elk. This change has all the indications of psychological castration for the juvenile spikes.

In the rutting season the female juvenile elk (yearling) does not have to leave her accustomed group. There is, in contrast to the situation of the juvenile spike bull, no direct threat and tension in store for her. Although subject to the rather violent herding action of the harem bull, the female elk yearling takes all her cues for feeding and resting, for moving and flight, from her dam or its group. If the elk dam is "cut out" of the harem by a rival bull elk, the female yearling usually breaks out of the group also and, like the calf, follows the dam into the new harem. However, in all these actions the yearling stays at least at the "critical distance" from the dam as long as there is a calf present. In elk harems there is no sign of female sex competition but the same group cohesion and compatibility prevail as at other seasons. This is in our opinion an important factor which keeps the groups intact and prevents dispersion, in spite of wide spacing, which even the most vigilant harem bull could not prevent.

For the yearling bulls (spikes), however, a highly threatening situation

[2] Tending as defined by T. McHugh (1958) is the closeup following of the cow by the bull.

arises with the onset of the rutting season. Not only is the spike chased out of his accustomed group by the now domineering harem bull, but after leaving he finds himself in a very insecure situation. In addition to well recognizable elk groups the juvenile now everywhere encounters roaming, unattached bulls which are bugling and challenging other males and searching for a breeding chance or a rival. Fright builds up like a chain reaction in the spikes and the result is confused drifting and, when exhausted, disregard of most other normally shown precautions against danger. Under the stress of fear from mature bulls these juveniles will often act irrationally and, as I have also shown previously (Altmann, 1956), rather meet and follow a pack train or invade a camp than face a bugling mature bull.

Winter Grouping

As the main rutting gradually draws to a close and the mature males are spent, there is occasionally a terminal expression of rutting behavior in the juvenile elk and moose, but the general regrouping of the elk and moose under the influence of the first severe winter weather and dwindling food supplies obscures a clear manifestation. The fall migration in the elk and the winter aggregation of the moose in the lower river drainages permit the juveniles to rejoin the others without danger. There is still, of course, a "peck order" of sorts within the loose groups. The juveniles rank low therein, almost always below the last adult animal, but quiet yielding and submission have taken the place of upheaval and persecution. In a lowly, but as such well-defined social rank, the juvenile elk and moose spend the winter months.

Vocal communications play a limited role in juvenile elk and moose. The spike elk bugle, or try to bugle, during the prerut. Juvenile moose in our experience are not vocal except for small grunts of warning or anger when disturbed. Juvenile elk and moose use in gait, in posture and in gesture the same signals as the adults and can send as well as receive these signals. This is different from the situation at the calf age when signals were practiced and executed but the adults did not attach any significance to them. For example, a band of elk cows would not be alarmed by a calf in high stepping gait but would immediately heed a yearling's warning gait by flight. Or, an adult moose would not counter the aggression gesture (ears folded back, head raised, mouth chewing) of a calf but would without delay respond violently to a threat by a yearling.

Play among juvenile elk is frequently seen, particularly in the prerut. Running, flight and fight games with adults and often with older calves in shallow water or in meadows are a regular elk activity on summer evenings.

In salt licks or in other critical areas of limited space the juveniles have to yield to the higher social rank of adults and even to the calves, who rank with their respective dams.

During most of the year the juvenile moose and elk are not aggressive, but this can be rapidly changed under special conditions. Such is the case in juvenile moose in deep, nonbearing snow cover, as shown also by Pruitt (1960), or in fence enclosures when the "cornered" animal attemps to fight its way out by attacking man or any other species in its way. The aggressive mood and intention of the juveniles is always clearly recognizable by folded-back ears, chewing, salivation and rising hair on hump and neck region, slow lifting of front feet and stamping of the ground a few times, as in adult animals. Striking is done with the forefeet in quick, drum-like barrages, often from above while rising on the hindfeet.

In considering the tense situation of the juvenile moose and elk and the condition of stress during many months, one cannot be surprised to find that this age group actually has heavy mortality losses (Peterson, 1955). The exact extent of the juvenile mortality rate is quite frequently obscured by difficulties in counting and recognition of juveniles in aerial and other counts.

The difficulties in social adjustment become more crucial when physiological burdens of malnutrition and parasitism during the winter months are added to lower the vitality of juveniles.

Toward the end of winter the majority of the observed juveniles, in particular the young moose, appeared very emaciated and ragged, but those who survived recovered in a remarkably short time. Healthy weight gain and glossy appearance of the pelage were reached usually within 6 to 7 weeks.

In the year following their problem age as juveniles, the elk and moose very gradually, but not completely, reach the social status of young adults. To a varying degree this new situation frees them the handicaps of the juvenile status, but a close observer may still notice the traces of last year's social difficulties in the critical period of the rutting season and in other competitive situations.

Summary

Among the age groups studied under a long-range plan concerning free-ranging wild ungulates, the juveniles in elk (*Cervus canadensis nelsoni*) and moose (*Alces alces shirasi*) were obviously a problem group. The role of these juveniles and their interaction with the social order of their species is investigated.

The juvenile moose undergoes a critical period when its dam chases it from its side before the birth of the new calf. Various difficulties in adaptation to the new situation for the juvenile are shown, among them its role as a satellite to adult males, the life in the margin and the formation of juvenile clubs.

After a brief flare-up of juvenile rutting behavior in the so-called "prerut" period, further stress situations are faced by elk and moose juveniles in the fall rutting season of their dams, when young males are driven out by the mature bulls, and females (moose only) have to cope with hostility of mature cows.

Differences in social structure between moose and elk groups are shown to affect the role of the juveniles. In general the results point to the role of the juveniles as a rejected and most erratic, non-conforming age group.

Accumulative effects of poor winter nutrition, parasitic infestation, and difficulties in social adjustment bring about a lowering of vitality of elk and moose juveniles toward the end of the winter.

The surviving juveniles, however, regain weight and health in early summer at a fast rate. Integration into adult social status is gradual with a variety of drawbacks, in particular during the next rutting season.

Literature Cited

Altmann, Margaret 1952. Social behavior of elk, *Cervus canadensis nelsoni*, in the Jackson Hole area of Wyoming. *Behaviour* IV, No. 2, pp. 116–143.

———— 1956. Patterns of herd behavior in free-ranging elk of Wyoming *Cervus canadensis nelsoni*. *Zoologica* 41, No. 8, pp. 65–71.

———— 1958. Social integration of the moose-calf. Animal *Behaviour* IV, Nos. 3 & 4, pp. 155–159.

———— 1959. Group dynamics in Wyoming moose during the rutting season. *Jour. Mammalogy* 40, No. 3, pp. 420–424.

Denniston, II, R. H. 1956. Ecology, behavior and population dynamics in the Wyoming or Rocky Mountain moose, *Alces alces shirasi*. *Zoologica* 41, No. 14, pp. 105–118.

Dodds, D. G. 1958. Observations of pre-rutting behavior in Newfoundland moose. *Jour. Mammology* 39, No. 3, pp. 412–416.

McHugh, Tom 1958. Social behavior of the American buffalo (*Bison bison bison*). *Zoologica* 43, No. 1, pp. 1–40.

Peterson, R. L. 1955. *North American Moose*. University of Toronto Press, pp. 66–67.

Pruitt, Jr., W. O. 1960. Animals in the snow. *Sci. Am.* 202, No. 1, Jan., pp. 60–68.

Reactions of American and French Species of Corvus and Larus to Recorded Communication Signals Tested Reciprocally

Hubert and Mable Frings,

Joseph Jumber,

René-Guy Busnel,

Jacques Giban,

Philippe Gramet

In 1953, it was found that starlings could be driven from objectionable tree roosts by broadcasting to them the recorded distress call of the species (Frings and Jumber, 1954). This led to further studies in the United States on the possibility of influencing the behavior of pest birds with recorded communication signals and through this to fundamental studies on acoustical behavior of these species. Similar studies were made simultaneously on pest birds in France. In 1954, 1955, and 1956, both the European workers and the American workers studied crows resident in their countries. The American workers studied also Herring Gulls and found ways to influence the behavior of these birds with broadcasts of recorded communication signals. These successes led the two laboratories involved to decide upon an exchange of recordings for the purpose of testing the possible intraspecific and interspecific semantic values of the calls. This paper, which is Paper No. 2101 in the journal series of the Pennsylvania Agricultural Experiment Station, reports the results of these tests to date.

Experiments on Crows

Tests in the United States

The only crow studied by the American investigators in the U.S. is *Corvus brachyrhynchos brachyrhynchos* (Eastern Crow). The species is the common crow generally distributed over the U.S. The subspecies studied is found in the eastern states northward from the Gulf states and northern Texas to Newfoundland and northern Manitoba (Bent, 1946). Three other subspecies are recognized (Bent, 1946): *C. b. paulus* (Southern Crow), in the southeastern part of the U.S.; *C. b. pascuud* (Florida Crow), in the Florida peninsula; and *C. b. hesperis* (Western Crow), in the western part of the range. A smaller species, *Corvus ossifragus* (Fish Crow), is also found in the eastern

Reprinted by permission of the authors and publisher from *Ecology* **39**: 126–131, 1958.

U.S., mostly in the southern states, occurring as far north as southern Massachusetts in the summer and not as far north in the winter. A third species, *Corvus caurinus* (Northwestern Crow), occurs in the extreme northwestern U.S. and thence northward to Alaska.

For this study, the calls of the Eastern Crow were recorded in the field on tape (at 71 in./sec) with either a Pentron, Model 9T-3C, or an Ampex, Model 350P, tape recorder. The behavior of the birds during the recording was observed to determine the possible significance of the calls. Copies of the recordings were made on continuous loop tape cartridges played by a special player (Message Repeater) through either a special amplifier designed for use with this player or a Stromberg-Carlson, Model AU-42, amplifier and University, Model PA 30, speakers. The Message Repeater and special amplifier were kindly supplied for these tests by the manufacturer, Mohawk Business Machines Corporation of Brooklyn, New York.

Tests with the calls were carried out during the daytime only. With this mobile broadcasting equipment in an automobile, some suitable location was selected and the sounds were broadcast at relatively high intensities—about 120 db at 1 m from the speaker. Ordinarily no crows were in sight at the start of the tests; therefore attractive or supposedly attractive calls were tested first. The recorded sequences were of either one or three minutes' duration, and they were repeated to give totals of six, nine or ten minutes.

No attempt was made to test all the calls of the Eastern Crow. Four signals were selected for testing, based on the possibility that these might have greatest utility in influencing the behavior of the bird: (1) the assembly call, given when crows sight an owl or cat; (2) the alarm call, given by a single crow which has sighted danger; (3) ordinary cawing, given by all individuals at times; and (4) begging cries of young nestlings. Attempts were made to capture normal adults for possible distress calls, but these proved fruitless; injured adults did not give distress calls. It is impossible to decide the relationship of these calls to those reported earlier in the literature (Bent, 1946) by syllables. Recordings of the calls studied here are on record with the International Collection of Animal Phonography (Frings and Frings, 1956).

During the summer of 1955 (July 5–Sept. 4), tests of these calls were made on Mt. Desert Island, Maine. The assembly call proved to be strikingly attractive to the crows. In 27 out of 30 tests, groups of crows numbering 2–30 came to the sound source within 1–5 minutes. The alarm call proved to be repellent, even at low intensities. Tests with this could be made only on crows already attracted or where they could be seen. In about 20 tests, it dispersed the crows with only one or two repetitions of the call, about 5–10 seconds. The other calls had no observable effects on the movements of the birds. These results have been reported in detail elsewhere (Frings and Frings, 1957).

During the winter of 1955–56 (Oct. 20–March 5), tests were made near State College, Pennsylvania, with essentially the same results. In 30 tests each, cawing and the sounds of nestlings proved to have no observable effects on the movements of the birds. In about 50 tests. the assembly call failed only six times to attract groups of 5–200 crows within 1–6 minutes. By using a stuffed Great Horned Owl (*Bubo virginianus*) as a visual reinforcement, these groups could be induced to approach the sound source and to remain nearby for long times. In about 30 tests, the alarm call proved to be repellent, except in the cases where the stuffed owl was present. Unfortunately, conditions beyond our control prevented tests of the alarm call on birds in large winter roosts.

These results may be summarized, therefore, as follows. The assembly call of the Eastern Crow, which is emitted by groups of crows which have sighted a cat or an owl, when recorded and broadcast to the birds in the field, is strongly attractive, bringing the birds in quite close to the sound source. When they have approached to a distance from which they can clearly see the sound source, they settle on some vantage point to observe. Only by visual reinforcement, with a stuffed owl for instance, can the birds be induced to approach quite close to the speaker or a person and to remain nearby. The alarm call, which is emitted by an individual crow on sighting danger, is repellent even at low intensities; thus mere intensity of sound is not the repellent factor. In many cases recordings of the calls of other species—gulls, ducks, wild turkeys, etc.—were broadcast without having any observable effects on the movements of crows. Likewise, the crow calls, except in a few cases, had no influence on the behavior of other birds in the neighborhood. These sounds are thus specific signals, and are used by crows for communication.

Pests in France

Three species of the genus *Corvus* are found in France, and during the winter intermingle in large flocks: *Corvus monedula* (in English, Jackdaw; in French, Choucas), *C. frugilegus* (Rook; Freux), and *C. corone corone* (Carrion Crow; Corneille noire). The social behavior of the Carrion Crow is much like that of the American Eastern Crow, but the social behavior of the other two species is more nearly like that of the American *Sturnus vulgaris* (Starling). In winter, the French species gather in large numbers for roosting at night and feed in flocks numbering from ten to hundreds during the day. These frequently include representatives of all three species, with *C. frugilegus* usually predominant.

The call with which the most detailed studies were made was the distress call of *C. monedula*, for the effects of broadcasting this call were very striking. This was selected for study from among a number of calls which were tested and found to have less effect or no observable effects on the flocks. The distress call was recorded on tape as emitted by individuals which were held by the legs or caught by a falcon, and then either played back from a disk record or from a tape cartridge by the Message Repeater through an amplifier and speaker mounted on a truck. The intensity was such as to give the sound a range of 1,500–2,500 m. Usually the distance from the truck to the flocks was 50–2,000 m. The flocks were feeding in fields and were always in sight at the beginning of the tests, unlike the situation in the U.S. The sound was emitted for about 20 seconds and then turned off. In about two minutes, there was another emission, and the sound was repeated thus 2–4 times. Most of the tests were made near Paris from November to March, 1954–55 and 1955–56.

Reactions to the sound were classified into three major and some minor categories. When the birds flew up from the ground, circled to gain altitude and approached the speaker, the reaction was called positive phonotaxis. If the sound was kept on, the birds circled near the speaker, generally vocalizing, and dispersed individually. If the sound was turned off, the birds circled higher and higher and disappeared as a group. If, after the birds started to leave, the sound was reemitted, they returned to the source. Positive phonotaxis was divided into five classes, designated as follows: $+++$, if the reaction was immediate and direct, $++$, if the reaction was good but not immediate, $+$, if only part of the flock was attracted, $+-$, if some were attracted while others flew away, and $+O$, if some approached the sound source while others remained on the ground. When the birds flew up from the ground and then away from or at some angle to the sound source, the reaction was called negative phonotaxis. Two classes were recognized:—, if the birds all flew thus, and $-O$, if only part flew thus while the others remained on the ground. In some cases there was no apparent reaction to the sound, and these were designated as negative, symbolized by o.

The general methods for recording and projecting the calls of the birds were thus similar to those used by the American workers, but the observations were made somewhat differently. In the tests in the U.S., usually no birds were in sight at the start and counts were made of the birds which were in sight at 30-second intervals during the broadcasting of the sound. In France, the birds were in sight at the beginning of the tests, and the reactions of the flocks were thus susceptible of classification into reaction types smaller groups and much more dispersed than those in France.

The results of the tests in France are summarized in Table 1, where the symbols are those defined above. It is clear that the distress call of *C. monedula* usually has great effect on the movement of flocks of the three species. In about 75% of the cases it serves to disperse the flocks, either directly or through circling flight which brings the birds closer to the sound source at first and later away.

Tests were also made at night with the distress call of *C. monedula* at a roosting place for about 2000 of these birds near Paris (Busnel *et al.*, 1955). With four minutes of sound at 10:30 P.M., the birds rose from the roost, circled in the air and left, not to return until six nights later. In seven similar tests at other places they stayed away from the roosts for 3–30 days. The distress call thus has effects with roosting corvines similar to the effects found for the distress call of the Starling in the U.S. (Frings and Jumber, 1954).

TABLE 1

Results of tests with the recorded distress call of *C. monedula* and the recorded assembly call of *C. brachyrhynchos* when broadcast to feeding flocks of French *Corvus* spp.

| Type of Reaction | Species Whose Call Was Broadcast: | | | |
| | *C. monedula* | | *C. brachyrhynchos* | |
	No. of react.	% of react.	No. of react.	% of react.
+++, ++ or + ...	20	40%	16	31%
+− or +o	8	16%	12	23%
− or −o	10	20%	6	11%
o	12	24%	18	35%

The symbols are explained in the test; those with +, indicate positive phonotaxis, with −, negative phonotaxis, and with o, no reaction.

Tests with Exchanged Recorded Calls

The investigators in the U.S. received from the French investigators, in the spring of 1955, the following calls of French birds: distress calls of *C. monedula*, *C. frugilegus*, and *C. corone*, and calls of nestling *C. frugilegus*. These were tested in the summer of 1955 at Mt. Desert Island, Maine, and in the winter of 1955–56 near State College, Pennsylvania, during the tests with the native crow calls. With the distress calls of all three species (20 tests with each) no observable results were obtained. During the summer, with the calls of young *C. frugilegus*, no observable reactions were obtained, but during the winter, some attractive properties appeared. In ten tests at this time, seven resulted in approaches to the sound source by a few crows: in two cases 2 crows, in three cases 3 crows, in one case 4 crows, and in one case 5 crows. These flew over slowly, as if investigating, and did not remain for more than one to two minutes at the most. Thus there was some attraction but not nearly so much as with the native call, and the reaction seemed more like curiosity than the purposive assembling elicited by the assembly call of the Eastern Crow itself.

The investigators in France received from the U.S. the following calls of the Eastern Crow: assembly call, alarm call, cawing, and the cries of nestlings. These were tested, along with distress call of *C. monedula*, near Paris in the winter of 1955–56. The alarm call, cawing and cries of nestlings proved ineffective in eliciting any observable reactions in flocks of the three species of corvines. The reactions to the assembly call, however, were much like those to the distress call of *C. monedula*, as shown in Table 1. While no statistically significant differences between the reaction to the two calls were found, the intensity of response to the American call seemed to be less than to the native call. With the French call, the birds circled near the speaker and dispersed one by one if the sound persisted. With the American crow call, the birds flew toward the speaker, did not circle, and dispersed in groups.

By April, 1956, therefore, it seemed that the Eastern Crow in the U.S. reacted very specifically to its own calls, the French calls arousing only slight reactions. On the other hand, the French birds reacted to both their own distress calls and to the assembly call of the U.S. crow, thus seeming to be less specific in their reactive potentialities. At this time, the French investigators came to the U.S. with a new recording of the distress call of *C. monedula*, and tests were made during June, 1956, with somewhat different results.

The first tests were made in Pennsylvania, near State College, on June 3–5. In five of the first six tests, using paired trials with the two calls, the French call had effects almost exactly like those of the assembly call of the Eastern Crow. The earlier results had been so decidedly negative that it seemed possible that the new recording might be different from the older one, even though to the human ear they sounded much alike. Accordingly, four tests were made with the older recording, with the same results as with the new recording. Thus there was a real difference between the reactions at this time and those during the previous summer and winter.

The next hypothesis was that the extreme hunting pressure on the crows in Pennsylvania during the breeding and planting season caused them to become reactive to almost any unusual sounds. Accordingly, a series of recorded sounds (duck vocalizations, mosquito wing sounds, etc.) were broadcast. There were no observable reactions to these, even when the crows were visible during the tests. It would seem, therefore, that mere unusual sounds were not responsible.

The difference in reactions seemed thus to be related either to seasonal or geographic factors, for the summer tests of 1955 were conducted in Maine. Accordingly, tests exactly like those in Pennsylvania, using paired trials of the assembly call of the Eastern Crow and the distress call of *C. monedula*, were made at Mt. Desert Island, Maine on June 12–14.

In 14 tests, no reaction was obtained to the distress call of *C. monedula*, just as during the previous summer, while the usual high reactivity to the assembly call was found. In fact, the difference in the reaction of these crows to the French call was so striking it seemed impossible that we could be testing the same call at all, while the reactions to the American call were exactly similar in Pennsylvania and Maine. Thus, there is a true difference in reaction to the French call between crows in central Pennsylvania and those in northeastern Maine, even though these are of the same subspecies.

Experiments on Herring Gulls

In the summer of 1954, the investigators in the U.S. studied the reactions of *Larus argentatus* (Herring Gull) to broadcasts of recorded communication signals of this species (Frings *et al.*, 1955a, 1955b). Briefly, four calls were clearly separable in origin and effects at feeding areas: a food-finding call, emitted by gulls on sighting food, which proved to be quite attractive to other gulls; an alarm call, emitted by gulls sighting danger, which proved to be strikingly repellent; and the mew call and trumpeting, both of great importance in breeding colonies but without clearly definable effects among feeding gulls.

Copies of these calls were sent to the French investigators for broadcasting to colonies of *Larus argentatus* (in English, Herring Gull; in French, Goëland argenté) and *L. ridibundus* (Black-headed Gull; Mouette Rieuse). The former is, of course, the same species as that in the U.S. The tests were made during the winter of 1955–56 with continental flocks of gulls. Since the calls of Herring Gulls had the same effects in the U.S. with *Larus marinus* (Great Black-backed Gull) and *L. atricilla* (Eaughing Gull), it seemed reasonable to expect that they would have similar effects in France, at least with *L. argentatus*.

The results were quite surprising—the calls were totally lacking in observable effects on the French gulls. This was later checked by Mr. G. Jansen of Rotterdam, Holland, who tried to use the recorded alarm call of the U.S. Herring Gull to drive gulls from an airport near Rotterdam without having any observable movement of the gulls, even when the call was broadcast from very short distances. In the U.S., flight from the sound source was achieved at distances up to 2 miles, with the intensity only about 95 db at 1 m from the speaker. Since recorded samples of the calls of European Herring Gulls have not yet been received for testing in the U.S., the explanation for this discrepancy remains unknown, but the results are given as an illustration of some possible subspecific differentiation in understanding of the signals. The tests in Europe were made during the winter and early spring, while those in the U.S. were made during the summer; the differences may thus be related to the time of year. Only further tests can decide the question.

Discussion

An acoustical note should be made on these tests. With field equipment, fidelity of reproduction is at times much reduced, and to the human ear at least the sounds broadcast to the birds are distorted or partially masked with background noise or hum. Yet they seem to be "understood" quite readily by the birds. It may be that the physical parameters determining the effectiveness for birds are not the same as those determining fidelity for the human ear. The similarity of the ears of birds and mammals, however, makes this seem not too likely. More likely, these communication signals are capable of being distinguished by the birds over high levels of background interference. This would be particularly the case for warning sounds, such as a distress call or an assembly call like that of the Eastern Crow.

What hypotheses might one set up to explain the results obtained? It is obvious that, in the species of *Corvus* we tested, three different levels of specificity in reactions to communication signals are represented—the Eastern

Crow in Maine during the summer and in Pennsylvania during the winter seems to be very specific in its reactions, this species in Pennsylvania during the summer seems to be less specific, and the three French species seem to be least specific of those tested. The difference between the behavior of the American *Corvus brachyrhynchos* and the French species of *Corvus* may be related to the fact that the American crows are usually found in flocks consisting of only one species, or in the southern part of the range two species, while the French birds associate interspecifically during the winter. Thus the French corvines might learn to react to more generalized features of warning sounds than their American congeners. As substantiation of this, the French species were found to react to the distress call when it was cut into sections or played backwards.

There are two important differences between the Eastern Crows in Maine and in Pennsylvania during the early summer. First, the crows in Pennsylvania are much more severely hunted than those in Maine, at least where these tests were made. It is conceivable that this might make them much more reactive to all warning sounds in Pennsylvania at this time. The exact similarity in reactions to the assembly call, however, lends little support to this idea. The second difference is that the crows living in Maine in the summer move southward for the winter to southern New England and Pennsylvania, while those in Pennsylvania move southward into the southern states (Bent 1946). This means that the crows tested during the winter in Pennsylvania are from a population equivalent to the tested during the summer in Maine. Further, they represent individuals which mingle generally only with other members of the same species. But the crows which move southward from Pennsylvania in the winter mingle with the different southern subspecies and, possibly of more importance, with the Fish Crow. This is reported as having a hoarser sounding vioce than that of the Eastern Crow (Bent 1946). The distress call of *C. monedula* is much more hoarse in sound than the call of the Eastern Crow. Is it possible that the crows which spend the summer in Pennsylvania, having just arrived in June from these associations, have learned to react to a wider gamut of warning sounds, and thus have become reactive to the coarser call of *C. monedula*? We believe that this is, at present, the most reasonable assumption.

This idea is supported by the following observations made by the American investigators and reported here for the first time. In Maine, two species of gulls are found together—*L. argentatus* and *L. marinus*—with the former by far in the majority. The latter always react quite typically to the calls of the former, but usually not the reverse. Eastern Crows also are often found feeding with Herring Gulls in Maine, and there is considerable cross-reactivity in calls, depending upon the population structure. It is interesting to note that, in a few cases, Herring Gulls in Maine responded similarly to the distress call of the French crow by flying in circles over the sound source. In tests with the distress call of *Sturnus vulgaris* (Starling), we have found that, with mixed roosts including *Molothus ater* (Brown-headed Cowbirds), *Quiscalus quiscula* (Common Grackles), or *Progne subis* (Purple Martins), the species other than Starlings will leave with the Starlings if they form a small fraction of the roosting birds, but may not if they form a large fraction. Thus it seems that minority groups flocking with other species may learn to react to the signals of the majority as to their own, but not necessarily the reverse. It has been well known to most naturalists since Aristotle that alarm calls of passerine birds which have sighted a hawk or cat attract individuals of other species.

The meaning of the subspecificity in the Herring Gull remains to be determined. A report from Europe suggests that the European Starling may also fail to react to the recorded distress call of its American conspecies, and that the European Starling may have a different signal.

We feel that all these observations suggest that birds develop basic communication signals within each species having features in common with those of related species, but sometimes with regional variations. In case in which individuals are exposed only to the signals of their own group, they may becomes quite specific in reactions. In cases where they mingle with other populations of their own species or with populations of related or non-related species, they may learn to respond to the signals of these.

These are probably behavioral isolating and hybridizing mechanisms—the substructure of evolutionary change, as Blair (1955a, 1955b, 1956) has studied in Amphibia and Fulton (1933, 1937) in crickets. For the birds, much work is needed before we shall be in a position to formulate even provisional theories. Studies should be made with different geographic and season populations of the same species and with reactions of birds to calls of related or distant species as functions of population structure. Only when the full "vocabularies" of many species are tested over wide geographic areas and with contiguous and distant populations of the same or related species will we be ready to develop theories relating the ecological, evolutionary, acoustical, and behavioral parameters of these behavior patterns.

From the standopint of possible practical utility in controlling the movements of economically important species, these results emphasize the need for careful studies on habits of birds if attempts to influence their behavior are to be made successfully. It may not be sufficient merely to broadcast recorded calls to birds to get specific results. Only critical observations of behavior as related to geographic distribution, seasonal movements and ecological relations can give the basic information needed for effective control measures.

Summary

In the U.S., Eastern Crows (*C. b. brachyrhynchos*) emit an assembly call on sighting an owl or cat which, when recorded and broadcast to crows in the field, causes aggregation near the sound source. An alarm call, emitted when the crows sight danger, when broadcast similarly, causes the birds to fly away.

In France, three species of *Corvus* (*C. monedula, C. frugilegus*, and *C. c. corone*) roost and feed together during the winter. Broadcasts of recorded distress calls, emitted when the birds are restrained or injured, cause the birds to approach the sound source at first and afterward to disperse. The distress call of *C. monedula* proved to be most effective. When broadcast at night near roosts, the call causes the birds to desert the roosts.

Using exchanged recordings, the distress calls of the French corvines were broadcast to crows in the U.S. There were no observable reactions by the birds in Maine during the summer and Pennsylvania during the winter. In early summer, in Pennsylvania however, the distress call of *C. monedula* induced crows to approach the sound source. In France, the three species did not respond to the recorded alarm call of the American species, but reacted to the assembly call of the American crow as they did to the distress calls of the French birds.

In the U.S., the Herring Gull (*L. argentatus*) responds to its own food-finding call when recorded and broadcast, by approaching the sound source and to broadcasts of its alarm call by dispersal. In France, with the same species, the calls elicit no response.

These observations suggest that these birds develop communication signals within each species having features in common with those of related species, but sometimes with regional variations within the species. In cases in which individuals are exposed only to the signals of their own group, they may become quite specific in reaction. In cases where they mingle with other groups of their own or other species they may learn to respond to the signals of these.

References

Bent, A. C. 1946. Life histories of North American jays, crows, and titmice. *U. S. Nat. Mus., Bull.* 191.

Blair, W. F. 1955a. Differentiation of mating call in spadefoots, Genus p*caphiopus*. *Texas J. Sci.* **7**: 183–188.

———. 1955b. Mating call and stage of speciation in the *Microhyla olivacea-M. carolinensis* complex. *Evolution* **9**: 469–480.

———. 1956. Call difference as an isolation mechanism in southwestern toads (Genus *Bufo*). *Texas J. Sci.* **8**: 87–106.

Busnel, R.-G., J. Giban, Ph. Gramet, and F. Pasquinelly. 1955. Observations préliminaires de la phonotaxis negative des corbeaux à des signaux acoustiques naturels ou artificiels. *Compt. rend. Acad. Sci.* **241**: 1846–1849.

Frings, H. and M. 1956. Recording animal sounds. *Science* **123**: 1088.

———. 1957. Recorded calls of the eastern crow as attractants and repellents. *J. Wildl. Man.* **21**: 91.

Frings, H. and J. Jumber. 1954. Preliminary studies on the use of a specific sound to repel starlings (*Sturnus vulgaris*) from objectionable roosts. *Science* **119**: 318–319.

Frings, H., M. Fings, B. Cox, and L. Peissner. 1955a. Recorded calls of herring gulls (*Larus argentatus*) as repellents and attractants. *Science* **121**: 340–341.

———. 1955b. Auditory and visual mechanisms in food-finding behavior of the herring gull. *Wilson Bull.* **67**: 155–170.

Fulton, B. B. 1933. Inheritance of song in hybrids of two subspecies of *Nemobius fasciatus* (Orthoptera). *Ann. Ent. Soc. Amer.* **26**: 368–376.

———. 1937. Experimental crossing of subspecies in *Nemobius* (Orthoptera: Gryllidae). *Ann. Ent. Soc. Amer.* **30**: 201–207.

Territory and the Regulation of Density in Titmice

H. N. Kluyver,

L. Tinbergen

Since the publication of Howard's "Territory in Bird Life" the behaviour aspects of territorial practice have been studied by many authors, but we are less well informed about its ecological significance. In particular, the presumed effect of territory upon density of population is still open to discussion.

Though he does not say so in so many words Howard (1920, p. 286) clearly assumes that for small passerines, territories have a minimum size beyond which the birds do not allow further crowding. In Howard's opinion, males which arrive in an area where the population has already reached this critical level will move around until they find unoccupied ground. If they do not succeed, they will be unable to breed.

On a priori grounds some limiting effect on the increase of local populations certainly is probable. It has been shown that the frequency of territorial quarrels increases with rising density (see e.g., Huxley, 1934; N. Tinbergen, 1939, p. 70). Thus an important condition for a limiting influence is fulfilled, and such effect has been assumed by several authors (e.g., Nice, 1937; Kluyver, 1951). But this thesis has not been supported by direct evidence, as Lack (1946) stresses.

The present authors have collected some information on this problem during bird census work in Dutch woods. In this paper we will show that density of population in the more attractive habitats is buffered to a certain extent. We will examine the possible explanations of this phenomenon, among which, in our opinion, Howard's thesis is the most satisfactory.

Kluyver's observations were made under the auspices of the Phytopathological Service, Wageningen. Tinbergen did most of his work under the "Instituut voor Toegepast-Biologisch Onderzoek in de Natuur", Oosterbeek, and continued it at the Zoological Laboratory of the University of Groningen.

We have to acknowledge valuable help from many sources. Many of the Wageningen observations were made by the late G. Wolda. During census work in 1946–1951 Tinbergen received much help from Miss J. G. Nijenhuis, Miss N. Croin, A. C. Perdeck, P. Sevenster, H. Veldkamp, N. Prop, B. Bennema, P. Glas, J. H. Mook and R. Simon Thomas. An important series of observations was put at our disposal by L. J. Kramer, the late A. J. Schravendijk, and A. J. Vegter. P. H. T. Hartley, R. E. Moreau, Dr D. Lack, and Dr B. Greenberg kindly criticized our manuscript and provided linguistic help. Finally we have to express our gratitude to Prof. L. J. Smid who gave us statistical advice.

Reprinted by permission of the Editorial Board of the *Archives Néerlandaises de Zoologie* and Swets & Zeitlinger Publishing Company, Inc., Amsterdam from *Archives Néerlandaises de Zoologie* **10**: 265–289, 1960.

Census Data

Between 1941 and 1952 Tinbergen and his collaborators determined densities of Great Tits *Parus major*, Blue Tits *Parus coeruleus* and Coal Tits *Parus ater* in the woods near Hulshorst, Guelders Prov., Netherlands. In a number of characteristic sampling areas territories were counted by mapping singing males during early morning song. The method has been described in detail by L. Tinbergen (1946).

The Hulshorst district consists largely of almost pure woods of Scotspine *Pinus sylvestris* with a rather poor bird fauna. Among these we studied a number of lots, varying in age between 35 and 70 years. Between these pinewoods are found narrow strips of mixed wood, 100 to 200 yards wide. For the greatest part these are situated on the borders of a small brook. These mixed woods are much more attractive to many species of songbirds than the pinewoods. Nevertheless, they are also of a comparatively poor type. Undergrowth of shrubs and herbs is scarce. The tree layer mainly contains oak *Quercus robur*, beech *Fagus sylvatica*, birch *Betula* spec., Scotspine, fir *Picea excelsa*, Douglas' fir *Pseudotsuga douglasii* and smaller numbers of *Quercus* cf. *rubra*, *Alnus glutinosa* and *Larix* spec. The tallest trees measure ca. 60 feet.

In both the pinewoods and the mixed woods nesting sites are present in sufficient numbers. The land owner placed nest boxes in the pinewoods which otherwise would not provide suitable nesting holes for Great Tits and Blue Tits. The mixed woods contain a great number of natural tree holes and moreover some nest boxes.

Density figures for mixed wood and pinewood are summarised in Fig. 1. In the first place, density per unit of area in the mixed wood was always much higher than density in the pinewood. This applies to all three species of titmice. Apparently they have a pronounced preference for the mixed wood.

Furthermore, fluctuations from year to year are much smaller in the mixed wood than in the pinewood. This is clearest in the Great Tit. In this species density in the mixed wood fell to 10 in 1942 whereas in all other years it fluctuated only between $13\frac{1}{2}$ and 17. The pinewood, on the other hand, had no Great Tits at all in 1942 and in the other years its population varied between 10 and 23. Apparently density in the mixed wood is buffered in some way.

This effect can be demonstrated more conveniently by plotting year for year density in the mixed wood against the accompanying value of density in the pinewood (Fig. 2A). Instead of proportionality between both figures (resulting in a straight regression line cutting the origin of the graph) one finds the points grouped on a line almost parallel with the abscissa. Thus, as density in the pinewood increases, density in the mixed wood remains almost constant. Nevertheless, it is clear that the regression line eventually must reach the point 0–0. So in its complete form it will include a part steeply rising from the origin to point 1942. This part has been extrapolated on Fig. 2A.

Density in the pinewood is an approximate index of total population

114

		MIXED WOOD HULSHORST	PINEWOOD HULSHORST		APD.
		♂♂ ON 25.5 HA	♂♂ ON 100 HA		
GREAT TIT	1941	13½	18	1941	22
	1942	10	0	1942	7
	1943	13½	10	1943	24
	1946	14½	11	1946	24
	1947	14½	19	1947	28
	1948	17	11	1948	21
	1949	14½	23	1949	37
	1950	14	10	1950	22
	1951	15½	23	1951	–
	1952	17	21	1952	–
		♂♂ ON 9.7 HA	♂♂ ON 80 HA		
BLUE TIT	1941	5	3.5	1941	0.8
	1942	6½	5.2	1942	2.6
	1943	6	–	1943	7.6
	1946	9	6.1	1946	6.1
	1947	6	4.7	1947	4.5
	1948	7	10.8	1948	11.6
	1949	7½	11.7	1949	11.8
	1950	6	4.0	1950	4.9
	1951	5½	3.5	1951	–
	1952	8	9.6	1952	–
		♂♂ ON 25.5 HA	♂♂ ON 100 HA		
COAL TIT	1941	14½	34	1941	7.2
	1942	14½	36	1942	10.5
	1943	22	45	1943	16.7
	1946	10	11	1946	7.6
	1947	12½	19	1947	6.
	1948	13½	19	1948	9.8
	1949	13	16	1949	7.3
	1950	10	13	1950	0.6
	1951	9½	13	1951	–
	1952	7½	12	1952	–

in the Hulshorst district, as the mixed wood covers only a very small part of this area. Thus a gradual increase in total population hardly raises density in the mixed wood except during the very first step of the process which we only know by extrapolation.

In the Blue Tit the correlation graph for density mixed wood and density pinewood shows a slightly different picture (Fig. 2E). Unfortunately the regression line cannot be drawn very exactly as the point 1946 fits badly. It is clear, however, that it has no horizontal part like in the Great Tit. Nevertheless, density in the mixed wood increases more slowly than density in the pinewood, at least within the range of observations. So we can speak again of a buffer effect. We are inclined to explain the abnormal values for 1946 as a chance effect in sampling, but we cannot prove this.

In the Coal Tit finally the situation is not quite clear. As compared with the other years, the points of high density (1941, 1942, and 1943; Fig. 2B) strongly suggest a buffer effect. Unfortunately, however, the later years have not given the opportunity of rechecking the distribution at high general density. In this period Coal Tits always have been scarce.

The observation points show only slight deviations from a straight line cutting the ordinate near point density mixed wood = 7, but the most probable interpretation seems to us a regression line rising through points 1950 and 1951 to points 1947 and 1948, bending in horizontal direction to points 1941 and 1942 and finally rising again to point 1943. A tentative explanation for point 1943 is given on p. 281. So only between density (pinewood) 8 and 15 density in the mixed wood would be buffered.

The total population of these species of titmice apparently strongly fluctuated in the Hulshorst district. These fluctuations occurred almost synchroneously in a much larger area. Through the kindness of the late A. J. Schravendijk, of L. J. Kramer and A. J. Vegter we can present population figures for the "Berg en Bos" wood near Apeldoorn, 15 miles SE from Hulshorst. As at Hulshorst, pinewoods dominate in this estate. The data have been included in Fig. 1. In general they show a similar trend as those for the pinewoods at Hulshorst. Thus the Great Tit minima for 1942, 1946, 1948,

Fig. 1. Number of breeding territories at Hulshorst. For comparison density figures for Apeldoorn (Apd) have been added, cf. text. 1 ha = 1 hectare = ca. 2.5 acres. Note. (1) The area covered in the pinewood counts at Hulshorst slightly shifted from year to year. On the average 100 hectares have been investigated each year for Great Tit and Coal Tit and 80 ha for Blue Tit. Average densities per 10 ha were the following:

	Great Tit	Blue Tit	Coal Tit
Mixed Wood......	5.6	6.8	5.0
Pinewood	1.46	0.83	2.18

(2) The Apeldoorn counts are expressed in pairs per 100 nestboxes. In some years parts of the wood have not been investigated. On the average 177 boxes have been inspected in each year. The pinewood at Apeldoorn contains a small amount of deciduous trees. Average density of Great Tits is somewhat higher than at Hulshorst.

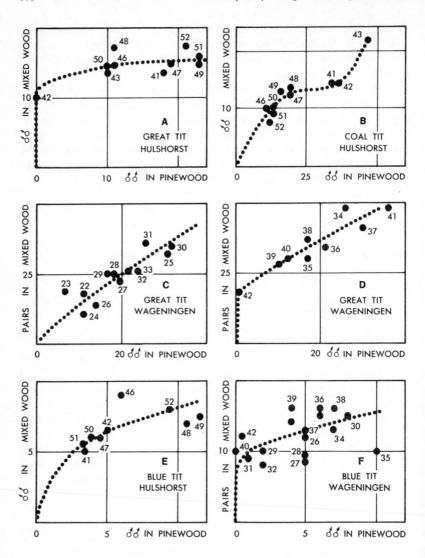

Fig. 2. Relation between numbers of titmice in mixed wood and in pinewood. Data from Fig. 1 and Table 1. Regression lines drawn at sight. Dotted: years of observation.

and 1950 were also found at Apeldoorn. The same holds good for the Blue Tit peak of 1948–1949 and the Coal Tit peak of 1943.

At Wageningen (Guelders Prov.) Kluyver collected a much longer series of observations on the estate "Oranje Nassau's Oord."

The woods of this estate are poor in natural nest holes. Nearly all Great

Tits and many Blue Tits therefore nest in boxes, which form almost optimal nesting sites for these species. Except in the years 1930–1933, boxes were present in excess throughout the estate. The number of first broods in these boxes was recorded year after year and these figures are used here as an index of population (Table 1).

TABLE 1

Numbers of breeding pairs at Wageningen (Oranje Nassau's Oord) in 60 hectares of mixed wood and in 61 hectares of pinewood.

Year	Great Tit (*Parus major*)		Blue Tit (*Parus coeruleus*)	
	Mixed Wood	Pinewood	Mixed Wood	Pinewood
1922	18	11		
1923	19	7		
1924	11	11		
1925	32	31	15	6
1926	14	14	12	5
1927	22	20	9	5
1928	25	18	9	5
1929	25	17	10	2
1930	35	32	15	8
1931	36	26	9	1
1932	26	22	8	2
1933	26	24	14	4
Av. 1922–1933	24.1	19.4	—	—
1934	48	26	13	7
1935	30	17	10	10
1936	34	21	16	6
1937	41	30	13	5
1938	37	17	16	7
1939	28	10	16	4
1940	30	12	10	0
1941	48	36	no observations	
1942	18	1	12	1
Av. 1934–1942	34.9	18.9	—	—
Av. 1925–1942	—	—	12.2	4.6

Great Tit

The Wageningen area comprises mixed wood as well as pinewood, the mixed wood being on the whole younger than that at Hulshorst, but richer in tree species. It has about the same average density of Great Tits. In earlier years, however, its vegetation was much poorer. This is clearly reflected in the census data (Table 1). Between 1922 and 1933 the density of Great Tits in the mixed wood was almost equal to that in the pinewood, but from 1934 onward it averaged about twice as much. Thus the Great Tits showed a clear preference for the mixed wood during these latter years but not during the earlier.

The change in 1934 was sudden. This has the following explanation. After 1930 the younger mixed plantations (which started as undergrowth in the older wood) had grown so far that they became a suitable habitat for Great Tits. There was, however, a shortage of nesting sites since there were only a few nestboxes. This situation changed in 1934, when more boxes were provided and the tits were enabled to utilise the young plantations fully. The attractiveness of the mixed part of the estate therefore increased abruptly.

The pinewood at Wageningen differs from most of the pinewoods at Hulshorst in having some shrub growth and taller trees. The average density of Great Tits is much higher than the average at Hulshorst. There, the old, well grown pinewoods have an equally dense population, but these are scarce and the average for the district depends mainly on the density of younger and slowly growing woods, which is low. Apparently the type of pinewood which prevails at Wageningen is more attractive to Great Tits than the lower woods at Hulshorst.

In Fig. 2C and 2D density in the mixed wood at Wageningen is correlated with density in the pinewood. In the years 1922–1933, when mixed wood and pinewood were almost equally attractive to Great Tits, density in the mixed wood was directly proportional to density in the pinewood. This is shown by the regression line which passes through the origin of the graph. But from 1934 onward, when the mixed wood became more attractive than the pinewood, the relation clearly changed. The regression line for this period, when drawn as a straight line, does not cut the origin. Density in the mixed wood changed much more slowly than density in the pinewood. Thus we can speak again of a buffer effect, present since the time when the attractiveness of the mixed wood had increased. It should be noted, however, that the regression line for 1934–1942 has no horizontal part as at Hulshorst, so that the buffer effect was less pronounced at Wageningen than at Hulshorst.

Blue Tit

The observations are summarised in Table 1. In several respects they differ from those on the Great Tit. In the first place density in the mixed wood always was much higher than density in the pinewood and even in the years before 1934 the Blue Tit preferred the mixed wood. This in our opinion reflects the fact that the Blue Tit has a stronger preference than the Great Tit for deciduous wood.

There is another difference between the figures for Blue and Great Tits. Between 1913 and 1924 density of Blue Tits in both the mixed wood and the pinewood was much lower than in the years after 1924. Since a similar increase was noted at other localities, we assume a general rise of the population of Blue Tits which was not caused by local conditions.

We shall analyze only the period 1925–1942, since the numbers in the earlier period were too small. In Fig. 2F density in the mixed wood is compared with density in the pinewood. The result is similar to that in the Great Tit 1934–

1942. Density in the mixed wood is not proportional to density in the pine-wood. It is already rather high when density in the pinewood is low. As the numbers in the pinewood rise, density in the mixed wood increases relatively slowly. Apparently the density of Blue Tits too was buffered in the mixed wood at Wageningen.

The "Buffer Mechanism" in the Great Tit

Both at Hulshorst and at Wageningen densities of Great and Blue Tits were high in attractive mixed woods and low in neighbouring pure stands of Scotspine. Fluctuations from year to year were small in the former habitat and considerable in the latter. As the total population in both mixed woods and pinewoods increased, density in the mixed wood rose much more slowly than density in the pinewoods. This buffer effect was very pronounced in the Great Tit at Hulshorst and in the Blue Tit at Hulshorst and Wageningen. The Great Tit records for Wageningen show it in a less marked but never-theless convincing form. Here the effect only occurred in the period when the mixed wood was rather attractive for the tits. Finally observations on the Coal Tit in Hulshorst suggest similar relations in this species.

We must now examine the mechanism which buffers density in the mixed woods. This requires knowledge of the life history of the different species. At present, only the Great Tit has been studied in detail. We will therefore first confine our attention to this species.

It may be useful first to summarise certain aspects of the Great Tit's biology. The phenomena of dispersal especially interest us here. Kluyver (1951) has studied these subjects in the woods near Wageningen already described in this paper, and we shall chiefly summarise his findings.

Ringing data show that a considerable number of Great Tits select a home range in autumn and early winter of the first year of life. After reaching this age many but not all Great Tits are very faithful to their homes.[1] Gen-erally speaking the further life of these individuals is confined to a range of about 50–80 hectares. The nucleus of this range is the area where the indi-vidual roosts during autumn and winter and where it breeds in successive summers; it has a surface of ca. 10 hectares. This area is named the "domicile." It should be noted that the domiciles of different individuals overlap to a considerable extent. So they certainly are not comparable with territories.

In early autumn (especially September) there is much fighting and threaten-ing among Great Tits. Both males and females participate in these quarrels which often occur on fixed spots. We are inclined to explain them as terri-torial fights, but we cannot prove this.

Aggressive behaviour is suspended in winter. During this season the birds roost in the domicile, but they spend the day in its larger surroundings, which, as already mentioned, do not cover more than ca. 50–80 hectares.

[1] The same has been found by Plattner and Sutter (1946).

The tits then flock together in the well known mixed parties. These scatter at dusk; every Great Tit then moves to its own domicile to roost.

The defence of territories can already be observed in late winter. Brian (1949) found that the boundaries between neighbouring territories were still rather vague in February. They become sharper in the course of spring, at least in densely populated areas like the mixed woods studied by us. In gardens at Wageningen, where the population of Great Tits is still denser, the boundaries between territories were very sharp, though they shifted slightly from one week to another. On the other hand fights between neighbouring pairs regularly were seen at low densities in the pinewoods. Here, however, the boundaries were not sharp.

At least in the mixed woods which we studied, the whole area is divided into territories during spring. For the pinewoods this is uncertain.

Within their domicile individual Great Tits do not inhabit exactly the same territory in successive springs; as a rule there is some shifting.

Many Great Tits are faithful to the domicile which they select in their first autumn. This fixation, however, is not absolute. For instance, when a habitat suddenly becomes very unsuitable by the cutting of trees or the removal of nestboxes, many tits will leave it. In such cases it was found that some of them move over considerable distances.

Displacements also occur under more normal conditions. In the mixed wood at Wageningen there is a category of birds which appear in autumn and emigrate in spring. In some winters this group is as numerous as the residents, in others they are scarce.

It is not known where these birds settle in spring. Some of them might be true migrants, which have wintered at Wageningen, but others probably do not go far away. It is possible that the latter settle in unattractive habitats, e.g., in the poor pinewoods. In this type of habitat regular observations of ringed birds were not made. Winter counts in poor pinewoods at Hulshorst revealed an increase of Great Tits in early spring, but this does not exclude other explanations.

Summarising we find that the distribution of Great Tits over different breeding habitats takes place in two phases. In rough outline it is already determined in autumn when many individuals settle in their final domiciles. In detail, however, it takes place in early spring when the breeding territories are established. Many birds remain faithful to the domiciles which they select in their first autumn of life. Nevertheless displacements at greater age do occur. There is, for example, a regular emigration from the mixed wood during late winter or early spring.

After this introduction, we can deal with our main point: the factors buffering density in the mixed woods.

In principle, density at a certain locality is determined by three main processes: reproduction, mortality and habitat selection (in a broad sense). We will discuss the possible influence of each of these factors in the buffer mechanism.

Reproduction

The Great Tits of the mixed woods do not form isolated populations which depend on their own reproduction for the recruitment of a new generation. Before settling the young birds may move over considerable distances (Kluyver, 1951). The latter are much greater than the dimensions of our mixed woods. Moreover the Wageningen ringing data show that birds which were born in the mixed wood often settle in pinewoods and vice versa. Krätzig found the same exchange between richer and poorer habitats. So eventual differences in reproduction rates between the pairs of mixed woods and those of pinewoods cannot account for the differences in density between both habitats, nor for the observed buffer effect.

Mortality

As we have seen, the rough distribution over different habitats has already taken place in autumn. Therefore we must examine how far mortality between autumn and spring can contribute to the buffer effect.

At first sight the remarkable distribution in 1942 might reflect an influence of mortality. In this year density in the mixed woods was 50–70 % of the average value, but density in the pinewoods fell to 0–7 % of the average. The winter 1941–'42 was very hard. It seems possible that the autumn population in 1941 was more or less normal in both mixed woods and pinewoods and that birds which had their domicile in pinewood suffered much more from frost and snow than those which had domiciles in the mixed wood.

Such differential mortality could operate either during roosting at night or by day. In the pinewoods at Hulshorst and at Wageningen most Great Tits roost in nestboxes, but in the mixed woods many make use of holes in trees. Possibly nest boxes are colder in winter nights than holes in trees. This might account for a difference in mortality. But inspections of nestboxes during and after the winter never revealed a significant number of dead titmice. Therefore we cannot accept that the disappearance of Great Tits in the pinewood was caused by a high mortality of the birds which roost in this habitat.

During daytime, on the other hand, many of the tits which have domiciles in the pinewood live under the same conditions as those which have domiciles in the mixed wood. This is especially noticeable at Hulshorst, where the width of the mixed wood is 100–200 m whereas the diameter of the range in which the birds wander each day is at least 650 m. (This figure is derived from the Wageningen ringing data; Krätzig (1939) found much higher figures.) This implies that all birds which have domiciles in the mixed woods at Hulshorst may spend a great part of the day in pinewood. On the other hand many birds roosting in pinewood may visit the mixed woods. In fact, flocks which move from the pinewood to the mixed wood and the other way round were often observed. At Wageningen the birds seem to concentrate in the mixed wood during winter days. At least, feeding shelves in the pinewood did not attract Great Tits whereas feeding shelves placed in the mixed wood were visited by birds roosting in the mixed wood as well as by birds roosting in the pinewood.

It seems probable that the mixed wood offers better conditions of food and cover during winter. These better conditions, however, are not the exclusive privilege of the birds which roost in the mixed wood. Many inhabitants of the pinewood share in them.

Also by day an influence of mortality is, therefore, unlikely. Hence the spring densities of 1942 probably do not reflect differential mortality.

Putting the question more generally, we must examine whether mortality could ever produce the buffer effect. We now meet a serious difficulty: we should know autumn densities and these have not been recorded. Theoretically, however, four possibilities can be distinguished.

A. Autumn density in both habitats has a constant value from year to year and the buffer effect is produced by winter mortality.
B. Autumn density fluctuates in both habitats.
  1. Autumn density in the mixed wood is not buffered and consequently directly proportional with autumn density in the pinewood. The buffer effect is produced by winter mortality.
  2. Autumn density in the mixed wood is not buffered. The buffer effect is produced by movements of the birds from one habitat to the other during spring.
C. Autumn density in the mixed wood is already buffered whereas it fluctuates in the pinewood. The buffer effect is produced by movements of the birds during dispersal in early autumn.

In the two last-mentioned possibilities habitat selection is the essential factor. Hence these will be discussed in the next section. We must examine here whether one of the first two possibilities can explain our observations.

A. Autumn density in both habitats has a constant value from year to year. A buffer effect could result if winter mortality of birds roosting in the mixed wood fluctuated between much narrower limits than winter mortality of the pinewood birds. This hypothesis can be rejected because the number of birds in autumn certainly is not constant in both habitats. Superficial observations in autumn already reveal huge differences in general density between one year and the next. Moreover, counts in late autumn show similar fluctuations. In a definite part of the mixed wood at Wageningen the following numbers of Great Tits have been recorded during nightly inspections of nest-boxes in early December: 1936, 59; 1937, 71; 1938, 110; 1946, 88; 1947, 43; 1948, 88; 1949, 77; 1950, 83; 1951, 98.

B (1). The number of birds which during autumn have a domicile in the mixed wood is not buffered but directly proportional with the pinewood population. A buffer effect will occur if winter mortality percentage in the mixed wood is density dependent, whereas in the pine wood it is not or to a smaller extent. To formulate this condition in a more general way: a buffer effect will result if the difference "percentage winter mortality in mixed wood less percentage winter mortality in pinewood" has increasing values with increasing density of population.

A strong argument against this hypothesis was already put forward. During winter birds roosting in the mixed woods are exposed to almost the same conditions as birds which roost in the pinewoods. Therefore, a great difference in mortality is not probable.

In our further discussion of this hypothesis we will treat the Hulshorst and the Wageningen data separately. For Hulshorst this hypothesis would include that winter mortality always leaves an almost constant number of survivors in the mixed woods. This seems only possible if mortality depended entirely on the following mechanism: the mixed wood has a fixed number of safe sites and all individuals which do not occupy such a safe site are killed. At first sight this seems very improbable, but in the case of the Great Tit the number of roosting holes could operate in this way as a limiting factor. Roosting holes, however, are present in great excess in the mixed woods at Hulshorst. We therefore cannot accept that the buffer effect at Hulshorst is produced by differential mortality.

As an alternative hypothesis one could assume that the number of safe sites in the mixed woods is constant because the supply of food is the same from year to year. Even if we neglect the fact that birds roosting in the mixed wood collect a great deal of their food in the pinewood, this relation cannot exist. In the first place, winter food density certainly is not equal from year to year (see below). In the second place, even if it was equal, the postulated effect would not occur. In winter the accumulation of new food almost stops. So the birds mainly depend on a stock of food which is present already late in autumn. Now our starting point was that autumn density of tits fluctuates. Hence in a year with many birds the stock of food would decrease in a much faster way than in a year with few birds. Instead of equal numbers of survivors, few of them should be expected in the former year and many in the latter. Hence, if the number of birds in autumn fluctuates—which happens—even a constant amount of food in the mixed wood would not lead to a constant number of survivors in spring.

At Wageningen, on the other hand, the situation is different from that at Hulshorst. Here the number of survivors in the mixed wood is not constant, although it is buffered. Hence the argument, which was given for Hulshorst, cannot be followed in this case. Nevertheless, the hypothesis put forward in this section most probably does not explain the Wageningen data. It postulates a sharp correlation between winter mortality and population density in the mixed wood. The data of Kluyver (1951) do not suggest such a marked correlation. An effect of density on mortality could be deduced only for severe winters (p. 125) and the estimates of the yearly mortality rate in adult birds (p. 100) do not point to a correlation with density at all. Thus the main condition for the hypothesis seems not to be fulfilled at Wageningen.

Summarising this section we consider it very improbable that mortality buffers density of Great Tits in the mixed woods at Hulshorst and at Wageningen.

Habitat Selection

In the preceding pages we found no reasons for assuming that either reproduction or mortality produce the density phenomena which we described. There remains only the alternative that the buffer mechanism is a component of habitat selection. We explain the census data for Hulshorst essentially in the following way: the mixed woods are "filled up" to a critical level and not further. The excess birds settle in the pinewoods. In some years, these are many, in others few.

At Wageningen, on the other hand, a fixed level of critical density cannot be distinguished but here as well the percentage of birds which settle in the pinewood increases as total population reaches higher values. A more detailed discussion of the Wageningen data will be given further below. We will first restrict our attention to the Hulshorst data.

One could give the following tentative explanation for the state of affairs at Hulshorst. Some element in the habitat, which every bird requires, is present in limited and constant supply in the mixed wood. Although many hypotheses can be made about the nature of this element, only two possibilities seem reasonable: the number of roosting holes and/or the number of nest sites is limited. Neither is the case, however. As already stated the mixed wood at Hulshorst contains a great number of tree holes (which are suitable for both roosting and nesting) as well as some nest boxes. Moreover, if the number of holes were to limit the population, this influence could be expected to act upon the numbers of Great Tits and Blue Tits taken together, because the latter species uses similar holes as the former. In other words, one would expect that only the combined population of Great *and* Blue Tits would be buffered. The percentage in which each species is represented in this sum would fluctuate in dependence on its general abundance. This clearly is not the case. The number of Great Tits in the mixed wood is almost constant despite big differences in the ratio Great Tits: Blue Tits as calculated for the district as a whole.

Other assumptions, viz. that the conditions of cover or the amount of food limit in a similar way density of the mixed wood, easily can be dismissed. Cover conditions are good throughout the mixed wood. That food supply in this habitat would attract a fixed number of Great Tits in every year seems completely improbable. In the first place the density of food varies very much from year to year. To mention one example: in the mixed wood beech mast is an important food item during the cold season. In some years it is present in enormous excess, in others it hardly can be found. In the second place, the total number of birds which seek a home is rather variable from one year to another. Even if food supply were constant and limited in the mixed wood, a great number of birds would be attracted by it in years of high population and a small number in years of low population.

So we cannot accept that the constant level of population in the mixed wood at Hulshorst is caused by the fact that the supply of things which the birds require is limited and constant in this habitat. In our opinion there is only one reasonable alternative hypothesis, namely, that the density of population of the same species is a factor in habitat selection. We assume that birds which seek a home are guided by two counteracting tendencies: a preference for mixed woods as such and an aversion to densely populated localities. Birds which settle early will choose a place in the mixed wood. The more this is filled up, the less attractive it will be for other individuals. In these circumstances, the latter will prefer a habitat which per se is less attractive, but where no dense population is present. Thus as the number of individuals in the district rises, there will be an increasing disposition to settle in the pinewoods.

This hypothesis implies that density in the mixed wood will increase until the attractiveness of the habitat is counterbalanced by the repelling influence of population already present. Therefore, we can expect that density in the mixed wood will rise to a certain critical level, a "level of saturation," and not further.

That in the Great Tit many adult individuals are faithful to the domicile of the preceding year forms no serious objection against our explanation. It only means that those adults which survived already occupy part of the positions when new birds try to settle.

The next question to discuss is, in which season does the repelling influence of population density operate?

We have seen that there are two phases in habitat selection: in autumn many Great Tits settle in their domiciles, and in spring the final breeding territories are established, These are counted in our censuses. We know further that part of the birds, which have settled in autumn, are killed during winter and that others emigrate in early spring.

In principle the density effect could operate in one of the two phases of dispersal or in both. We can deduce that it works at least in spring, but we have no observations which allow a conclusion about the autumn period.[2]

If the density effect does not operate in spring, we have to assume that it is restricted to the autumn. In winter, however, many birds die. Of course this winter mortality cannot be equal year after year. Thus the number of survivors would fluctuate from one year to another. This is in contradiction with the census data for Hulshorst, which show very small fluctuations. We therefore must conclude that the density effect works at least in spring. This implies that the birds are redistributed to a certain extent during this season.

Unfortunately, we have no conclusive information on this redistribution. In principle, it might imply either an emigration from or an immigration into

---

[2] Kluyver (1951, p. 122–123) brought forward evidence for large scale emigrations of juveniles in autumn. His data strongly suggest that these emigrations are density-dependent. It is not known, however, whether these displacements influence density in the mixed wood to a greater extent than density in the pinewoods, in other words whether they contribute to the buffer mechanism or not.

the mixed wood. It seems probable that movements in both directions may occur. When the total population has decreased very much during winter (as in 1942), we must assume a displacement from the pinewood into the mixed wood. On the other hand, in years with a more normal density the Wageningen ringing data show that part of the population emigrates before spring from the mixed wood. This suggests that in autumn or winter the mixed wood is filled beyond the saturation level and that excess birds disappear. Although it is very probable that true migrants are scarce among these emigrating birds (Kluyver, 1951, p. 31) we do not know whether the latter move into the neighbouring poor habitats. These movements need to be studied more intensively before we can state whether they contribute to the buffer effect.

We should add here that spring densities in the mixed wood can be adjusted to a certain extent by local movements of birds which do not leave their original domiciles. We have seen that the domicile has a larger surface than the average territory. Thus birds living on the borderline between mixed wood and pinewood can select either habitat for their final breeding territory. Especially at Hulshorst, where the mixed woods are narrow strips, 1–2 territories wide, this factor might have considerable influence.

Finally, it should be stressed that besides displacements from the mixed wood to poorer habitats and the other way round, there also might be an exchange between mixed woods and still more attractive habitats.

We now must consider whether the critical level or "level of saturation" is the same in all types of habitat. In our hypothesis we supposed that the critical level represents the density value at which, according to the innate standards of the bird, the attractiveness of the habitat is counterbalanced by the repelling influence of population density. Certainly, the attractiveness of different habitats is not equal. Thus we can expect the critical level to be low in unattractive habitats and high in attractive ones. This in fact seems to be true. Parts of the woodland district at Hulshorst have a still denser population of Great Tits than the mixed woods. These are, among others, the gardens near houses. Apparently this habitat is still more attractive to Great Tits than the mixed woods. As the latter are saturated in most years, the former must also be filled up to the critical level. This consequently is higher than the critical level in the mixed wood. Apparently these gardens are so attractive, that the birds which inhabit them endure more members of their own species than do the birds which live in the mixed woods.

On the other hand, the pinewoods are clearly less attractive to the tits than the mixed woods. Therefore we may expect that here the critical level is lower.

Hence the important question arises, what happens when the pinewoods are also saturated to the critical level. There are no poorer habitats which then may harbour the remaining birds. There are then two alternatives: the birds may attempt to settle in any of the already saturated habitats or they may not settle at all. At present we cannot give a definite answer to this question.

If we were to assume that our explanation could also be applied to the Coal Tit (which is not proven, see below), we have one observation which might throw some light on this problem. In 1943 the population of Coal Tits at Hulshorst was very high. As compared with 1942 both the mixed woods and the pinewoods had a remarkable increase in density. This might indicate that the saturation level in pinewood was passed and that the excess birds settled in all the habitats. If this interpretation is right, population density in the mixed woods is only buffered as long as the pinewoods are undersaturated. Therefore an effect on the total size of population would be doubtful.

So far we have considered only the census data for Hulshorst. At Wageningen density of population in the mixed wood (1934–1942) was buffered to a certain extent, but it was not as stable as at Hulshorst. Nevertheless we believe that the Wageningen data must be explained in the same way as those for Hulshorst. The argument previously given makes it very probable that at Wageningen, too, the buffer effect is a product of habitat selection. An influence of limited supply of nestboxes or a food influence seems hardly probable. Hence we assume again an influence of density in habitat selection.

Three factors might explain why density in the Wageningen mixed wood is not buffered to the same extent as at Hulshorst.

1. The difference in attractiveness between mixed wood and pinewood is smaller at Wageningen than at Hulshorst. Now it is evident that our suggested principle will be the more effective, the greater the difference in attractiveness between "rich" and "poor" habitat. Where the latter is very unattractive, the birds will do their utmost best to find a place in the former, and there will be a strong tendency to fill this up to the saturation level. The tendency will be weaker when the poor habitat is still fairly attractive, like the pinewood at Wageningen. In such case we cannot expect that the mixed wood will be filled till the exact limit of tolerable density. It therefore seems quite natural that density in the mixed wood at Wageningen was not buffered to such extent as at Hulshorst. In this regard the older series at Wageningen (1922–1933) is of interest. In these years there was hardly a difference in attractiveness between mixed wood and pinewood. Accordingly, there was no buffer effect at all.

2. At Wageningen, habitats which are still more attractive than mixed woods cover a relatively larger area than at Hulshorst. In years of low total population, this might imply that the mixed woods are not filled till the critical level. We do not know whether this factor has real significance.

3. In relation to its surface the mixed wood at Wageningen has a relatively shorter borderline than the mixed wood at Hulshorst. We have mentioned the possibility that birds living at the borderline move from one habitat

to the other without leaving their domicile. This might be an important factor in the regulation of density in the mixed wood. The shorter border-line would lessen the effectiveness of this factor at Wageningen.

The differences between Wageningen and Hulshorst suggest that local conditions at Hulshorst favour the operation of the density effect in habitat selection. Further investigations will have to show to what extent local conditions may obscure it. We have shown the phenomenon to exist, but we cannot give an exact delimitation of its influence. Thus in several regards our observations invite further research. In the first place, more observations of density in attractive and unattractive habitats are desired. Further density measurements in autumn and winter would be very welcome. Finally a large scale investigation of the movements of individuals from one habitat to another is very much needed.

We have concluded that the density effect in habitat selection operates at least in spring. We must examine now by what elements of behaviour it is produced. It might be caused by aggressive action, by avoiding behaviour or by both. Now both are essential features of territorial practice, which is at a peak in spring. Therefore, we accept as the simplest explanatory hypothesis that the population effect in habitat selection is an immediate consequence of territorial behaviour. The Great Tit is a territorial bird, and in spring the mixed wood is divided completely into territories. The buffer effect implies that the size of these territories does not decrease in proportion with a rise in total population, but more slowly. It seems justifiable to regard this total population as a more or less exact expression of the number of birds which try to settle in any given year. At Hulshorst a marked increase in this number hardly lowered the average size of territories in the mixed wood. At Wageningen a definite minimum size of territory was not reached, but the decrease was relatively small.

When speaking more generally, it is of course not necessary to postulate such a relation with territorial practice. A similar effect could be reached when animals were only mutually hostile (without settling at an individual territory) or when they merely avoided each other.

The above explanation implies that we accept Howard's principle for the populations of Great Tits, but under restricted conditions. In the first place it should be added that the limit of compressibility of territories is not the same in every habitat. Further we conclude that this principle can buffer density in attractive habitats only as long as the population in less attractive environments of the same district has not yet reached the "level of saturation." We do not know what happens when more birds are present.

We should stress here that we realize we have not provided a direct proof for Howard's thesis. Such proof would require much more knowledge about behaviour and movements of individual birds than we have at present. We feel, however, that the facts reported here are most easily explained by Howard's hypothesis.

The "Buffer Mechanism" in the Blue Tit and the Coal Tit

Very little can be said about the buffer mechanism in the two other species, as their life history has not been studied sufficiently. We can conclude that the census figures are not in contradiction with the explanation which we gave for the buffer effect in the Great Tit. (A tentative explanation for the abnormal values for Coal Tit 1943 has been given above). It is impossible, however, to exclude in a strict way the alternative hypotheses. We may add that both the Blue Tit and the Coal Tit defend territories.

Discussion

The census data, presented in this paper, show that density of population in three species of titmice was buffered to a certain extent in densely populated mixed woods and fluctuated much in neighbouring pinewoods, where the population was low. Krätzig (1939, p. 32) has found the same phenomenon. Referring to Great Tits he writes about the favourable habitats: "dass diese Typen offenbar wegen ihrer stärkeren Laubholzdurchmischung als Siedlungsgebiete bevorzugt werden. Es sind dieselben Waldteile, die auch zahlenmässig nur geringe jährliche Siedlungsveränderungen aufweisen . . ." and he adds that density in the neighbouring poorer habitats clearly sinks in unfavourable years.

Before Krätzig, Errington (1934, 1943) and Errington and Hamerstrom (1936) described similar relations in other species. According to these authors Bobwhite Quails (*Colinus virginianus*) and Muskrats (*Ondatra zibethica*) have a more or less constant density in the most attractive habitats whereas poorer sites are only occupied in peak years. Finally, the observations of Southern and Morley (1950) suggest analogous conditions in the Marsh Tit (*Parus palustris*).

When examining the nature of this buffer mechanism, we have concluded that at least in the Great Tit density of population is an important factor in habitat selection. We assume that the birds have an aversion for densely populated localities. Such a population effect in habitat selection has been suggested in several other cases.

For instance, Errington (l.c.; 1946) assumes it in his explanation of the regulation of density in Bobwhite Quail and Muskrat. Siivonen (1941) supposes the same factor as releaser of mass emigrations in the Waxwing (*Bombycilla garrulus*). Finally Crombie (1944) in his experiments with grain boring insects found a pronounced correlation between population density and the intensity of emigration among the larvae of *Rhizopertha dominica* and *Sitotroga cerealella*.

In the Great Tit movements of individuals seem to play an important role in the regulation of density. Kluyver (1951) assumes that the emigrations of juveniles in autumn chiefly radiate from densely populated areas. In this paper we have postulated movements in spring which adjust density in the more attractive habitats. These findings support Errington's view that displacements and the innate standards of tolerable crowding are important factors in density regulation among higher vertebrates.

We found reasons to suppose that at least in spring the density effect in habitat selection of Great Tits is produced by territorial behaviour. Although for definite proof more observations of behaviour are required, we accept Howard's thesis as the most satisfactory explanation. So we assume that more birds settle in the pinewoods as territories in the mixed wood approach the limit of compressibility.

We concluded that this limit is not equal in all kinds of habitats but varies in relation with the attractiveness of the latter. During our observations the limit was never reached in the unattractive pinewoods. So we do not know whether Howard's principle still works when density in the poor habitats has reached the critical level. Probably the latter condition generally is prevented by the above mentioned emigrations in autumn.

As far as concerns these autumn emigrations it is still unknown whether they have relations with territorial practice. In fact, there is a marked rise in hostility during the fall, but it is not certain whether real territories are established. A thorough study of autumn behaviour in ringed birds would be very valuable.

According to our assumption Great Tits are guided during habitat selection by two counteracting tendencies: a preference for certain habitats and an aversion for densely populated localities. The distribution over different habitats therefore is not the effect of habitat preference only, but of both dispositions.[3]

The biological significance of this principle of density regulation becomes clear, when we ask, what would happen if the birds were guided only by their preference for certain habitats and not by their aversion for crowding. The population then would be concentrated almost exclusively in the attractive habitats. When the population increased the densities of birds in these attractive habitats would become very great. We know that such concentrations of animals are in general unstable. There would follow an unfavourable trend in the rates of reproduction and mortality, eventually accompanied by an exhaustion of the resources of the habitat. On the other hand the surrounding unattractive habitats would be utilised to a very small extent. In the long run the species in question could only maintain a much smaller population than it does in reality. Thus the interaction of habitat preference and the aversion for concentrations prevents the development of topheavy populations in favourable habitats and ensures the utilisation of less attractive

---

[3] This point seems of importance for the interpretation of the results of bird censuses. It implies that the ratio of densities in different habitats is not a simple expression of the degree to which the birds prefer one to another. We think it probable that this effect is not restricted to the Great Tit, but is found in other species as well.

environments. The fact that individuals avoid concentrations probably will favour their survival.

This is a rather vague statement, based only on general ecological principles. But we cannot go further than this. At present we do not know at what densities the populations of the favourable habitats become "unsafe." Neither do we know whether shortages of food or some other factor (e.g., an increased risk for predation or disease) would dominate in such unfavourable development. So the hypothesis of the food value of territory (which is often linked with the thesis that territory limits the population) remains untouched in this study.

In its effect on survival the buffer mechanism has some resemblance to the emigrations of Lemmings and, probably, with similar but less conspicuous phenomena in several other species. The Lemming emigrations lower the density in favourable habitats which are heavily populated. Moreover part of the animals which emigrate find suitable habitats, which they otherwise would not have reached (Kalela, 1949). On the other hand, these emigrations do not start until the density in the favourable habitat has already reached a very dangerous level. Hence this regulation is less effective than that in the Great Tit, where the limit of density in the mixed wood seems rather safe.

Summary

1. We have studied densities of the spring populations of Great Tit, Blue Tit and Coal Tit (*Parus major, P. coeruleus,* and *P. ater*) in two woodland districts in Holland. Both districts contained attractive mixed woods (high densities) and unattractive pinewoods (low densities). Fluctuations from year to year were small in the former and considerable in the latter. As the number of tits increased, density in the mixed wood rose much more slowly than density in the pinewoods. Apparently some mechanism buffers density in the mixed woods.

2. The nature of this buffer mechanism is examined in the Great Tit. Reproduction and mortality can be excluded as possible causes; apparently the mechanism is a component of habitat selection. As a limiting influence of nesting holes, roosting holes and food can be rejected, we assume the following explanation. Great Tits have an aversion for localities which bear a dense population of the same species. The birds seem to prefer mixed woods to pinewoods, but as the mixed woods become more densely populated, excess birds settle in the pinewoods. Thus the attractiveness of the mixed wood per se is counterbalanced by the repelling influence of the population already present. In one case this resulted in the mixed wood being always filled up till a constant level.

3. The limit of tolerable crowding is not the same in all habitats but higher in the more attractive ones. During our observations this limit probably never was reached in the pinewoods.

4. Dispersal of Great Tits over different habitats takes place in autumn and in spring. We conclude that the buffer mechanism works at least in spring. It is unknown whether it acts also in autumn. A partial redistribution of birds during spring must be assumed.

5. Local differences in the census data are discussed. They are most easily explained by the assumption that the buffer mechanism is the more effective, the greater the difference in attractiveness between rich and poor habitat.

6. Innate standards of tolerable crowding and displacements of individuals seem to be important factors in the regulation of density of Great Tits. Besides the principle discussed in this paper, emigration of young birds in autumn (probably density dependent) much influences the number of birds which settle in a given area (Kluyver, 1951).

7. Great Tits are territorial birds. In spring the mixed wood is completely divided into territories. Since the density effect works during this season, we assume that it is a consequence of territorial behaviour. A complete proof for this assumption cannot be given, but it seems to us the most reasonable hypothesis.

8. The census data for Blue Tit and Coal Tit agree with the above explanation, but it is not possible to exclude alternative hypotheses.

9. The biological significance of the buffer mechanism in the Great Tit is discussed and some comparisons are made.

Appendix: Statistical Analysis

Professor L. J. Smid of Groningen University kindly undertook the statistical study of our data. His comments are quoted here.

We consider two neighbouring woods, a mixed wood of O_1 ha and a pinewood of O_2 ha. By way of simplification we suppose that in a certain year n tits (males) of a certain species (Great, Blue or Coal Tit) must settle in the two woods. Then, if the territories have a surface of 1.6 ha in the mixed wood and of 8.0 ha in the pinewood, the numbers of tits are

$$n_1 = O_1/1.6 \text{ and } n_2 = O_2/8.0; \; n_1 + n_2 = n.$$

Now the following "hypothesis of proportionality" can be set up: In any case the tit makes no difference between a certain area of mixed wood and ac (in our case $c = 5$) times larger area of pine wood. Then in other years also, with higher or lower values of n, the proportion of the numbers would be

$$O_1 : (1/c)O_2.$$

If a diagram is made in the (n_1, n_2)-plane, the points are to be expected on a straight line through the origin (Fig. 3). In reality there are of course many causes for accidental deviations in the ratio c. Thus if n is given, not always the same division in n_1 and n_2 will be obtained, but there is a certain probability distribution on the line $n_1 + n_2 = n$, around the indicated point.

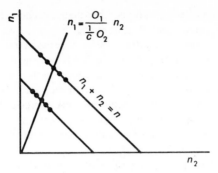

$$n_1 = \frac{O_1}{\frac{1}{c}O_2} \, n_2$$

$$n_1 + n_2 = n$$

Fig. 3.

If there were no other accidental deviations than those in c, then a higher value of n would correspond to an almost proportionally enlarged distribution. (Exact proportionality is impossible because n_1 and n_2 must have integral values.)

On the other hand it may be thought that a tit cannot breed on a territory which is smaller than a certain area of A ha. A rather oversimplified scheme is obtained by supposing that the attractiveness of a territory is measured by the surplus $(O_2/n_2) - A$ in the pinewood and by $c[(O_1/n_1) - A]$ in the mixed wood and that in the ideal equilibrium

$$(O_2/n_2) - A = c[(O_1/n_1) - A].$$

If $n_1 + n_2 = n$ is variable, this formula represents a part of a hyperbola in the (n_1, n_2)-plane (Fig. 4).

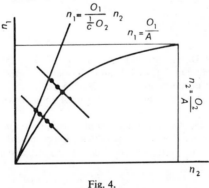

$$n_1 = \frac{O_1}{\frac{1}{c}O_2} \, n_2 \qquad n_1 = \frac{O_1}{A}$$

$$n_2 = \frac{O_2}{A}$$

Fig. 4.

In reality a probability distribution around the regression curve would be obtained. We do not suggest of course that this simple formula really represents the regression curve.

In this case it may be said that density is buffered, in the first place in the mixed wood.

We now will neglect all deviations other than those in c, for example those caused by counting errors and the sampling deviations caused by the smallness of the areas of the woods. The correctness of these neglections is questionable.[4] Then if the hypothesis of proportionality holds true the distribution of n_1/n_2 is independent of $n_1 + n_2$. This independency can be checked by testing whether the rankings according to these two quantities are correlated. This may be done by means of Kendall's coefficient rank correlation[5] which is ordinarily denoted by τ. As in the alternative hypothesis an increasing value of $n_1 + n_2$ tends to be accompanied by a decreasing value of n_1/n_2, a one-sided test may be used.

Each of the 5 cases produces a value of τ which is significantly negative, and thus leads to rejection of the hypothesis of proportionality.

Finally, we remark that even the simple fact that in each of the 5 cases τ turns out to be negative provides a significant test against the hypothesis of proportionality.

	Number of years of observation	Probability of obtaining or exceeding the observed value of τ (in case of the hypothesis of proportionality)
Great Tit. Wageningen (1934–1942) .	9	0,0012
Blue Tit. " (1925–1942) .	17	0,023
Great Tit. Hulshorst (1941–1951) .	9	0,0063
Blue Tit. " (1941–1951) .	8	0,016
Coal Tit. " (1941–1951) .	9	0,0063

References

Brian, A. D., 1949: Dominance in the Great Tit. Scott. *Naturalist* **61**: 144.

Crombie, A. C., 1944: On intraspecific and interspecific competition between larvae of graminivorous insects. *J. exper. Biol.* **20**: 135.

Errington, P. L., 1934: Vulnerability of Bob-white Populations to Predation. *Ecology* **15**, 110.

Errington P. L., 1943: An Analysis of Mink Predation upon Muskrats in North Central United States. Iowa State Coll. Agr. Exper. Sta. Res. Bull., **320**.

Errington, P. L., 1946: Predation and Vertebrate Populations. *Quart. Rev. Biol.* **21**, 144.

Errington, P. L. & F. N. Hamerstrom, 1936: The Northern Bob-white's Winter Territory. Iowa State Coll., *Agr. Exper. Sta. Res. Bull.*, **201**.

Howard, H. E., 1920: *Territory in Bird Life*, London.

[4] Moreover, in the Hulshorst data the area of the observed pinewood is not the same every year. We replaced the observations by fictitious observations in a wood of the mean area, by enlarging or reducing the number of tits proportional to the area.

[5] Cf. M. G. Kendall, *Rank Correlation Methods*. London, 1948.

Huxley, J. S., 1934: A natural experiment on the territorial instinct. *Brit. Birds* **27**, 270.

Kalela, O., 1949: Über Fjeldlemming-Invasionen und andere irreguläre Tierwanderungen. *Ann. Zoöl. Soc. Zoöl. Bot Fenn.* **13**, no 5.

Kluyver, H. N., 1951: The population ecology of the Great Tit. *Ardea* **39**, 1.

Krätzig, H., 1939: Untersuchungen zur Siedlungsbiologie waldbewohnender Höhlenbrüter. Ornithol. *Abh.* **1**, Berlin.

Lack, D., 1946: *The Life of the Robin.* 2nd. Ed., London.

Plattner, J., 1946: Ergebnisse der Meisen- und Kleiberberingung in der Schweiz (1929–1941). *Ornithol. Beob.* **43**, 156, and **44**, 1. With postscript by E. Sutter.

Siivonen, L., 1941: Über die Kausal-Zusammenhänge der Wanderungen beim Seidenschwanz. *Ann. Zoöl. Soc. Zoöl. Bot. Fenn.* **8**, no. 6.

Southern, H. N. & A. Morley, 1950: Marsh tit territories over six years. *Brit. Birds* **43**, 33.

Tinbergen, L., 1946: Dé Sperwer als roofvijand van zangvogels. *Ardea* **34**, 1.

Tinbergen, N., 1939: The Behavior of the Snow Bunting in Spring. *Trans. Linn. Soc. New York* **5**, 1.

Social Interactions in Discrimination Learning with Special Reference to Feeding Behavior in Birds

Peter H. Klopfer

The Problem

A full understanding of at least two problems central to current evolutionary and ecologic thought depends on a greater knowledge of particular learning processes and the learning capabilities of specific animals.[1] For example, in order to assess the significance of mimicry in a variety of invertebrate and vertebrate groups, it is necessary to know under what conditions and how rapidly, if at all, the potential predators can learn the necessary discriminations. Or, in other cases, it may be essential to discover why a predator fails to discriminate between a model and its mimic when the resemblance between the two is less than perfect (Brower, 1958; de Rutter, 1952; Remington, 1957). Further, when dealing with sympatric species, we are limited by our ignorance of the ontogenesis of the behavior which preserves the distinctiveness of the species' niches. Some of this distinctiveness may represent learned traditions, and the learning processes which are involved are doubtless influenced by intraspecific social interactions.

In this study, the first of a series designed to analyze the role of traditions in the determination of species-specific behavior, we have investigated the role of imitation in discrimination learning. To accomplish this, comparisons were made of the rates in which a discrimination could be established in single and paired birds.

Empathic Behavior

The term "empathic behaviour" has been used to embrace all types of motor mimicry (Klopfer, 1957). The various mechanisms by which such imitation can occur can be listed as follows:

1. *Secondary conditioning:* this is a type of learning akin to Type I conditioning of Konorski (Thorpe, 1956; Konorski, 1948), except that the

[1] These experiments were carried out at the Madingley Field Station of the University of Cambridge during the tenure of a U.S. Public Health Post-doctoral Research Fellowship. The auther wishes to record his appreciation for their helpfulness to Drs. W. H. Thorpe and R. A. Hinde. The design of these experiments grew out of discussions with Professor G. E. Hutchinson and Dr. M. Mead. The author is indebted to the following for having offered their criticism of the manuscript: Drs. R. A. Hinde, R. MacArthur and W. H. Thorpe. Graphs were prepared by M. Klopfer.

Reprinted by permission of the publisher from *Behaviour* 14: 282–299, 1959.

unconditional stimulus is an alarm, or similar, response of one individual to which another will show a response. When, for example, a duck was trained to avoid a particular feeding-dish by shocking it with a strong electric current, a process which elicited an intense alarm response, a duck observing the procedure subsequently avoided the dish, too, even in the absence of the shocked duck and without having himself experienced the shock (Klopfer, 1957).

This process may account for many of the cases, usually recorded anecdotally, where imitation occurs. A feeding-response may serve as a stimulus to another bird, too, of course, and where the secondary conditioning is of this nature rather than of the sort which leads to an avoidance reaction, it may be difficult to distinguish from the phenomenon known as local enhancement. A useful operational distinction can be made, however (see below).

2. *Social facilitation:* Thorpe has defined this as "contagious behavior." It is distinguished from the foregoing by the fact that the performance of an act by one individual, which is followed by the performance of a similar act by another individual, has an effect strictly limited in time. Thus, if a bird is restive as the consequence of having not been fed, it may become quiet when placed with fully fed birds, and vice versa (Thorpe, 1956). The effect, however, is temporary, and seems always to require the continued presence of the companion.

3. *Local enhancement:* This is simply a special case of social facilitation which involves an animal having its attention directed towards a particular part of the environment by the activity of another (Thorpe, 1956). This is presumably the process by which the cream-stealing habit of tits (*Parus* spp.) has spread, the activity of one bird calling the attention of others to a source of food (Hinde and Fisher, 1952). Here, too, the temporal factor is limiting. Where this is not the case, i.e., where the actor's example is still effective after some hours, we may speak of secondary conditioning having occurred, the difference being one of degree, or stability.

4. *Visual imitation:* Thorpe has reserved this term for the copying of improbable acts, with a connotation of self-consciousness on the part of the performer. This is a concept impossible to define operationally except in a negative sense. For the time being, we must consider this category to include those types of learning which are inexplicable in terms of the others. There appears to be no convincing evidence indicating that this category is needed to explain any aspect of avian behavior, but the possiblity can clearly not be excluded. Justification for this qualification will be found in the experiments on unnamed numbers (Koehler, 1955).

It should be emphasised that these categories are not intended to represent qualitatively distinct types of learning. Dinstiguishing sections along a continuum is necessarily an arbitrary task, but no less useful for that.

Methods

The material used consisted of wild adult male Greenfinches (*Chloris chloris*), trapped one to three months before the commencement of the experiments and housed in large flight aviaries until needed. The experimental cages were of half-inch wire-mesh, 6 × 6 × 6 feet, and were raised several inches off the ground so as to allow the complete removal of spilled seeds. The cages were placed along the edge of a wood, somewhat separate from other aviaries, and were positioned, with the aid of opaque screens, so that the occupants of one cage were not, when feeding, visible to occupants of other cages. Each cage was supplied with perches and cover, the latter consisting of a bundle of twigs, grasses and leaves loosely held by a square of wire-mesh suspended from the roof. A half-inch wire-mesh partition running from top to bottom divided each of these cages into two equal compartments. The foodbox was situated in the middle of this partition (Fig. 1). For convenience, the two halves of each cage are referred to as actor's pen and observer's pen, and their occupants as actor and observer respectively.

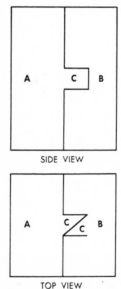

SIDE VIEW

TOP VIEW

Fig. 1. Diagram of aviary: A = actor's pen; B = observer's pen; C = feeding box.

The conditions of training are best described separately for each of the experimental groups, but the following procedure was standard for all groups: 24 hours before the start of the training period, the two patterns which the birds were to be taught to discriminate (Fig. 2) were placed alongside the seed pan for a 20-hour period. These two patterns were circles of fiberboard,

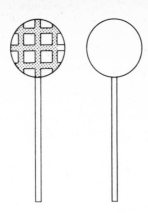

Fig. 2. Negative and positive patterns.

about 8 inches in diameter, one of which was painted white, the other white with red stripes which intersected at right angles. Preliminary trials had shown that untrained birds either showed no greater fear of one pattern than the other, or else were somewhat more reluctant to approach the striped pattern. Hence, this latter was used as the "positive" pattern or stimulus, with which the reward was associated, and the former was the "negative" pattern or stimulus, a response to which went unrewarded or punished. At the start of the training, the birds were deprived of food for one and one half hours and then presented with the positive pattern on which was placed a sunflower seed. It remained in the cage until the bird finally approached it and fed, a process which took anywhere from 1 minute to two hours on first presentation. After two presentations of the positive pattern, by which time the response latency was usually less than five minutes, the patterns were successively presented in a random sequence, each pattern remaining in the pen until the bird had alighted upon it and fed. In the case of the negative pattern, a sunflower seed from which the kernel had been removed and replaced with a small quantity of moist aspirin was substituted for the edible seed. This substitute was not sufficiently repugnant to the birds to totally inhibit their chewing on the seed, except upon repeated exposures.

A total of 12 successive presentations was made each day, although after the first day the time allowed for a response was limited to two minutes. Prior to each day's trials, both actor and observer were deprived of food for a brief period to assure prompt responses, generally for 15 minutes when the temperature was below 25° F., 30 minutes between 25° and 35° F., 45 minutes 35° and 45° F., and 60 minutes at higher temperatures (which, unhappily, were rare indeed!). Whenever a bird did not respond at all during two successive positive pattern presentations, the period of deprivation was increased 15 to 30 minutes. This was rarely necessary, and then only for the first few days of the trials. The rationale for the variation in deprivation period with temperature comes from some preliminary work by H. F. Rowell (personal communication) indicating a decrease in response latency with a decrease in temperature. In any case, the deprivation period was not so long as to more than slightly enhance the feeding tendency and was a convenience rather than a necessity.

The sequence of presentations was randomised and each bird was given the sequence. Twelve presentations were made each day until the bird had demonstrated that it was discriminating between the two patterns. The total number of presentations of positive and negative paterns was equal during each two-day period, while the ratio of one pattern to the other varied only within the limits of a 5: 7 and 7: 5 ratio on any one day. The time of attainment of the criterion was rather arbitrarily established as the third consecutive day of which no more than two errors had been made (a less arbitrary criterion is given below). An error consisted of not making a response when the positive pattern was presented, or in making a response at the presentation of the negative pattern. A response was defined as touching the seed with the bill. In almost every instance this touching was followed by chewing of the seed, for as birds learned not to chew the aspirin-filled seeds they simultaneously tended to avoid touching them, or even to alight on the negative pattern. A bird that did alight on the negative pattern almost always chewed the seeds as well.

The period until the attainment of the criterion is referred to as the pre-criterion period, that following, the post-criterion period. The duration of the two periods was equal; that is, if a bird required ten days to reach criterion, the training continued for an additional ten days. Thereafter, if there was reason to continue training, the period of exposure to the patterns was reduced to one minute. Data of this last period are not included with the post-criterion period. For convenience, it is known as the over-learning period.

Observations were made from a blind located about four feet from the foodbox. The birds were observed through holes of less than one-half inch diameter, so there is no question of their having been able to respond to cues given by the experimenter. The patterns were rapidly removed and exchanged after each two-minute presentation with the aid of wooden handles which projected from the patterns. Of course the experimenter was visible to the birds during this part of the procedure.

Records were kept of the birds' activities during the course of each presentation; a stopwatch helped measure the response latencies; and note was made of the frequency of behavior which could be interpreted as displacement reactions. Details of this follow.

A total of 8 sets of experiments are called for in this type of analysis. These are necessary in order to gauge separately the influence of the relevant variables, namely: the effect of habituation to the patterns which must be discriminated, the effect of the observer on the actor during the latter's training period, the effect of the actor on the observer during the latter's training, and the effect of the observer's witnessing incorrect responses by the actor. Thus the following groups are required:

A. Actor trained in the absence of an observer.
B. Actor trained in the absence of an observer and with pretraining habituation to the two patterns.
C. Actor trained in the presence of an observer.
D. Actor trained in the presence of an observer and with pretraining habituation to the two patterns.
E. Observer observing the actor from the start of the latter's training and with the actor remaining in his pen during the observer's training.
F. Observer introduced into his pen only after the attainment of the criterion by the actor, with the actor remaining in his pen during the observer's training.
G. As E, with the actor removed during the observer's training.
H. As F, but with the actor removed during the observer's training.

The A experiments serve to establish the learning speed in the absence of any possible distracting effects of a companion, while the B experiments should reveal whether an increased learning speed on the part of the observers was due to their having become habituated to the patterns during the actors' training. The F experiments eliminate the possiblity of secondary conditioning with a negative stimulus, as the observers observe primarily correct responses. The significance of the remaining categories will be self-evident.

In as much as seasonal changes in factors affecting learning speed could not be controlled, the experiments were scheduled so as to allow for randomisation of such effects. The dates of each experiment are recorded on the abscissae of the various graphs. All training was done between 8 AM and 12 noon, and the exact time any particular bird was trained was systematically varied from day to day.

Data

The basic data are given on the accompanying graphs. It will be noted that no distinction is made between positive and negative errors. The explanation for this lies in the fact that the two types of errors cannot be treated as independent variables. Thus, when a bird mistakenly feeds from the wrong pattern, he often declines to feed again for some minutes, irrespective of the pattern set before him. This was particularly the case during the first three days of training. By equating the two types of errors, it also becomes possible to adjust for nonresponses to the negative pattern which are due to a general disinclination to respond rather than to specific avoidance behavior. Where the former obtains, the positive pattern will be treated in the same fashion. Thus, whenever the animal's behavior with respect to the two patterns becomes random, it will be reflected by the score.

It can be shown that discrimination is significant at the 99% level (sign test) whenever the total number of errors, irrespective of the proportion of negative to positive errors, does not exceed 5 errors in 2 consecutive days. It may be added that once such a level of performance is attained, unless conditions are changed, this level is maintained or improved upon for the duration of the experiments. In comparing learning rates, it is this criterion of no more than 5 errors in two days that will be used, this being a more natural and significant criterion than that used to establish the subdivisions of the training period.

Learning Speed

From the graphs depicting the performance of the 4 birds of Group A, each of which was trained individually, it will be seen that the required discrimination was learned very quickly. Discrimination was significant at the 99% level (sign test) in the first two days, in two cases, and by the second and third day in the remaining two. Thus it appears that as few as two encounters with the negative pattern can suffice (cf. de Ruiter, 1952). The latency of the initial response to the positive pattern on the first day of training was less than 5 minutes in three of the cases, although an hour in the fourth. This would indicate that prolonged habituation to the experimental apparatus was not essential and, since space and time were at a premium, justified the elimination of Groups B and D. In this connection, it must be brought out that the learning abilities of wild birds can be severely impaired when the training

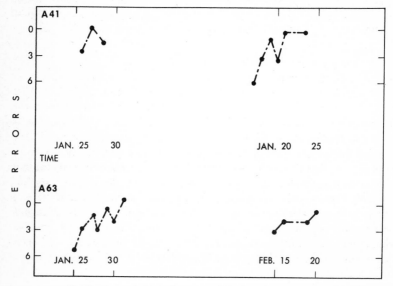

Fig. 3. Group A: Learning rates of single males

occurs under unnatural conditions (cf. Klopfer, 1957), so it is of no slight significance that the conditions of confinement and testing were sufficiently akin to the birds' normal environment to allow rapid learning.

The speed with which the birds of Group C, who were watched by observers during their training, attained a significant level of performance was noticeably less, being 5, 6, 6, and 7 days respectively, as compared with the 2, 2, 3, 3 days required by the Group A birds. The latency of the first response was also considerably greater, times (in minutes) being 13, 15, 49, and 120. Presumably the presence of the observer in the adjacent pen was a distracting factor. The nature of the distraction is examined later. By far the most important aspect of this group's behavior lies in the fact that after the training of the observers was begun, the actors, who had been discriminating in a consistent fashion, suddenly began responding randomly. From the graphs can be seen that actors and observers tended to oscillate between random and nonrandom levels of performance, the two birds in a general way fluctuating somewhat out of phase with one another. It is as if the actors, watching the observers making responses to the negative pattern, thereby learned to respond to the negative pattern too. Then, after a series of encounters with this unrewarding stimulus, they relearned the discrimination. In the meantime, a similar process was occurring in the case of the observers, so that a circular causal chain was established. It was not practical to continue these trials for a prolonged period, but it will be seen that one pair of birds was still oscillating after three weeks. During the last days, in two cases, moist sucrose oectoacetate was mixed with the aspirin in the seed. This is a substance which, to the human palate, has an extremely bitter taste, similar to quinine, though without the toxic properties of quinine salts. Even this presumably strong stimulus did not suffice to stop the oscillations. (It is possible that this substance was not as distasteful or perceptible to these birds as was supposed.)

Since the actors' trials always followed those of the observers, sometimes directly, or after an interval of up to an hour, there was always a delay of about 24 hours between an actor's performance and that of his observer. This would clearly indicate that the oscillations of at least the observer cannot be attributed to social facilitation or local enhancement. This argument is developed further below. In the case of the pair E-62 and O-62, in fact, the onset of the oscillations was delayed three days, the performance of both birds showing that they were making the discrimination satisfactorily for that period. Apparently the errors of the birds are mutually reinforcing, thus gradually initiating the fluctuations. In any case, of the four members of Group E, three failed to attain the criterion during the course of the experiments, a time which was never less than ten days, while the fourth was discriminating satisfactorily in four days and showed no fluctuations. Their latencies for the first responses were 14, 15, 7, and 10 minutes respectively—somewhat shorter than the latencies for Group C.

Group F birds, who were introduced into the pens adjacent to those occupied by actors who had previously attained criterion, were discriminating at a significant level after two and three days, in two instances. A third bird was still performing at a relatively poor level after II days. Of the entire collection of 15 birds, this was the only one consistently to show a low-level discrimination. There is no evidence which supports any explanation for this anomaly. The experiments with the fourth bird of this group had to be discontinued because of continual fighting between it and its actor. (By this date, late in February, a high proportion of the males were showing intensely aggressive behavior towards one another, which was the principal factor limiting this particular series of experiments.) At the termination of an aggressive encounter the participants frequently chewed the wire of their

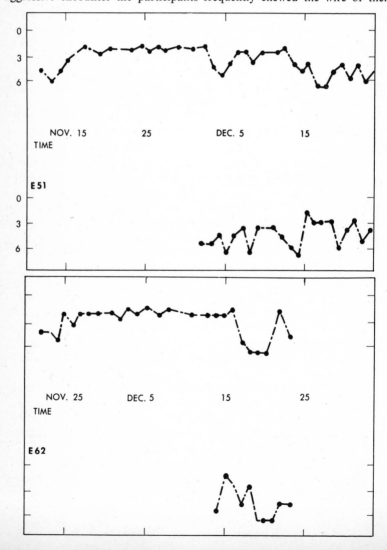

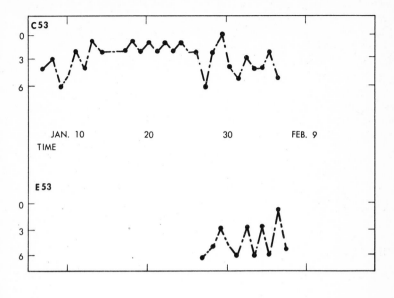

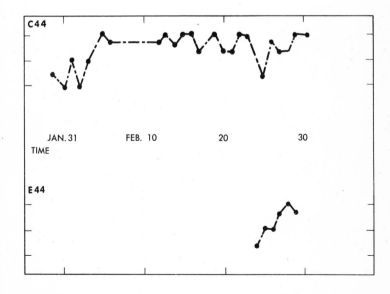

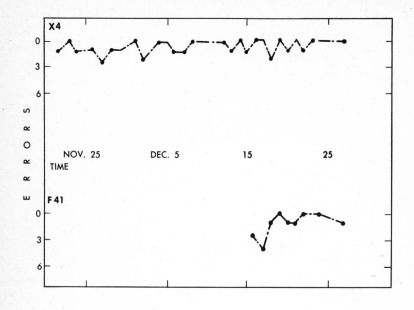

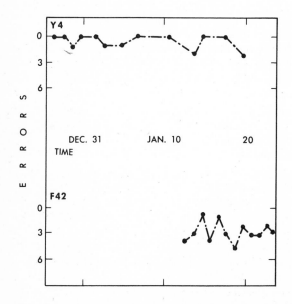

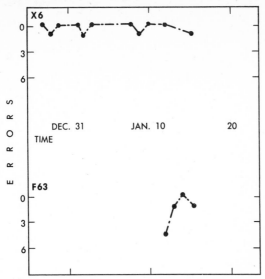

Fig. 4. Groups C and E: Actors (C) with untrained observers (E)

food-box, the patterns, or, if a seed was present, chewed it. Since a response to the negative stimulus which is due to redirection activity or displacement and one due to a failure to discriminate can be distinguished only on a *post hoc* basis, a continuation of these trials was pointless. What these data do suggest, however, is that the observation of correct responses is not, in the case of the Group F birds, sufficient to accelerate the learning process to a measurable degree, for the performance of this group was equal to but not superior to that of Group A. Their initial latencies were 10, 2, and $\frac{1}{4}$ minutes, which figures are also markedly similar to those for Group A. Alternatively, the observations by the observers could have produced a degree of learning just sufficient to compensate for the distracting effect of the partner. It will be, recalled that the mere presence of another bird had retarded the learning rate of Group C birds.

Results from the Group H birds, which were obtained in Durham, North Carolina,[1] one year later, indicate the absence of any reenforcing effects of the observation of correct responses. In these particular trials, slight modifications of the usual procedures had to be made. These, in addition to the altered climatic conditions, may have altered motivational levels thereby making quantitative comparisons with the preceding groups unsafe. Response periods were shortened from two to one minutes, and trials were held throughout the day, not only in the morning. In addition, two of the pairs consisted of adult females, rather than males.

It will be seen that the Group H observers witnessed about 14 consecutive trials with pretrained actors. Although the graphs indicate that the actors did make some errors, these were largely due to failures to feed. Feeding

[1] Thanks are due to W. Conway and the New York Zoo for expediting shipment of the birds.

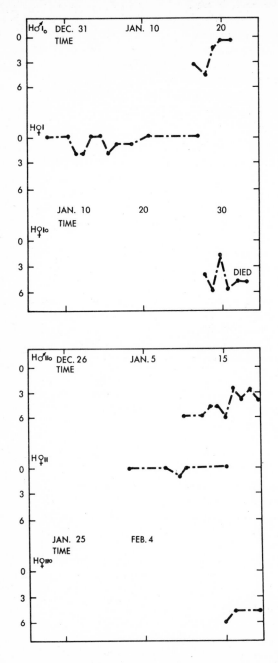

Fig. 5. Group H. H_I and H_{II}: Actors; H_{Io} and H_{IIo}: Observers

from the incorrect, or negative, pattern occurred 2, 3, 5, and 1 time, respectively, in the 4 pairs. The observers either did not learn the discrimination in the time allowed, or did not learn faster than the Group A birds. For the reasons given above, the differences in learning speed cannot be judged as to their significance, but the failure of the birds to learn in the absence of personal experience with the patterns is obvious.

Social Facilitation and Local Enhancement

It is conceivable that in Groups C, E, and F the learning rates were influenced by the kinds of effects we have called social facilitation and local enhancement. The degree of their influence can be assessed in the following manner:

If the relatively slow rate of learning of birds in Group C was due to their having been adversely influenced by the response-attempts of their observers in the adjoining pens, then the ratio of the number of the observer's response-attempts in the presence of the negative pattern to the number in the presence of the positive pattern should differ significantly from the same ratio for birds of Groups F. A response-attempt refers to a bird's entering or alighting upon the foodbox when the pattern is in the pen adjacent to its own. For statistical purposes, responses during the precriterion period of the first three birds from each of the two groups have been pooled. An attempt was counted as such only when it preceded or occurred simultaneously with the response of the bird which was being tested.

Group	Observer's response-attempts to the negative pattern / total number of response-attempts to both patterns
C	53/113
F	15/23

The approximate confidence intervals of these proportions (95 % level) are 0.35 to 0.55 and 0.43 to 0.85. The raw data given below indicate that the pooling procedure in no way distorted them.

Bird	Observer's response-attempts	
	Negative pattern	Positive pattern
C–62	20	24
C–51	6	3
C–53	27	33
F–41	0	3
F–42	8	0
F–63	7	5
C–44	7	10

Obviously, due to differences in the lengths of the precriterion period, it is the proportions which are significant, rather than the absolute number.

If anything, the proportion of response-attempts made by their observers to the negative pattern is somewhat greater in the case of the Group F birds. As these birds learned far more rapidly than their counterparts in Group C, it seems clear that social facilitation, as here interpreted, cannot be a significant factor. The same must be said for local enhancement which, in these experiments, is operationally indistinguishable. At the least, if the alternative explanation for F is true, i.e., that the distracting effect of the bird in the adjacent pen was masked by empathic learning, we can still conclude that social facilitory effects can be readily overcome.

We can, in addition, compare the number of times a bird, in Groups C and F, entered the foodbox following a response-attempt by its partner. The proportions given below represent this information:

Group	Proportion of responses following a response-attempt		
	Negative pattern	Positive pattern	Totals
C	14/53	36/60	50/113
F	4/15	8/8	12/23

These figures suggest that birds in both groups are equally susceptible to the social facilitory influence of their partners, which was indeed what was predicted.

Secondary Conditioning

A series of preliminary experiments had failed to establish any consistent differences in responses and general behavior upon the presentation of the two patterns, except, of course, the alighting upon or avoidance of one or the other pattern. A few birds billwiped ostentatiously after their first encounter with the aspirin-filled seed, but the occasions when this happened were too rare to be significant. It did appear, however, that there might be a difference in the frequency with which excursions were made to the water or gravel dish, depending on which stimulus had been presented. These data are tabulated below:

Number of excursions to the water or gravel dish during the presentation of the negative pattern/number during the presentation of the positive pattern (precriterion period only).		
Group A: 2/1	Group C: 5/0	Group F: 0/0
5/2	7/5	7/1
2/1	1/1	4/3
0/0	2/0	

In 8 cases there were indeed more excursions made during the presence of the negative than positive pattern, and in 3 cases there was no difference. This proportion is significant at the 99% level (sign test), so we are entitled to conclude that more trips to the water or gravel dish do occur when the negative pattern is presented. Is there any reason for believing this could provide an unconditional stimulus for the observing bird? There are three explanations possible for this behavior, only one of which would provide reasonable grounds for assuming the occurrence of secondary conditioning. The excursions could be (a) in the nature of a displacement or redirection activity; they could be (b) a response to the taste of the aspirin; or they could be (c) a function of the available time, since a bird which failed to respond to a pattern would have more of the two minutes available for other behavior than one which did respond. This latter situation would obtain if the bird's excursions were randomly distributed in time or else a function of the temporal interval since the last excursion.

If explanation (b) is not correct, then the same ratio as that given above should obtain if we count only excursions made before the bird has touched the seed. These figures indicate that in 9 instances the number of excursions made during the presence of the negative pattern was greater than the number made during the presence of the positive pattern, and in two cases there was no difference. This ratio is similar to the one above, so explanation (b) can be discarded as a valid hypothesis. The actual figures are given below:

Number of excursions made during presentation of negative/number during presentation of positive patterns (prior to bird's touching the seed)		
Group A: 2/0	Group C: 4/0	Group F: 0/0
5/0	5/0	4/0
2/0	1/0	3/2
0/0	1/0	

It seems fair to assume that conflicting response tendencies will be greatest during the precriterion period, when the discrimination is being established. If this assumption is correct, and if explanation (a) is also correct, then the proportion of excursions during the presence of the two patterns should not be the same in the postcriterion as in the precriterion period. These figures are only available for Group C:

Excursions made during the presence of negative/positive pattern	
Precriterion period	Postcriterion period
5/0	1/0
7/5	8/2
1/1	7/1
2/0	3/2

The proportions are similar, which inclines one to take the view that displacement or redirection activities are not involved and hence cannot serve as unconditional stimuli. Obviously, the necessity of assuming a reduction in conflict with the establishemnt of learning, while reasonable, prevents explanation (a) from being rigorously excluded. By default, however, (c), the greater amount of time available during the presence of the negative pattern, seems the most likely explanation for the difference in the number of excursions.

Conclusions

From the previous discussion, the following facts emerge:

1. Under the conditions of the experiment, birds did not learn to avoid a stimulus as the consequence of having observed the learning process of their partners (Group E).

2. In the presence of untrained partners, learning speed was considerably reduced (Group C), while the presence of trained partners did not have this effect (Group F).

3. Birds could be made to ignore a discrimination which they had previously learned by observing wrong responses by an untrained partner (Group C).

The fact that the trained partners of the Group F birds never oscillated (although in only two instances were the experiments continued for a period long enough for oscillations to be established), may be attributed to the fact that these birds had been overtrained for a period much longer than was the case with the Group C birds. It is clear, then, that for oscillations of the described type to occur, the discrimination in question must not have been established for a protracted period. It is not yet certain whether the Group F birds would have learned as rapidly as they did had they ever observed their partners making errors. Since at least one Group E bird showed, initially, equally rapid learning until its partner began oscillating, it would appear that an absolute failure to observe errors was not a necessary condition for rapid learning.

What these results indicate is that, under the conditions for empathic learning which existed, a feeding response can be established more readily than an avoidance response (e.g., Group C and E fluctuations). This occurs apart from social facilitation or local enhancement-type effects. The maladaptiveness of the oscillatory behavior of the Group C and E birds would argue against any high degree of insightful behavior being involved. Apparently the sight of one bird feeding on a particular pattern can serve as an unconditional stimulus of considerable strength; sufficient, at least, to temporarily override the negative effects of the aspirin-filled seed. It will be noted that such a situation would be highly disadvantageous to a species unless linked with a general wariness of new foods or feeding sites. On this basis one might predict that wherever this situation does exist, the species involved will have restricted food habits. Conversely more opportunistic species should be able to learn avoidance responses with greater ease, relative to the ease of learning a feeding response. One might also suggest that the degree of social flocking will be found to show a positive correlation with the ability to learn avoidance and other responses through empathic processes. Examination of these hypotheses as well as an analysis of empathic learning in bisexual and varied-age groups is continuting.

Similar experiments conducted under more natural conditions and with less artificial stimuli have yielded identical results (Klopfer, 1958). Thus, paired Greenfinches, males and females, in 9 cases out of 10 required longer to learn a discrimination than their single controls. In the more explorative Great Tit (*Parys najor*), the results were almost the reverse, a result which accords almost too perfectly with what was predicted (Klopfer, unpublished data and 1958).

Summary

A full understanding of the ontogeny of species-specific food preference requires a knowledge of the effects of social interactions on discrimination learning. In this study, learning rates and processes were compared in paired and single birds.

The term "empathic behavior" has been proposed to cover all forms of motor mimicry. Processes involved may include conditioning, social facilitation, local enhancement or visual imitation, though these distinctions are not fundamental. There is evidence supporting the operation of all these in avian behavior, except the last.

Greenfinches (*Chloris chloris*) were trained to feed from one of two patterns and to avoid the other, with whole and aspirin-filled sunflower seeds serving as positive and negative reinforcement. Single birds learned the discrimination rapidly, as did birds which had been allowed to observe a previously trained bird performing. Birds which were being trained in the presence of an untrained partner, however, required much longer. When birds of this last group were permitted to observe the training sequence of their untrained partners, their performances, which had previously been correct, repeatedly fluctuated to a random or nondiscriminatory level. The partners, in turn, then also began to fluctuate between random and nonrandom levels.

Behavioral data preclude the operation of local enhancement or social facilitation. Thus, the results are interpreted to mean that, under the conditions that prevailed, a feeding response can be established more readily than an avoidance response, apparently as the result of conditioning (the unconditioned stimulus being the sight of another bird feeding). The suggestion is made that birds which show this type of learning pattern in nature will prove to be conservative in their feeding habits when compared with opportunistic species whose learned avoidance responses should be more stable.

Bibliography

Brower, J. (1958). Experimental studies of mimicry in some North American Butter-flies. *Evolution* **12**: 32–47; 123–136; 273–285.

Hinde, R. A. and Fisher, J. (1952). Further observations on the opening of milk bottles by birds. *British Birds* **44**: 393–6.

Klopfer, P. H. (1957). Empathic learning in Ducks. *Amer. Nat.* **91**: 61–63, 1957.

———. Influence of Social interactions on learning rates in birds. *Science* **128**: 903.

Koehler, O. (1955). "*Zählende*" *Vögel*. Acta XI Cong. Int. Ornith.

Konorski, J. (1948). *Conditioned Reflexes and Neuron Organization*. Camb. U. Press, Cambridge.

Remington, J. E. and C. L. (1957). Mimicry, a test of evolutionary theory. *Yale Scientific Mag.* 32 (1).

de Ruiter, L. (1952). Some experiments on the camouflage of Stick Caterpillars. *Behaviour* 4, p. 222–32.

Thorpe, W. H. (1956). *Learning and Instinct in Animals*. Methuen, London.

3 / Individuals and Those of Other Species

The papers in this section deal with behavioral aspects of prey-predator relations. There are, of course, other ways in which individuals of different species may interact, particularly species whose ecologic requirements are similar and which therefore compete for certain resources. This aspect of interspecific relations is treated in another volume of this series (Arthur S. Boughey, *Population and Environmental Biology*, Dickenson, 1967) and therefore is not considered here.

Experimental Studies of Mimicry.
IV. The Reactions of Starlings to Different Proportions of Models and Mimics

Jane Van Zandt Brower

Introduction

One of the basic tenets of Batesian mimicry has been that in order for a mimetic color-pattern to evolve and be maintained, the model must occur in greater frequency than its mimic. This is because a vertebrate predator in learning to associate unpalatability with a specific color-pattern would presumably have more frequently to experience unpalatable individuals (the models) than palatable ones (the mimics). That the selective advantage of mimicry is reduced when the model species is rare, has been suggested for several African mimetic butterflies by Carpenter (1932), Ford (1936), Carpenter (1949), and reviewed by Sheppard (1959). These authors showed that in areas where, or times when, the model frequency was low, the degree of perfection of the mimetic pattern was much lessened. This phenomenon has come to be known as breakdown of mimicry and is also known to exist (from unpublished work) in the North American mimic butterfly, *Papilio troilus* L.

There is thus considerable indirect evidence in support of the idea that a higher frequency of models is necessary for the maintenance of mimicry in nature. Nevertheless, no experimental studies have been made to discover the effect of different proportions of models and mimics on the ability of predators to learn to reject them. The present study was therefore undertaken to investigate this problem with caged Starlings [*Sturnus vulgaris* (L.)] as predators, and mealworms (*Tenebrio molitor* L.) as artificial models and mimics.

The Birds

The Starlings used in these experiments were trapped as adults at Milton, Berkshire, England, in the winter of 1957–1958 and were banded and released at the completion of the study. Eight bird cages were constructed, each measuring 24 inches wide × 30 inches high × 30 inches deep, with plywood sides, half-inch wire-mesh front, back, and top, and a galvanized steel tray floor. The front of each had a metal strip five inches high, across the base of the cage, in the middle of which was a sliding door through which experimental insects were introduced. The floors were lined with newspaper, and each cage had a plastic water bottle and a dish of P. Sluis Universal bird food, a commercial mixture imported from Holland. In addition, each bird was given grit, cuttlefish bone, and two drops of cod liver oil per day.

Eight Starlings were trapped for each of two series of experiments and were caged individually. Because of the plywood sides and the positions of the cages, the birds could not see one another's reactions. Unlike the Scrub Jays of the previous studies on mimicry (Brower, 1958a, b, c), the Starlings were shy and required from two to three weeks to become tame enough to be used. In the first series, early in the taming period, two birds failed to eat the food provided and died. These were replaced and no further deaths occurred. However, all were not equally calm: of the eight in the first set, four were useable, and in the second group again only four of eight could be used, although a fifth was tame enough, but would not eat mealworms. Shyness did not appear to correlate with sex; in the second set there were two males and three females that were tame, and two males and one female that were shy. The characters used for determining the sex were taken from Witherby et al. (1938) and were: bill color, eye color, presence or absence of spotting and of sheen, and shape of feathers. All were adults in the second set except one first-winter male (bird 1). The sexes of the first set were not determined.

Artificial Models and Mimics

In this investigation, mealworms colored by means of quick-drying cellulose paints were used for experimental food as a substitute for actual species of models and mimics. By applying a band of paint to the third and fourth abdominal segments with a small camel's hair brush, and allowing it to dry and become odorless, three categories of mealworms were made:

1. edibles: banded with orange and dipped into distilled water.
2. models: banded with green and dipped into a 66 per cent aqueous solution of quinine dihydrochloride.
3. mimics: banded with green and dipped into distilled water.

The purpose of the orange-banded edible mealworms was first to show that birds can associate orange, often a warning color in nature, with palatability, and second, to be certain that the paint itself was not unpalatable to the birds. The green paint was chosen for the unpalatable models because it is usually associated with protectively colored, highly edible insects, and therefore the birds probably would not have and a previously learned aversion to green. The mealworms were banded and treated according to the categories above before the start of each day's experiments. With this method, models and mimics were visually identical so that the mimic was "perfect."

Procedure

The experimental procedure was based on a modification of that used in mimicry experiments with butterflies (Brower, 1958). For the first group of four Starlings four different proportions of green-banded model and mimic mealworms were selected, and each bird was assigned one.

    A. 1 mimic: 9 models (ten per cent mimics).
    B. 3 mimics: 7 models (30 per cent mimics).
    C. 9 mimics: 1 model (90 per cent mimics).
    D. A control bird (100 per cent mimics).

A table of random numbers was used to obtain randomness in the order of presentation of the mimics and models in each of the proportions for any given series of ten trials. For example, at 30 per cent mimics, the mimics were presented in the fourth, seventh, and eighth trial in one series of ten trials, third, fifth, and ninth in the next, etc., until 16 sets of ten trials were completed. Thus the birds could not learn to predict the order of mimics and models. In addition to green-banded models and mimics, orange-banded edibles were also given to the Starlings, for the reasons stated above and to assure that they were hungry throughout the experiments. If a bird refused to eat an edible mealworm, the experiments were temporarily suspended until its appetite returned, and that trial was disqualified. As in the earlier work with butterflies, each trial consisted of offering a sequential pair of mealworms, one model *or* one mimic, and one edible to a bird. A random number table was again used to determine the order of presentation of each in such a way that runs of more than two of each kind were prevented, as fully described in the earlier paper (Brower, 1958a).

The random series for each proportion (ten per cent mimics, 30 per cent mimics, 90 per cent mimics, 100 per cent mimics) was determined prior to the experiments and the same sequences used with the first set of four Starlings were repeated for the second, with the addition of one new proportion, six mimics to four models (60 per cent mimics).

It had been planned that the Starlings would be introduced to their respective proportions of mimics and models at the outset of the first series of experiments. This was an attempt to simulate a natural situation in which a bird might be confronted with a population of models and mimics of a given relative frequency. However, there were initial difficulties in finding an odorless substance which was unpalatable enough to cause the birds to learn to reject the model mealworms on sight alone.

In these preliminary trials, solutions of sucrose octa-acetate, bitter aloes, a commercial bird repellant, and ten per cent and 20 per cent aqueous solutions of quinine dihydrochloride were all found to be insufficiently distasteful. But a 66 per cent solution of quinine dihydrochloride was so unpalatable to the Starlings that they soon learned to reject models on sight alone. By this time, they had already partially learned from the other unsuitable substances that model mealworms (green-banded) were less palatable than the orange-banded edibles. As a result of these difficulties, the birds of the first set of experiments were not introduced to their respective proportions of models and mimics until trial 61, whereas the second set of Starlings got the prescribed proportions of models and mimics from trial 1, as originally planned. In spite of this initial difference in the two groups, both were given a total of 160 trials with their respective proportions of models and mimics.

During an experiment, one banded mealworm at a time was placed on clean, white filter paper in a petri dish, after its head had been crushed with forceps so that it would not walk. When it was immobile, the dish was put into a bird's cage through the sliding metal door. As soon as the dish was inside, I moved out of sight so that I could observe the bird and yet it could not see me. This was done because they were relatively shy, and in addition to reduce the possibility of a bird getting a cue as to the palatability of a mealworm from some inadvertent gesture or expression on my part. The complex behavior of the Starlings towards mimics, described below, very strongly indicates that they were not taking cues as to palatability from the experimenter.

Each mealworm was left in a cage for one minute during which time the bird might: (1) not touch it (NT); (2) peck it (P); (3) kill it (K); (4) eat it (E). The category of response and the reaction time of each bird were recorded, and general notes on its behavior during an experiment were kept. In the preliminary trials, edibles were seized in ten seconds or less by all the birds, as were mimics by the control bird of the first group, so that the refusal to touch a mealworm for one minute was considered ample as a criterion of rejection. On most days, each bird was given ten trials, that is, was presented with 20 mealworms, as each trial consisted of a randomized pair, one model *or* mimic, and one edible.

Data

The First Group of Starlings

During the first eight trials with 66 per cent aqueous solution of quinine dihydrochloride as the unpalatable substance for the models, only models and edibles were given to the experimental birds. Bird A pecked three models and ate one, but touched none further in these trials. Similarly, bird B learned after eating one and pecking the next that the models were unpalatable and did not touch the rest of the ones given in these trials. Bird C, apparently more sensitive to quinine, had found the models unpalatable earlier when they were dipped in 20 per cent solution. In all eight trials with a 66 per cent solution, this bird did not touch the models, and hence had already learned to reject them on sight alone. However, it also rejected three edibles on sight during this period, which shows it had not yet learned to associate the color of the band on the mealworms with their palatability.

The control bird, D, ate all the mimics and edibles presented throughout the entire series, showing that both green-banded and orange-banded mealworms dipped in distilled water were palatable.

Following these eight trials, the four Starlings were offered ten per cent, 30 per cent, 90 per cent, and 100 per cent mimics (control), respectively. Thus bird A got one mimic in every ten trials. At irregular intervals this bird, and bird B which was given 30 per cent mimics, pecked the green-banded mealworms (models or mimics) although usually did not touch them. This learning behavior is similar to that shown by the Scrub Jays in the earlier mimicry experiments (Brower, 1958a, b), and again indicates that although the model is unpalatable and not eaten, the birds occasionally renew their experience with it, that is, make an "error" by pecking it. On the other hand at trials 42 and 107, bird A pecked a mimic and ate it. However, in 14 other trials, the mimic was not touched. Bird A ate the edibles in all trials.

Again, bird B which received 30 per cent mimics, or three in each ten trials, pecked models occasionally, but did not even touch most of them. At trial 25, it pecked and killed a mimic, but its behavior indicated that it associated the green-banded mealworm with unpalatability. The other 19 mimics offered were not touched. After trial 66, this Starling would no longer eat the edibles, pecking and leaving several over a period of three days, with the result that experiments with this bird were ended prematurely.

Having seen that experimental populations of ten per cent and 30 per cent mimics were relatively spared from predation, one can now compare these with the results for bird C which got 90 per cent mimics, nine in every ten trials. The deterrent effect of the initial trials with 20 per cent quinine already mentioned, lasted not only through the eight preliminary ones with 66 per cent solution, but into the proportion experiments. For 20 trials, no green-banded mealworms were touched; two models and 18 mimics escaped predation, whereas all 20 edibles were eaten, as well as all subsequent ones given to this bird. At trial 21, a mimic was pecked, at 22 another was eaten. However, in the next three trials one model and two mimics were not touched. From then on, most mimics were eaten, and the one model in each ten trials was usually pecked. At trial 51, a model was not touched, apparently because it followed a model which was pecked at trial 50. At trials 67, 74, 110, and 115, mimics were either pecked or not touched, in three instances one or two trials after the bird had experienced the unpalatable model.

This series of experiments was carried out between 28 January and 10 March 1958.

The Second Group of Starlings

After the first group of Starlings was released, a new set was obtained in order to present each individual with a different proportion of models and mimics from the outset of the experiments, and in addition to investigate an intermediate proportion between 30 per cent and 90 per cent mimics. Five Starlings appeared to be satisfactory for use in this series and were given the following proportions: 10 per cent, 30 per cent, 60 per cent, 90 per cent, and 100 per cent mimics, the last being a control bird. Shortly after the trials began, the control bird would no longer eat mealworms, so that before trials were discontinued with this bird, it had eaten only 10 mimics and 11 edibles and pecked and not touched a total of 7 of each. The one which got 90 per cent mimics is the nearest to a control for this series. In the statistical analysis, the control bird from the first set was used in comparisons with the second set in so far as it had received only mimics and edibles and had not been subjected to the various distasteful substances.

All four Starlings ate the edibles throughout the experiments. Bird 1 (ten per cent mimics) learned that the model was unpalatable after eating two and pecking one in the first six trials. Thereafter most were not touched, with occasional errors when a model was pecked, or in three instances, eaten. In the entire series, only one mimic was eaten, at trial 26, but 15 were not touched so that these results were similar to those for bird A (ten per cent mimics) in the first series, in spite of the fact that in that experiment the bird had previously experienced the model.

At first bird 2 (30 per cent mimics) pecked or did not touch models and also mimics, indicating that it was associating the green-banded mealworms with unpalatability, regardless of their actual taste. After trial 55, ten mimics and five models were eaten, but more than half of the mimics in the experiment were not touched.

The new proportion studied in this series was six mimics to four models (60 per cent mimics). Because this bird, 3, was getting more than half mimics, it was thought that perhaps it would peck almost every green-banded mealworm presented, and then finding it palatable in six out of ten trials, would learn to eat the mimics. However, this was not so. It was evident that bird 3 found the models unpalatable: all but one were only pecked or were not touched. Although 18 mimics were eaten, 72 were not touched, and 6 were only pecked.

As in the first series, bird 4, which was given 90 per cent mimics, ate most of them, showing that if the model is rare enough, mimicry is much less effective. It is interesting to note that periodic rejection of the mimics was closely related to the recent prior presentation of a model. Thus in trials 5, 16, 24, 52, 53, 54, 55, 66, 67, 68, 73, 85, and 97, mimics were not touched, or were pecked or killed, just after the bird had experienced the unpalatable model. There were only 100 trials for bird 4 because this individual was reluctant to eat as many as 20 mealworms per day, and so fell behind the other three birds.

This series of experiments was carried out between 26 March and 22 April 1958.

Statistical Analyses of the Data

The First Group of Starlings

In so far as the first set of Starlings had a period of conditioning with models which the second did not, the data from the two groups were analyzed separately. Tables 1 and 3 show the reactions of the two groups to mimics. Comparisons within each set were made by the chi-squared method to show whether or not the differences in the reactions of the individual birds to the various proportions of models and mimics were in fact real. The null hypothesis was that there was no difference in the reactions of two Starlings to their respective proportions of mimics. The four necessary 2 × 2 contingency tables were analyzed by the chi-squared test with the use of the Yates correction factor. Table 2 gives the chi-squared and P values for the first set of four Starlings for the comparison of the number of mimics "not touched—pecked—killed" *versus* "eaten," that is to say, *not eaten versus eaten* for each two birds. It can be seen that when the mimics were relatively rare (10 per cent, 30 per cent), there was no significant difference in the number "not

TABLE 1

Data for the reactions of Starlings in group 1 to mimics

	Bird A	Bird B	Bird C	Bird D
Mimics	(10%)	(30%)	(90%)	(100%)
Eaten	2	0	119	160
Killed	0	1	0	0
Pecked	0	0	3	0
Not touched	14	19	22	0
Totals	16	20	144	160

TABLE 2

Comparisons of birds (mimics not eaten *vs.* eaten)

	X^2	P values
Bird A (10% mimics) − Bird B (30% mimics) = 0.77, 1 d.f.,		$0.50 > P > 0.30$
Bird B (30% mimics) − Bird C (90% mimics) = 56.00, 1 d.f.,		$P < 0.001$
Bird C (90% mimics) − Bird D (100% mimics) = 28.21, 1 d.f.,		$P < 0.001$
Bird A (10% mimics) − Bird C (90% mimics) = 34.73, 1 d.f.,		$P < 0.001$

touched—pecked—killed" (not eaten *versus* "eaten" by the two birds. But between these two and the 90 per cent frequency of mimics, and between the 90 per cent and 100 per cent frequencies, the difference in the number eaten and not eaten was highly significant. This means that although significantly more remained uneaten when they were relatively rare, still when they comprised 90 per cent of the total "population" of models and mimics, significantly fewer were eaten than when 100 per cent mimics was given to a bird.

Figure 1 is a graph comparing the percentage of models and the percentage

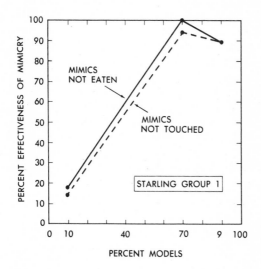

Fig. 1. Effectiveness of mimicry at different proportions of models and mimics.

effectiveness of mimicry, that is, the number of mimics *not eaten* divided by the total number of mimics given to each bird, for the first group of Starlings. It also shows the percentage effectiveness of mimicry when the number of mimics *not touched* was divided by the total given to each bird.

The Second Group of Starlings

The data for the four Starlings of the second group (Tables 3 and 4) were treated in the same statistical manner as in the first set. (It will be recalled that this set of birds was given the proportions of models and mimics from the outset of the experiment in contrast to the first group.) It can be seen that as before when the mimics were relatively rare (10 per cent, 30 per cent), there was no significant difference in the reactions of the Starlings to them. However, it is surprising to note that even when the mimics were at a fre-

TABLE 3

Data for the reactions of Starlings in group 2 to mimics

	Bird 1	Bird 2	Bird 3	Bird 4
Mimics	(10%)	(30%)	(60%)	(90%)
Eaten	1	0	18	75
Killed	0	1	0	1
Pecked	0	10	6	4
Not touched	15	28	72	10
Totals	16	49	96	90

TABLE 4

Comparisons of birds (mimics not eaten *vs.* eaten)

X^2		P values
Bird 1 (10% mimics) − Bird 2 (30% mimics) = 0.85, 1 d.f.,		0.50 > P > 0.30
Bird 2 (30% mimics) − Bird 3 (60% mimics) = 0.00, 1 d.f.,		P = 1.00
Bird 3 (60% mimics) − Bird 4 (90% mimics) = 74.94, 1 d.f.,		P < 0.001
Bird 4 (90% mimics) − Bird D (100% mimics) = 25.50, 1 d.f.,		P < 0.001
Bird 1 (10% mimics) − Bird 3 (60% mimics) = 0.75, 1 d.f.,		0.50 > P > 0.30
Bird 1 (10% mimics) − Bird 4 (90% mimics) = 36.39, 1 d.f.,		P < 0.001
Bird 2 (30% mimics) − Bird 4 (90% mimics) = 50.46, 1 d.f.,		P < 0.001

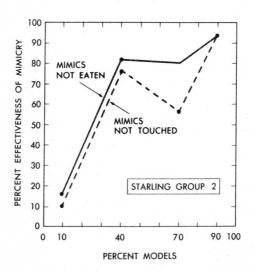

Fig. 2. Effectiveness of mimicry at different proportions of models and mimics

quency of 60 per cent, slightly outnumbering the models, the bird did not react in a significantly different way from those which got only ten per cent or 30 per cent mimics. In fact, bird 2 (30 per cent) and bird 3 (60 per cent) failed to eat almost the same percentage of mimics.

Figure 2 is a graph comparing the percentage of models given to these four birds, and the control bird from group one, with the percentage effectiveness of mimicry for both the number of mimics *not eaten* and the number *not touched*, as in Figure 1. The three points for 90 per cent, 70 per cent, and 40 per cent models indicate that 80 per cent or more mimics were not eaten. At ten per cent models, 17 per cent mimics escaped being eaten, just as in the first group of Starlings, and 11 per cent were not touched, compared with 15 per cent in first group (see Figure 1).

Behavior of the Starlings

As in earlier experiments with Scrub Jays (Brower, 1958), the Starlings showed characteristic behavior patterns when offered an unpalatable model and its visually identical mimic. In the first group, bird A (10 per cent mimics) ruffled its feathers and wiped its beak a total of 13 times out of 160 (8 per cent) when given a model or mimic, considerably less frequently than the Scrub Jays. This Starling sometimes also behaved in a way which indicated a state of indecision or conflict when it was given a model or mimic. It would flap its wings as though about to fly and then preen vigorously or scratch its neck with one foot (probable displacement activities) and not peck the mealworm.

Similarly, bird B (30 per cent mimics) wiped its beak and ruffled its feathers a total of 12 times out of 66 (18 per cent) when it was given a model or mimic, but gave no further visible reaction. For bird C (90 per cent mimics) very interesting behavior was observed. This bird gave the feather-ruffling and beak-wiping reactions to the models or mimics in eight out of 160 trials (5 per cent). The behavior which was unique to this bird, however, was that of mouthing and rubbing the mimics which followed trials in which a model was offered. This consisted of the bird turning the mealworm with its beak and pressing the insect against the floor of the cage for as long as 40 seconds. It apparently was uncertain of the palatability of green-banded mealworms and tested each before eating it, occasionally to the point of leaving it altogether. During the experiments, this Starling mouthed 26 out of 144 mimics (18 per cent) and also five edibles out of 160 (3 per cent), of which it was sometimes suspicious, but nevertheless ate.

Bird D, the control, gave no such reactions to the mimics and edibles, all of which were palatable.

In the second group, bird (10 per cent mimics) ruffled its feathers and wiped its beak in 64 out of 160 trials (40 per cent) when a model or mimic was given; bird 2 (30 per cent mimics) in 66 out of 160 (41 per cent); bird 3

(60 per cent mimics) in 13 out of 161 (8 per cent); and bird 4 (90 per cent mimics) in six out of 100 (6 per cent). In addition, bird 4 gave this reaction to the edible in 6 out of 100 trials (six per cent).

Now it has been noted in both groups that when a bird merely pecked or killed a mimic, but did not eat it, a conflict situation was sometimes evident. First, it might be hesitant in seizing the mimic, and then, once it had done so, the Starling would treat the mealworm as though it were an unpalatable model by rubbing it on the floor of the cage, pecking it up and dropping it successively, and feather-ruffling followed by vigorous beakwiping. The importance of this behavior will be considered below.

Discussion

In this investigation, experiments were carried out in which caged Starlings were used as predators, and modified mealworms as artificial models and mimics to test the effectiveness of mimicry at different proportions of models and mimics. The results suggest a new interpretation of one part of mimicry theory. It has long been assumed that when a mimic outnumbers its model, the mimic will no longer be at a selective advantage because learning predators will not tend to associate the mimetic pattern with the unpalatability of a relatively rare model.

These experiments indicated that under conditions of nearly perfect mimicry, this may not be so. First, it was seen that when a Starling was given 60 per cent mimics, there was no significant difference in the number of mimics rejected by this bird and by two other birds which got 30 per cent and ten per cent mimics, respectively. Thus the birds learned to associate the color with unpalatability nearly as well if the models were slightly more rare than the mimics than if the models greatly outnumbered them. Two other Starlings behaved in a way which strongly indicates that mimicry can be partially effective when the model is quite rare compared with its mimic. These two birds received only 10 per cent models, and yet for each, 17 per cent of the mimics offered were not eaten. There was furthermore a correlation of those which were not eaten with the recent experience of a bird with the model. This suggests that a relatively perfect mimic will derive some protection from predation even if it outnumbers its model by nine to one, and that the mimics spared will most likely be those encountered by a bird soon after it has taken a model. Thus the results of this study show that mimicry may be far more effective under certain conditions in which a mimic outnumbers its model than had previously been expected on the basis of indirect evidence.

A second important finding from these experiments is that with a highly unpalatable model, mimicry may be effective even if mimics are attacked by a predator. In several instances during the experiments, mimics were pecked (and presumably tasted) and yet rejected by Starlings which had had experience with models. That this occurred with an artificial mimic of known palatability is noteworthy because it affords a control on similar behavior shown by the Scrub Jays towards mimic butterflies (Brower, 1958). In the instance of the Viceroy (*Limenitis archippus archippus* (Cramer)), a mimic of the Monarch (*Danaus plexippus* (L.)), several were only pecked or killed, and not eaten by the Jays, and at the time it was difficult to assess whether the birds could not discriminate the mimic from the model even after pecking it, or whether in fact the mimic itself was relatively unpalatable. The present experiments give some basis to the alternative that birds which have experienced models can peck a palatable mimic, and yet because they have learned that its particular color-pattern is unpalatable, they will reject it. The learned association of unpalatability with a specific color-pattern is not immediately negated by a *new* association of palatability with the same pattern. In fact, a learned negative response to a visual stimulus appears to dominate a positive "taste stimulus" under the conditions of the experiment.

Another point of similarity between these experiments with Starlings and the previous ones with Scrub Jays is that after learning to avoid the models, both species of birds occasionally made errors by pecking, killing or eating the models (or mimics). That such an error pattern could serve as an adaptive mechanism for a predator to detect changes in the relative frequency of models and mimics in time seems almost certain, and as Fisher (1930) has suggested seems an essential feature of mimicry theory.

Summary

1. Experiments were carried out to test the effectiveness of mimicry at different proportions of models and mimics with Starlings (*Sturnus vulgaris*) as predators and mealworms (*Tenebrio molitor*) as artificial models and mimics.

2. A band of green cellulose paint was used to mark the "model" mealworms which were made unpalatable by being dipped into a 66 per cent solution of quinine dihydrochloride. "Mimic" mealworms were identically banded, but dipped into distilled water, as were orange-banded "edible" mealworms.

3. It was found that birds which received 10 per cent, 30 per cent, and even 60 per cent mimics (the balance being models) rejected about 80 per cent of the mimics by associating their color band with that of the unpalatable model. Mimicry is thus effective when mimics are more frequent than models.

4. Two birds which were given 90 per cent mimics (only 10 per cent models) nevertheless rejected 17 per cent of the mimics, indicating that when a model is highly unpalatable, and a mimic relatively "perfect,"

mimicry may be effective even when a mimic outnumbers its model by as much as nine to one.

5. Under the conditions of the experiment, the selective advantage of mimicry is far greater than believed by previous investigators.

Acknowledgments

This work was carried out in the laboratories of Dr. E. B. Ford, F.R.S., at Oxford University under a National Science Foundation regular postdoctoral fellowship. I am most grateful to Dr. Ford for constructive discussions during the course of these experiments and for reading and criticizing the manuscript. Dr. Lincoln P. Brower gave invaluable assistance in discussing the design and statistical analyses of the experiments, in reading and criticizing the manuscript, and in obtaining the birds. Dr. N. Tinbergen of Oxford University offered helpful suggestions concerning the distasteful substances and the preparation of the artificial models and mimics. Mr. Michael King of Oxford University kindly gave me much assistance in the trapping and care of the Starlings.

Literature Cited

Brower, Jane V. Z., 1958a, Experimental studies of mimicry in some North American butterflies. I. *Danaus plexippus* and *Limenitis archippus archippus*. *Evolution* **12**: 32–47.

————, 1958b, Experimental studies of mimicry in some North American butterflies. II. *Battus philenor* and *Papilio troilus*, *P. polyxenes*, and *P. glaucus*. *Evolution* **12**: 123–136.

————, 1958c, Experimental studies of mimicry in some North American butterflies. III. *Danaus gilippus berenice* and *Limenitis archippus floridensis*. *Evolution* **12**: 273–285.

Carpenter, G. D. H., *Pseudacraea eurytus* (L.) (Lep. Nymphalidae): a study of a polymorphic mimic in various degrees of speciation. *Trans. R. Ent. Soc. London* **100**: 71–133.

————, 1932, Mimicry. *Sci. Prog.* No. **104**: 609–625.

Fisher, R. A., 1930, *The Genetical Theory of Natural Selection*. pp. 146–169. Clarendon Press, Oxford.

Ford, E. B., 1936, The genetics of *Papilio dardanus* Brown (Lep.). *Trans. R. Ent. Soc. London* **85**: 435–466.

Sheppard, P. M., 1959, The evolution of mimicry; a problem in ecology and genetics. *Cold Spring Harbor Symp. Quant. Biol.* **24**: 131–140.

Witherby, H. F. et al., 1938, *The Handbook of British Birds*. London.

Insect Survival and Selection for Pattern

H. B. D. Kettlewell

Because insects are a major source of food, they have, in the last 80 million years, evolved highly efficient survival mechanisms. Except for the smallest, they have been driven by natural selection into one of two main lines of defense; the one is the antithesis of the other. The first group depends on revealment, the second on concealment. Recently both have been extensively studied.

In the first groups, insects in many different orders have developed chemical repellents to make them distasteful, odoriferous, or dangerous. In order to enhance these characters, they frequently advertise their presence by conspicuous patterning with red or yellow and black stripes, or, in its simplest form, a white coloration. Aggregations of aposematic insects wearing such uniforms are normally found in many parts of the world. These are the Müllerian mimics.

Insects in the second group have specialized in producing color patterns which mimic niches available to them in nature; they include mimics of other, poisonous insects (as in the case of the Batesian mimics). At an early period the backgrounds on which insects most frequently camouflage themselves, such as tree trunks, rocks, or dead wood, must have been copied successfully. More important still, many of these insects avoided overspecialization and developed an ability to vary in response to frequent environmental changes. In these insects the gene complex has, from antiquity, been built up with a premium on cryptic patterns, and to these ends the genetic armory has retained those mutants which have been of use in the past. It is this second group with which I am largely concerned in this article. The two groups, however, have a common denominator in that in both a balance must be struck by each gene which controls both pattern and physiological fitness, having regard to the advantages and disadvantages of each.

Group 1 : Aposematic Insects

Recently advances have been made in the analysis of the chemistry of "repellents" in insects with warning coloration, but, as yet they are incompletely understood. Many different poisonous substances have been found, such as hydrocyanic acid in the hemolymph of Zygaeninae (Lep.) (*1*), choline esters (possibly $\beta\beta$-dimethylacrylyl choline) in the moth *Arctia caja* L. (*2*), and a digitalis-like substance in the locust *Poekilocerus bufonius* Klug (*3, 3a*). Histamine (as well as acetylcholine) is also present in Zygaeninae (at con-

Reprinted by permission of the author and publisher from *Science* **148**: 1290–1296, 1965.
Copyright 1965 by the American Association for the Advancement of Science.

centrations up to 250 μg/g), and it is found in "enormous amounts" (2) in the locust *P. bufonius*. Histamine appears to be virtually absent, however, in *A. caja*, though an "active agent . . . far more efficient in increasing capillary permeability" is present (2). On the other hand, histamine is present in very high concentrations (750 μg/g) in the warningly colored moth *Hypocrita jacobaeae* L., not, so far as is known, in association with any other toxic substance (2), though I believe one will be discovered later.

A further important contribution is the finding that certain aposematic insects themselves feed on toxic plants and that in some instances the poisons in the plant are related to those in the insect. These insects therefore may have developed an enzyme mechanism enabling them to survive the ingestion of such plants, and also to make use of the toxins synthesized by them (4). Thus, asclepiad species, the food plants of the butterfly *Danaus plexippus* L. and the locust *P. bufonius*, are rich in glycosides, which have a profound effect on mammalian hearts (5). In each of these insects the digitalis-like substance has been isolated (3a, 4). The fact that this situation exists in both the New and the Old World, and in such diverse orders, suggests that this protective mechanism must have been evolved independently in each hemisphere at an early time.

Aposematic coloration offers one great advantage over crypsis: it permits insects to move freely and fly in safety by day. By contrast, most insects that depend on camouflage only must remain motionless in daylight on specialized backgrounds; they fly only under cover of darkness.

White is the simplest warning color, and it is effective with predators whether they have color vision or not. Butterflies of the genus *Pieris* are relatively rarely attacked. Many white moths fly in daylight. In England, *Cycnia mendica* Cl. (Lep.) is sexually dimorphic—males are black and females white. The males fly by night, and mating takes place shortly before dawn; females, however, fly by daylight, when they oviposit. In a closely related species, *Spilosoma lubricipeda* L., in which both sexes are white, up to 700 μg of histamine per gram of body tissue has been demonstrated (2, 6). It would indeed be interesting to know the histamine content in the two sexes of *C. mendica*. In Ireland, *mendica* is monomorphic, both sexes being white. We know little of its natural history there and nothing of its chemistry.

In every species a particular behavior sequence or display is associated with its own particular color pattern (7). This may be complex and involve a series of defensive mechanisms, each brought into play in order, according to the seriousness of the situation (8). Few of these sequences have been analyzed in the field, though many have been studied in the laboratory (9). Recent work by Brower (10) and others has given convincing proof of the efficiency of warning coloration as protection against predators.

An example of the sophisticated sequences which exist in nature is the survival mechanism of *Arctia caja* L. This moth passes the day motionless in deep vegetation. The fore wings, which entirely cover the hind wings and body when the moth is at rest, have disruptive coloration, with alternate black and white markings. When forcibly disturbed, the moth exposes its crimson hind wings and body in a series of jerking movements. If an attack is driven home, however, bubbles of fluid are secreted from the crimson collar surrounding the cervical (prothoracic) glands (*11*), which contain the acetylcholine-like substance. A second toxic, though nondialyzable, chemical is found in even greater concentration in the abdominal tissues of the female, and injection of 5 to 10 μg of a saline extract of this chemical per kilogram is sufficient to kill a guinea pig in 2 to 10 minutes (*2*). In addition, the cervical glands secrete a strong-smelling fluid, and it has been recorded that the sharp tibial spines are capable of producing a painful sting (*2*).

I have tested this moth's defenses by presenting it to two very different species of birds in the wild. In July and August 1963 I was daily able to offer many species of living moths to an immature robin, *Erithacus rubecula* L. After the bird had fed on palatable noctuids, it was given a specimen of *Arctia caja;* on the first such occasion it pecked the moth, refused in, and then flew away. A large number of specimens of *caja* were presented subsequently, but never again did this bird approach this species. The impact of a single encounter with *caja* is even more convincingly shown in experiments I undertook with a mallard duck (*Anas platyrhynchos*) between 1953 and 1963. This bird was found in the wild on the first or second day after hatching, and was hand-reared. Subsequently it had complete freedom and flew about the district for 10 years. During this period it was, on most days in summer, offered various insects in sequence, both palatable and unpalatable. (For these tests no attempt was made to take into account the normal resting positions of the insects.) In July 1954 the mallard was offered its first *caja*, which it immediately pecked and attempted to swallow. It rapidly regurgitated the moth and "beakwiping" took place. On subsequent days the mallard was offered other *caja* among the palatable species which it ate, but it never touched them. More remarkable is the fact that, throughout the following nine years of its life, this bird never again pecked this species after its first experience, even though this insect was available for 1 month only in each year. The warning color pattern is therefore seen to be a highly successful deterrent by day after an original encounter (*12*). *Arctia caja* normally flies late at night, and pairing takes place at midnight.

In 1948 it was recorded that *Euprepria pudica* made a rasping noise in flight (*13*), and, in an editorial footnote (*13*), I mentioned that the males of *caja* were capable of stribulating, and that I had observed that this also took place during wing movements. More recently this observation has been confirmed by others (*14*). I have, however, been unable to trace the source of the sound, but it is likely to be caused by a timbal organ. It is possible that some component of the sound emitted acts as a warning to bats. Among the scores of Lepidoptera wings I have examined under bat roosts, I have never found any of this species. Maybe, then, this highly distasteful species depends on warning color by day and warning sound by night.

Aposematic Müllerian mimics can gain no special protection during night life. They are active by day only when they depend on uniformity of a conspicuous pattern; any variation of this is likely to be disadvantageous and is certainly of rare occurrence in nature. Nevertheless, a few species of Heliconidae (*Rhopalocera*) in South America are polymorphic, each with clearcut morphs (*15*).

By contrast, it is strange to find that in aposematic nightflying moths there can be great genetic variability of pattern. In Britain, the two species with most frequent and extreme aberrational forms are both aposematic: *Arctia caja* L. and *Abraxas grossulariata* L. Because both species are common and highly toxic, it is likely that there has been little selection for an exact pattern by visual predators in the recent past; the emphasis may have been on their physiological requirements. In recent work on another highly repellent aposematic moth, *Utetheisa pulchella* L., I have shown that great variability exists in inbred stock, which is only disclosed when unusual environmental conditions are imposed (*16*). More recent work by us (*17*) has revealed a similar situation in *Arctia caja*.

It is a fact that melanic (dark-colored) forms of aposematic insects are of great rarity, and this character, with few exceptions, is inherited as a recessive (*18*). This implies that melanism in the past has conferred little advantage to the species' survival. I know of only two exceptions. The two-spot ladybird, *Adalia bipunctata* (Col.), has warning coloration and is highly distasteful. It contains 150 milligrams of histamine (*19*) per gram of body tissue, and this is unlikely to be the only toxin. Under certain conditions one or the other of two common melanic mutants, which are allelic, are substituted for the normal red form in up to 90 percent of a population (*20*). Both of these mutant forms are inherited as Mendelian dominants. The second exception is found in the moth *Spilosoma lutea* Huf., a near relative of *S. lubricipeda* E. Though it has a similar color pattern, it is not so repellent to birds and may contain little histamine (*19*). It is one of the commonest and most widely distributed moths in Britain. On the Lincolnshire sand hills, however, and on Heligoland, a black form, *S. lutea* f. *zatima* (Cramer), is found as a polymorphism, and the black color is dominant to the normal white color. There is evidence that here the moth rests by day on the dead stumps of elder and other shrubs which grow on the dunes, and that it is cryptic (*21*). Gull species, many of which are highly insectivorous (*22*), are likely to be the most influential predators; it is well known that they accept species repellent to other birds.

Summary: Group 1, Aposematic Insects

In aposematic insects we are dealing, therefore, with at least three different situations. Firstly, selection in Müllerian insects must favor conformity. Secondly, in abundant aposematic species in which the deterrent substances are sufficiently unpleasant, predation is relaxed by day, and freedom of pattern is the result; no degree of nocturnal predation can affect this directly. Thirdly, and rarely under certain circumstances, aposematic insects may forfeit their warning coloration for melanism because of cryptic or physiological advantages; because these melanic forms are dominant today, it is likely that they have frequently proved to be successful alternatives in the past.

Group 2: Cryptic (and Batesian Mimetic) Insects

Cryptic insects, in contrast to Müllerian aposematic species, maintain and may exhibit genetic variability of pattern. These situations can be considered under two headings.

1. *Polymorphisms*. These enable species to exploit more than one niche at the same time and place. Recent work on the Batesian mimic *Papilio dardanus* L. (Lep.) has given clear proof of the part played by a gene, a supergene, and the gene complex (*23*). Because of its implications, I give a résumé of the findings.

2. *Recurring mutations*. Mutants have been retained in the gene complex and may be of great antiquity. In melanic forms of Lepidoptera they probably reflect successful adaptations to different environments in the past history of the species. Many cryptic nightflying moths today have industrial melanic forms (forms occurring in manufacturing areas during and since the Industrial Revolution), and these are inherited as dominants (*24*). In this paper I am suggesting that two separate mechanisms may contribute to this, and it is these I am largely concerned with here.

Polymorphisms

One of the most complex polymorphisms found in insects is in the butterfly *Papilio dardanus* L. (Lep). This species is a Batesian mimic, and its distribution can be divided into three areas: Africa north of the Sahara, Africa south of the Sahara, and Madagascar. Throughout its range the males are yellow and tailed. In Madagascar the species is monomorphic, both sexes being tailed and yellow (*25*).

In Abyssinia 80 per cent of the females are tailed and yellow and 20 per cent are tailed mimics (*26*). Over the greater part of the continent, however, the female has no fewer than 14 forms, which mimic local races of distasteful species of butterfly. Four other forms occur which are nonmimetic. All are tailless. In extensive breeding experiments from stock from all these areas, the following observations were made.

1. In the female, each color morph is controlled by a major gene.
2. All the forms examined were allelic, and the order of dominance could reflect their order of ancestry.
3. This "H locus" constitutes a supergene. The dissimilar mimetic phases are controlled by combining, in a number of ways, variation in a few simple characters.
4. Nonmimetic forms are maintained by heterozygous advantage.

5. Perfection of local mimetic pattern is attained by selective changes in the gene complex. An allele from the east coast of Africa expresses itself quite differently in a west-coast gene complex, where its model is absent.
6. The inheritance of tails is controlled by a single pair of alleles which are autosomal and sex-controlled, but not linked with the "H locus." Heterozygotes have intermediate and variable tail length.

The polymorphisms of *Papilio dardanus* are of ancient origin, and in recent work I have suggested that those contributing to industrial melanism today may also be of great antiquity (*27*). It is in fact possible to make a comparison the mechanisms controlling each situation. On the one hand, many of the *dardanus* forms fly together at the same time. By contrast, the various melanic forms of a species are usually not required at one and the same moment in the same place, but occur spaced out in time according to the degree of darkness demanded by natural selection is a changing environment.

I hope to provide evidence that two mechanisms are concerned in a cycle of melanism. Firstly, different melanic allelomorphs replace one another, and secondly, the expression of each can be changed by modification of a gene complex which has made use of it on previous occasions. Conversely, if a melanic mutant is put into a gene complex in which it has not been present at some earlier time, dominance is rapidly broken down.

Recurring Mutations: The Natural History of Industrial Melanism

Since the Industrial Revolution in the latter half of the 18th century, black forms of many cryptic, nightflying moths have replaced light specialized forms in most manufacturing areas throughout the Northern Hemisphere (with the exception of the tropics).

It is unlikely that in Britain immediately prior to that time more than 10 percent of those species which today exhibit industrial melanism had melanic polymorphisms (*27*). The majority of these forms must therefore have arisen by mutation. We know from old collections that most of these earliest melanic mutants were near-dominant. Though the specimens taken around 1860 are different from those found today, they were always clearly distinct from f. *typica*. The important point, therefore, is that melanic mutants, occurring within a preadapted gene complex, have not had to adjust their patterns on each successful occasion, except in minor details. Crosby (*28*) has suggested, from his computer models, that modification of dominance could not be achieved because of the dearth of heterozygote material on which natural selection could work. Later in this paper I provide experimental data which contradict his computer results. Nevertheless, though dominance-modification does take place, it is the replacement of one form (allelic or otherwise) which is the more important factor in the history of industrial melanism.

Though *Biston* (*Amphidasys*) *betularia* L. has been the species most thoroughly investigated, about 20 others have been studied by us in both laboratory and field experiments. In Britain, with the help of a large number of parttime lepidopterists, I have obtained a comprehensive record of many of these. From this it appears that two separate factors contribute to the natural history of industrial melanism. Firstly, present-day melanic mutants are darker than those taken in the last century. Secondly, different melanic mutants may replace those of an earlier wave of melanism. Thus, f. *carbonaria*, the blackest form of *B. betularia*, has usually been preceded by one of a number of intermediate forms (collectively referred to as f. *insularia*), whose phenotype frequencies, however, never rise above 40 percent of a population (*29*). One form of the f. *insularia* complex has been shown to be allelic to f. *carbonaria* (*30*). According to theory, multiple allelomorphism is likely to occur in many species with several melanic forms. Each at mutation is found to be dominant to f. *typica*, though one melanic form (usually a later mutant) is epistatic to an earlier one.

The natural history of industrial melanism and the wave of spread of different melanic mutants can be clearly demonstrated in many Lepidoptera species in Britain. *Cleora rhomboidaria* HG. (= *gemmaria* Brh.), a common and widely distributed geometrid, was, in the last century, a pale moth with darker patterning. It was highly cryptic on dead wood and palings throughout London and elsewhere. This f. *typica* was rapidly replaced by a dark grey form (f. *perfumaria*). More recently a jet black form (f. *nigra*) has spread through populations in areas as distant as Norwich and Portsmouth. The rapid replacement of one melanic form by another is seen similarly in *Phigalia pedaria* F., *Polia nebulosa* Hufm., and *Cleora repandata* L. In this last species the melanic form, which at present constitutes over 90 per cent of the population in central industrial England, is similar in appearance to one that is still found today as a balanced polymorphism (constituting up to 10 per cent of the population) in the relict Caledonian pine forests of the Black Wood of Rannoch (*31*). Here the advantages which melanism confers are entirely different from those in an industrial environment. Melanic polymorphisms are found far from industrialization in the vicinity of latitude 60°N. One third of the Shetland species have melanic forms, as no doubt they always have had in the past (*32, 33*). Recent work has shown that one of the advantages conferred here is "aerial crypsis"—protection due to the fact that dark-colored insects are less conspicuous in flight in twilight than light ones (*34*). The Shetland melanic forms so far investigated are, like industrial melanic forms, inherited as dominants (*32*). A few of these Shetland species have, in fact, similar industrial melanic forms which are today spreading through industrial areas of Britain. This finding underlines the all-important fact that black coloration can give advantages in a number of quite different ways under very different conditions (*18*). Because situations in which it has done so have arisen in past environments over eons of time, the gene complex is geared for the production of such mutants. Thus, only to a limited extent can industrial melanism be considered an exceptional type of polymorphism.

The Breakdown and
Buildup of Dominance

The earliest *Biston betularia* f. *carbonaria* were different from the majority of present-day heterozygotes in that they had more patches or lines of light coloration on their wings (*29*); such patterning is rarely seen today (Fig.1). Modern heterozygotes are entirely black except for a few white dots situated at the front of the thorax, and they have a white costa on the hind wings.

Coll. F. Bond, about 1872
Coll. Gregson, old pin
Coll. Gregson, old pin
Coll. Sidney Webb
Coll. Cooke, old pin

Fig. 1. (left) Modern heterozygotes of British *Biston betularia* f. *carbonaria*. Intermediates never occur. Though intermediate *B. betularia* individuals are common phenotypically, they have a different genetical origin (= f. *insularia* complex). (right) Earliest specimens of f. *carbonaria* from collections made in the last century.

Even the dots have disappeared in a high proportion of f. *carbonaria* from Manchester, Chester, and elsewhere. These insects are not necessarily homozygous f. *carbonaria*, is in these places, after 120 years, the gene frequency of f. *typica* is still of the order of 10 to 15 per cent. The very great visual disadvantage of the light form must therefore be compensated by a physiological advantage of heteroxygous over homoxygous f. *carbonaria*. Selection in fact favors the darkest heterozygotes.

In the last eight years I have attempted to test this by two series of large-scale breeding experiments: firstly, by outcrossing for three generations "industrial" f. *carbonaria* (from Birmingham) to *betularia* stock from southwestern England where this form does not occur; secondly, by outcrossing f. *carbonaria* to *Biston* (*Amphydasys*) *cognataria* Gn from Canada, where f. *carbonaria* does not occur.

Breakdown of Dominance Breeding Experiments in which f. *carbonaria* (Industrial Origin) Were Outcrossed to Nonindustrial Stock from Britain

Heterozygous *Biston betularia* f. *carbonaria* from Birmingham were crossed with f. *typica* from southwest England. Clearcut segregation occurred in all broods. Randomly selected individuals of f. *carbonaria* were then crossed with wild-type f. *typica* from southwest England. After three generations, some f. *carbonaria* differed from the original specimens of industrial origin: their jet black color was peppered with white dots. These individuals on the one hand bore little resemblance to the earlier f. *carbonaria* caught in the last century, but on the other they were different from those of today (Fig. 1). It is assumed, therefore, that the original f. *carbonaria* allele, as present in the middle of the last century, has been replaced by another having a more extreme effect. Yet, as a powdering of white scales then appeared, we have evidence that some relative adjustment of the new allele had in fact taken place.

Outcrossing f. *carbonaria* to North American *Biston* (*Amphidasys*) *cognataria* Gn

The species *cognataria* is found throughout the North American continent; a black form, f. *swettaria* Barnes & McDunnough, occurs around industrial areas, particularly in the eastern United States; only f. *typica* is found over large areas of Canada. Crosses between *cognataria* and *betularia* are highly fertile, and crossing produces no gross disturbance of sex ratio. The two species differ in several recognizable characters, however: f. *typica* of *cognataria* is somewhat darker than that of *betularia;* it hatches earlier in the summer and over a much shorter period; the larvae feed at a great speed and most have pupated by the end of August. Quick feeding and early hatching are no doubt essential for avoiding the sudden onset of Canadian winters. By contrast, imagines of British *betularia* hatch from May to August and larvae can be found till October.

Experimental Evidence

After four generations of outcrossing hybrid *betularia* f. *carbonaria* to wild Canadian stock, a gradation of insects occurred in all broods. Dominance was completely broken down (Fig. 2). At this stage approximately 94 per cent of the genes present would be of Canadian origin, but even after three generations there was no clearcut segregation.

Fig. 2. *Biston cognataria* f. *typica* (Canada) × *B. betularia* f. *carbonaria* (Industrial Britain), showing the breakdown of dominance after four generations of outcrossing.

Buildup of Dominance

Random intermediate *carbonaria* hybrids were mated to *betularia* f. *typica* of British industrial origin. In the *first* generation clearcut segregation appeared (Fig. 3).

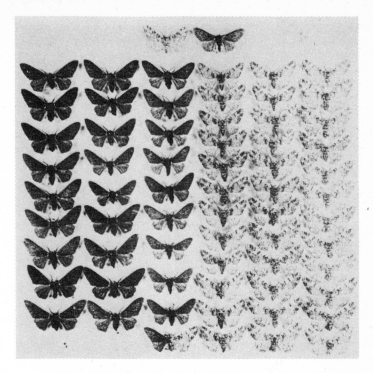

Fig. 3. The buildup of dominance in the first-generation progeny of crosses of *B. betularia* f. *carbonaria* hybrids and f. *typica* of British industrial origin.

The question posed was whether dominance-modification had been built up locally in urban areas since the Industrial Revolution, or whether dominance-modifying genes were universally present throughout the British *betularia* population. To test this, intermediate f. *carbonaria* hybrids were crossed to *betularia* f. *typica* from southwest England. Clearcut segregation took place again in the first generation (Fig. 4), but there were significantly fewer black f. *carbonaria* in the extreme of category 6 (Fig. 5, col. 7) than in the comparable crosses from industrial Britain.

These breeding experiments, therefore, show the following points.

1. There are genes present in British *betularia* which ensure the expression near full dominance in f. *carbonaria* for the character of blackness.
2. It makes little difference whether the modifying genes come from an industrial area where the phenotype frequency of *carbonaria* is 90 per cent or from a rural district where f. *carbonaria* does not occur.
3. The modifying genes in British *betularia* are themselves dominant but not linked to f. *carbonaria*. The majority of them may be universal throughout Britain.

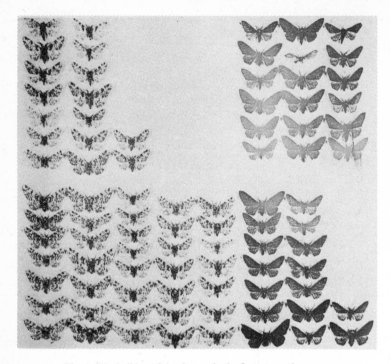

Fig. 4. The buildup of dominance in the first-generation progeny
of crosses of *B. betularia* f. *carbonaria* hybrids and f. *typica* of British
nonindustrial origin.

4. From this it appears that on each occasion that a mutation takes place,
this particular mutant is guaranteed dominance at inception.

Summary: Group 2, Cryptic Insects

1. Batesian mimics are considered in this article as cryptic insects which
have copied animate creatures which are highly mobile and poisonous. In
order to spread its risks, a species may mimic a large number of different
aposematic insects. Nevertheless, the degree of unpalatability is relative, and
a Batesian mimic must always accrue advantage if it is able to acquire a degree
of even moderate distastefulness.

2. *Papilio dardanus*, which must always have been a most attractive species
gastronomically, copies a large number of repellent species which have for
millennia inhabited the same areas. The various mimetic forms are controlled
genetically by a supergene which has come to be responsible for switching
pattern elements in such a way that crossing over between the genes controlling them is near zero.

3. The majority of cryptic insects, however, depend for survival on copying

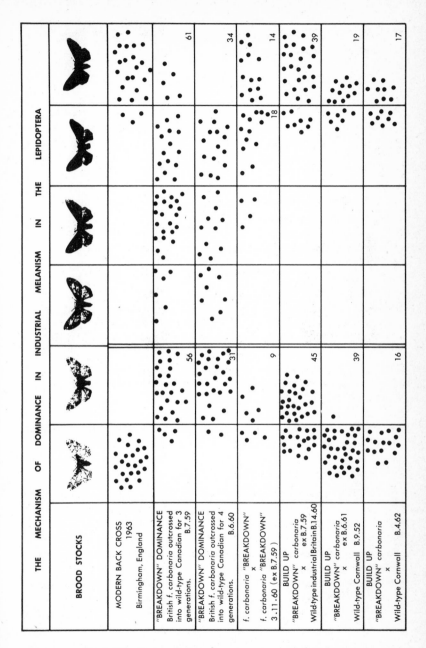

Fig. 5. Distribution of phenotypes into six categories in broods showing "breakdown" and "buildup" of dominance. (Crippled and worn insects were not scored.)

backgrounds which, though immobile, vary from time to time according to the meteorological and environmental conditions imposed. Melanic forms have for several reasons conferred advantages during different periods in the past. Recently a new environment brought about by the polution of the air by smoke has fortuitously favored these same melanic forms. We refer to these as "industrial melanics."

4. The natural history of industrial melanism in Britain, as investigated in the field and by breeding experiments in the laboratory, suggests that different melanic forms of a cryptic species can spread through a population and replace f. *typica* in as short a time as 50 generations (*35*). Large-scale experiments in an industrial area in which individuals were marked and then released showed that in *betularia* there was a 30 per cent advantage of f. *carbonaria* over f. *typica*. The converse was true in nonpolluted districts. Waves of different industrial melanic forms, which may be allelomorphs, have spread and then been replaced by others. Nevertheless, each allelic form can be modified by changes in the local gene complex. How dominance-modifiers can be held in a population throughout those periods in which melanic polymorphisms do not occur (and in which no black forms occur except by mutation) is difficult to explain. The antiquity, periodic recurrence, and importance in the past of melanism suggest that genes controlling it may play a special part in a gene complex, analogous to the polymorphism of *Papilio dardanus*. It has been shown in *B. betularia* that dominance-modifiers, themselves dominant, are present in two very different and widely separated populations in Britain [from (i) industrial and (ii) nonpolluted areas of western England]. It is in fact likely that they are universal throughout Britain and that they guarantee dominance at each mutation. Such modifiers for British f. *carbonaria* were found to be absent in Canadian stock.

It is suggested that different alleles, presumably mutations within the same cistron developed in the past, have been selected during the adaptations of industrial melanic forms and that these control the deposition of melanin and its distribution in slightly different ways.

References and Notes

1. D. A. Jones, J. Parsons, M. Rothschild, *Nature* **193**, No. 4810, 52 1962; Feigl, F. *Spot Tests in Inorganic Analysis* (Elsevier, Amsterdam, ed. 5, 1958), p. 276.
2. G. W. Bisset, J. F. D. Frazer, M. Rothschild, M. Schachter, *Proc. Roy. Soc. London* **B152**, 255 (1960).
3. M. Rothschild and J. Parsons, *Proc. Roy. Entomol. Soc.* **27**, No. 6 (1962).
3a. J. Parsons, *J. Physiol. London* **169**, 80 (1963).
4. ———. "A digitalis-like toxin in the Monarch Butterfly *Danaus plexippus* L.," *ibid.*, in press.
5. R. Paris, in *Chemical Plant Taxonomy*, T. Swain, Ed. (Academic Press, London, 1963), pp. 337–358.

6. M. Rothschild, *Proc. Roy. Entomol. Soc.* **38**, 159 (1933).
7. A. D. Blest, *Zoologica* **49**: 3, 1964.
8. H. B. D. Kettlewell, *Endeavour* **18**: 200, 1959.
9. J. V. Z. Brower, *Am. Naturalist* **94**, 271 (1960).
10. ———, *Evolution* **12**, 1 (1958).
11. V. G. Dethier, *J. N. Y. Entomol. Soc.* **47**, 131 (1939).
12. M. Rothschild, *Entomologist* **97**, 73 (1964).
13. A. Valetta, *ibid.* **81**, 102 (1948).
14. M. Rothschild, in press.
15. J. R. G. Turner and J. Crane, *Zoologica* **47**, 141 (1962).
16. H. B. D. Kettlewell, *Entomologist* **96**, 102 (1963).
17. ——— and C. J. Cadbury, in preparation.
18. H. B. D. Kettlewell, *Ann. Rev. Entomol*, **6**, 245 (1961).
19. J. F. D. Frazer and M. Rothschild, "Chemical Defence Mechanisms," *Proc. Intern. Congr. Entomol., 11th, Vienna, 1960.*
20. E. R. Creed, thesis, University of Oxford (1963).
21. W. E. Collinson, personal communication.
22. R. Sparck, *Proc. Ornithol. Congr. 10th* (1950), pp. 588–591.
23. C. A. Clarke and P. M. Sheppard, *Heredity* **14**, 163 (1960).
24. H. B. D. Kettlewell, *Proc. Roy. Soc. London* **B145**, 297 (1956).
25. C. A. Clarke and P. M. Sheppard, *Genetic* **44**, 1347 (1959).
26. ———, *ibid.* **45**, 439 (1960).
27. H. B. D. Kettlewell, *Proc. Roy. Inst. Gt. Brit.* **36**, 164 (1957).
28. J. L. Crosby, *J. Theoret. Biol.* **5**, 35 (1963).
29. H. B. D. Kettlewell, *Heredity* **12**, 51 (1958).
30. P. M. Sheppard, *Nature* **202**, 215 (1964).
31. H. B. D. Kettlewell, *Proc. Intern. Congr. Entomol., 10th* (1958), vol. 2, pp. 831–842.
32. ——— *Heredity* **16**, 393 (1961).
33. ——— and R. J. Berry, *ibid.*, p. 403.
34. ——— *ibid.*, p. 415.
35. ——— *ibid.* **9**, 323 (1955); *ibid.* **10**, 287 (1956).
36. I wish to thank Professor E. B. Ford for reading the manuscript, Professor P. M. Sheppard for discussion, and the Hon. M. Rothschild for her help on recent work on insect toxicology. C. J. Cadbury assisted me greatly in carrying out the large-scale breeding experiments, with the help of a grant from the Department of Scientific and Industrial Research, for which I am grateful.

Predators and Anti-Predator Behavior of the Black-Headed Gull (*Larus ridibundus* L.)

H. Kruuk

1. Introduction

The group of aerial predators on the brood in Ravenglass includes Corvids and Larids.

Of the Corvids, only the carrion crow (*C. corone*) preys on the gulls, but it seems justified to consider the hooded crow (*C. cornix*) as well, since their ecology and behaviour are very similar, and they replace each other in different parts of the black-headed gull's range. The range of the carrion crow and hooded crow together entirely overlays that of the black-headed gull.

The diet of the crows is extremely variable. They are known to prey regularly on eggs and young birds (Witherby et al., 1938; Bergman, 1939; Niethammer, 1942; Meidell, 1943; Axell, 1956; Gerber, 1956); only very occasionally do they attack small birds or wounded large birds (Witherby, 1938; Mattson, 1948). They are reported by Noll (1913), Bergman (1939), and Makatsch (1952) to take eggs of black-headed gulls.

Other Larids known to take eggs and young of black-headed gulls are herring gulls (*Larus argentatus*) and lesser black-backed gulls (*Larus fuscus*) but it is probable that other large gulls do the same (Witherby et al., 1938; Niethammer, 1942; Kantak, 1954).

The damage herring gulls do to the broods of other birds is creating a serious conservation problem in many countries (V. Dobben, 1934; Otterlind, 1948; Tinbergen, 1953; Mörzer Bruyns, 1958) especially because of a vast increase in their numbers over the last decades (Voous, 1960). The black-headed gull will be exposed to this all the more since this species itself shows an increasing tendency to nest along the coast, which is the habitat of the herring gull. In England the percentage of colonies along the coast remained about the same for 1913, 1938, and 1958 (28 %, 28 %, and 26 % respectively), but although in 1938 only 44 % of the individuals nested in coastal colonies, this figure was 65 % in 1958; no data are available for 1913 (calculated from Hollom, 1940; Gribble, 1962). A centuries-old black-headed gull colony of several thousand pairs on Walney Island in the Irish Sea decreased in numbers after the first herring gulls arrived in 1929, and had vanished by 1958. In this period increasing numbers of large gulls have been seen by several observers to prey on this colony; now there is a large mixed colony of herring and lesser black-backed gulls.

Reprinted by permission of the publisher from Behaviour (Supplement) **XI**: 7–31, 1964.

2. Predation by Carrion Crows

The picture, given by Tinbergen et al. (1962) for predation by carrion crows and herring gulls in the Ravenglass colony in 1960 and 1961, has been largely substantiated; it remained about the same in 1962 and 1963.

Our peninsula was frequented by a limited number of crows which probably bred from two to six miles away. In the gulls' breeding season, they mostly fed in pairs, but sometimes solitarily or even, though more rarely, in flocks of up to 12 individuals. In 1962 and 1963 the colony area was visited daily by at least two different pairs. From direct observations, tracks in the sand and some regurgitations, we obtained a qualitative impression of their diet, which consisted mainly of shellfish, etc. from the beach, carcases of black-headed gulls which had been left by foxes, vegetable matter, and insects. Fighting often occurred between pairs and frequently one pair managed to drive another pair out of the area at least temporarily. Fighting also occurred often within flocks, especially over food (see also Lockie, 1956).

Over a period of close watching by many observers, crows have been seen to take an egg or chick from the gulls on only very few occasions. In 1962 and 1963 we observed three successful and two unsuccessful attempts by crows to take an egg or chick, of which two attempts were made outside the main colonies and the other three on the edge of the colony. Two of the successful attempts were concerned with chicks (one of which was stolen directly afterwards by a herring gull), and one with either an egg or a small chick.

There is a discrepancy between what is known about the predatory nature of crows and their low predation records in the colony of black-headed gulls —we would expect them to take a larger share of eggs and chicks. This discrepancy could be caused either by a direct preference for other food items in this particular region, or by a protective mechanism of the black-headed gull.

To decide this, a simple experiment was carried out. Black-headed gulls' eggs were laid out on the beach in several clutches of three. The centre of this "artificial colony" was about 150 m from the edge of the real colony. The clutches were evenly spaced out, 3–4 m apart. The area was watched from a hide placed on the top of a dune at about 200 m distance; on other occasions it was left alone and conclusions were drawn from tracks and shell remains. This artificial set up differed from the natural one in several respects: (a) adult gulls were absent; (b) no nest material was used; and (c) the habitat was different (no vegetation; different ground colour; completely flat).

Since (b) and (c) affect mainly the camouflage of the eggs, which has been shown to afford some, but only little, protection against crows, the situation on the beach differed from that in the colony mainly in the absence of adult gulls.

The results may be summarised as follows:

Date of experiment*	No. of eggs laid out	Time during which eggs were left out	No. of eggs gone	Evidence
17/5/63	36	6 hours	all	Crow tracks, few shells
27/5/63	36	30 hours	all	Crow tracks, few shells
28/5/63	60	4 hours	57 by crows, 3 by herring gulls	watched

* Some additional remarks may be made about the third experiment. Of 57 eggs, 18 were taken by one single crow (within $2\frac{1}{2}$ hours) and 39 by one pair of crows. At one time the pair carried off 18 eggs and ate 5 within an hour. Eggs were mostly carried away and buried somewhere in the dunes and only 12 out of 29 were eaten on the spot. The solitary crow invariably carried the eggs to a small dune valley at the other side of the estuary, about 1.5 km. away. The pair chased off the solitary crow far out of sight, and at the end when they were eating some leftover, they were chased off by another pair after a fierce fight between the two males.

These observations show that crows do take black-headed gulls' eggs if not opposed by the black-headed gulls and that they can take very large numbers in a short time. Only a small proportion of the eggs were directly eaten (45 of the 57 eggs taken in the third test were buried). This "caching" habit of crows causes predation to exceed their direct needs. How big their total capacity is I do not know (it was limited in this experiment by the number of eggs), but certainly it is very considerable. Therefore, the presence of the black-headed gulls in the colony area must in one way or the other afford a very effective protection of the brood.

3. Predation by Herring Gulls and Lesser Black-Backed Gulls

In 1960, 1961, and 1962, three pairs of herring gulls nested or attempted to do so in or near the black-headed gull colony; in 1962 a pair of lesser black-backed gulls nested there as well and one pair settled without producing eggs. All these nests were deserted before the eggs hatched—in 1960 and 1961 this was mainly due to human disturbance; in 1962 to predation by foxes. In 1963 no nesting attempts were made at all but three pairs of lesser black-backed gulls and one pair of herring gulls occupied territories. These so-called resident large gulls prey to a large extent on the black-headed gulls. In contrast to the flock birds, they behave territorially, with frequent threatening and fighting. The nests are always far apart (up to several hundred meters), entirely solitarily (as described by Wynne-Edwards, 1962).

Apart from this resident population, large numbers of herring gulls and lesser black-backed gulls, mostly immature, were living near the colony. They lived entirely on the shores, their droppings consisting mainly of fragments of *Mytilus* and a few other molluscs, and some crustacean remains. They passed over the colonies without visibly reacting to the presence of the black-headed gulls.

The chief predation of resident gulls is on very young chicks; in 1962 and 1963, 31 out of 95 observed attempts were successful, these concerned 22 chicks and 9 eggs. The success of 2 other attempts could not be established. However, this is obviously only a small fraction of the total predation by large gulls in this colony. The bulk of observations are from the end of May (which is the peak time of hatching of the black-headed gulls' eggs); only a few predation attempts occurred before May and none after the first half of June. Especially in that part of the 1962 season, the general impression was that the resident herring gulls and lesser black-backed gulls did almost all their searching for food in or around the colony. In 1963, predation was much lower than in 1962; only 30 attempts were observed against 65 in 1962, although the number of large gulls involved was about equal and the observational effort was if anything larger. This might have to do with the fact that in 1963 no nests were made. On 14th June 1963, a continuous watch was kept over circa 2,000 nests of black-headed gulls from 3 until 23.000 hours. Lesser black-backed gulls were seen to take only 2 chicks, of which one might have been dead.

We have only very little evidence of the actual diet of these resident gulls but almost certainly when they have nests, they live practically exclusively on eggs and chicks. In 1962, from a herring gull's nest in the black-headed gull colony, the eggs were replaced a few days after laying by hatching eggs from a nearby herring gull colony. The young herring gulls were fed by the adults—of six feeds, four were black-headed gull chicks and two consisted of bread or unrecognisable food. This brood was destroyed the following night by a fox. Two dead black-headed gull chicks were collected from another herring gull's nest without eggs which had no other food items.

The large gulls were never observed to store food, and the predation pressure of large gulls therefore does not exceed their feeding capacity. Mrs. J. McFarland has kindly allowed me to quote her observations on the daily intake of herring gulls in captivity. An adult male herring gull, which had been in captivity for a year, was given black-headed gulls' eggs only, on five different days. Fish and biscuits were fed on the other days. The number of eggs eaten on these five days is given in Table 1.

TABLE 1

Number of black-headed gulls' eggs eaten per day by a herring gull in captivity

Date	No. of eggs presented	Eaten	Eaten half (or less)	Untouched
5/6/63	12	10	2	0
10/6/63	15	12	0	3
14/6/63	15	15	0	0
17/6/63	15	10	4	1
19/6/63	15	13	0	2
Total	72	60	6	6

This bird thus consumed on average just over 12 eggs per day. Even though wild herring gulls might eat slightly more, their capacity remains far below that of carrion crows because they do not store eggs.

Summarising: while most of the large gulls do not prey on the black-headed gull at all, a few individual specialists take a good many eggs and chicks. The number of prey items taken in a breeding season by a resident large gull many times exceeds that taken by the crow, although the total capacity of the herring gull or less black-backed gull is smaller.

4. Hunting and Storing Methods of Crows and Large Gulls

On the few occasions when crows were seen taking prey from the Raven-glass colony, this happened after a very sudden stall from a fast flight—the crows were never seen to circle over the colony like the large gulls. However, in Sunbiggin Tarn, crows did circle over the colony, although much higher (8–10 meters) than a large gull would do, and only for periods of up to twenty seconds. Only once was a crow seen to come down from that height, descending vertically in a series of steps.

The crows visiting the eggs I had laid out on the beach (see II. A. 2) circled slowly over the eggs at about five metres above the ground for up to thirty seconds before alighting. After a few eggs had been taken, they alighted at the eggs directly on arrival. In the experiments with hens' eggs, which will be mentioned later, crows reacted similarly to eggs outside the colony. Apparently only a small area underneath was searched because the crows did not usually react to an egg until they were directly above it. They then stalled in air and came down vertically or in a spiral with deep wingbeats. Hens' eggs inside the colony were approached much more rapidly with a faster searching flight; the crows mostly alighted in the way described above for actual predation in the colony and much nearer to the eggs than outside.

Bergman (1939) found eggshells in alder bushes in a black-headed colony and suspected crows of taking the eggs. It could well be that in his case, the relatively high crow predation was made possible by their use of the alder tree as a safe watchout post (as described for the American crow, *Corvus branchyrhynchos*, by Preston, 1957) from which they preyed upon the nearby nests. Axell (1956) describes predation by crows on herring gulls where a pair of crows approached a herring gull sitting on eggs, and whilst the gull flew off in pursuit of one of the crows, the other crow removed the eggs. I never saw this behaviour, but it might well have been used by crows for robbing solitary nests outside the colony.

The caching of eggs appeared to be an important element in the preying behaviour of crows. Sometimes an egg was cached only a few metres from the place where it was found, but usually a crow flew at least a few hundred meters with the egg in its bill before it alighted. It walked to a suitable place, dropped the egg and started digging nearby with its bill. It dropped the egg into the hollow, wiped sand over it with a few quick movements of the bill and then often put leaves or moss on top. The whole procedure took less than a minute and the covering of the cache was so well done that, even if the burying had been watched at very close quarters, a buried egg was very difficult for a human observer to find. Crows did return to these caches, but the great difficulty I had in finding them made it impossible to get an impression of the rates of return.

Since no differences have been observed in the hunting behaviour of the herring gull and the lesser black-backed gull, my description, based on the herring gull, refers to both. A particular pair might spend a long time on a dune top or a ridge in a sparsely populated part of the colony or outside it. Starting from there, they might hunt either in flight or walking. One bird, more often both, would fly off and then go rather slowly back and forth over part of the colony. This hunting flight was always between two and six metres above the ground, rather fast, looking downwards and often moving the head from side to side. Now and then one of them stalled, hovered and alighted almost vertically. The herring gull might interrupt this sequence by either flying on before it began to descend, or it descended part of the way and then flew on. If it did alight it mostly did so very near to the prey and sometimes even picked up the prey whilst still in the air. An egg was very often swallowed whole but sometimes it was opened and the contents eaten on the spot. Otherwise it was carried off in the bill. A chick could be carried in the same way and eaten either in flight or later on the ground. Often chicks were swallowed alive. On a few occasions, herring gulls were seen to forage whilst walking through the colony, eating the contents of nests on the spot.

5. Reactions of the Black-Headed Gulls

The gulls' reactions depend on the behaviour of the predator. Therefore, we will discuss these reactions to crows and large gulls in situations where the predator (a) flies over the colony, (b) stalls and alights in the colony and (c) sits or walks in the colony. A stuffed carrion crow and herring gull were used in order to compare directly the reactions to the predators sitting in the colony.

(a) A crow or large gull flying in a steady flight over the colony area, at a height not exceeding ten metres, might release two different behaviour patterns in the black-headed gull. (i) Fleeing. On the ground, a gull in the flight path might fly up and away from the approaching bird, make a short circle in the air and alight again on its territory. This usually happened in silence but kek-calls might be heard. (ii) Attack. Some birds might pursue the predator in the air and follow it for some distance uttering tremulous-calls. This chase, however, hardly ever ended in actual contact for either the pursuer soared up in time or the predator evaded him. Diving attacks ("swoops") might also be observed where the attacking black-headed gull approached the target at an angle from above, and then soared (for further description, see Manley 1960b). All this might be repeated several times by one pursuer, and several pursuers might take part.

In Table 2, observations of reactions to crows and herring gulls flying over the colony are summarised. It has to be borne in mind that while only a few birds attack at the same time, there is no limit to the numbers that may flee simultaneously. The category "ignored herring gull" was not counted in 1962; the figure 68 is the count for 1963. No reactions to birds flying above ten meters have been counted.

TABLE 2

Observations of reactions to crows and herring gulls flying over colony or roost

| Situation: | Reactions of black-headed gulls | | | |
	attack	attack + fleeing	fleeing	ignored
Crow over colony	1	28	5	3
Herring gull over colony	30	0	1	68*
Crow over roost	0	2	22	0
Herring gull over roost	0	0	0	*

*Occurring frequently, but no counts are available.

From Table 2, we can draw several conclusions: (a) a flying crow is reacted to far more often than a herring gull; (b) the reaction to crows more often contains a fleeing element (in 67% of the reaction to crows, only in 3% of the reactions to herring gulls $x^2 = 29.4$, P < 0.001); (c) the relative frequency of reactions involving attack is not significantly different for the two predators (for crows in 90%, for herring gulls in 97% of the reactions). All these percentages relate to the total number of occasions in which black-headed gulls reacted at all. I had the impression that the sudden appearance of a crow tended to make the gulls flee; by taking landscape into account, it was often possible to predict whether an approaching crow would make the gulls flee or not. Also, on four occasions, when crows flew over a colony on a dune, the gulls sitting on the slope facing the approaching predator did not react, whereas those on the opposite slope, which could not have seen the crow approaching, fled when it appeared. The reverse was never observed.

Also in Table 2, reactions to crows and herring gulls flying over roost flocks outside the breeding colonies are summarised. Comparing these data with those for the colony, we conclude that (a) attacks are very much restricted to the breeding areas of the black-headed gull and (b) here again, crows are more often reacted to than herring gulls; (c) the most common reaction to crows on the roost is fleeing.

The fact that crows are so much more often reacted to than herring gulls could be due to a subsequent waning effect (see also Schleidt, 1961)—herring gulls are much more common in the breeding area than crows.

(b) The reaction to a stalling and alighting crow was only rarely observed in the purely natural situation but many incidents were watched in the tests with hens' eggs (II. A. 6.2). The gulls sitting on the ground near the place where the crow came down, flew up and away from the crow, often not further than one metre, sometimes with a few kek-calls. Then they turned back and either attacked the crow (which might have alighted by then) or returned to their nests. The attacking gulls uttered the tremulous call. The attacks consisted of a rapid aerial approach and, although the crow almost always managed to avoid physical contact, it was obvious that the gulls tried to peck or grab it with their bills. Usually, many gulls attacked simultaneously.

When flying off, the crow was pursued over a short distance but it always easily outflew its pursuers. A herring gull stalling over the colony invariably elicited a great number of tremulous calls in the gulls below. No other response followed if the herring gull flew on, but if it actually came down, the gulls below still uttering this call would fly straight at the approaching predator. The herring gull was also often pursued when flying off.

Thus, to stalling predators of both kinds, the gulls reacted with ground-to-air attack, often preceded by brief fleeing, particularly from crows.

(c) Once a predator—crow or herring gull—alighted in the colony, it elicited different reactions. Most black-headed gulls kept some distance away but a number of them performed diving attacks. In these, the gulls swooped down from up to five metres, uttering tremulous calls and some-times, at the nadir of the swoop, the "K-waaaarh-call" (Manley, 1960a). Some of these attacks might be made from the ground and have an almost horizontal approach. During these attacks, the enemy might be hit with the feet, or sometimes with the bill or the whole body as well. Attacking gulls might also defaecate.

The attack-frequency waned soon after the predator alighted, especially if it kept still; walking around immediately revived the attacking. There was also a long-term waning effect—a herring gull nesting in the colony is soon left alone.

If the predator was eating a prey in the colony, the behaviour of the neighbouring gulls might contain other elements—several birds stood close to an eating crow or gulls with rather a long neck and wide-open eyes, wait-ing to try and eat the spoils when the predator left.

Whereas black-headed gulls usually ignored walking crows and herring gulls outside the colony and, for instance when feeding on the shore, would pass within two metres of them, they would occasionally attack them far away from any colony; this also happened at the winter feeding places (see also Markgren, 1960). In all my observations, this was started off by one black-headed gull swooping at it repeatedly and other gulls joining in.

A stuffed herring gull and a stuffed carrion crow were presented to test the reactions of the black-headed gull to these two predators in a more standardised situation when both were motionless. The following method was used:

A model was presented on one end of the top of a T-shaped stand, the horizontal part of which was 1.20 metres and the vertical part 1 metre long. This stand, which itself was ignored by the gulls, could be moved at will. Reactions of the gulls to the mounted bird were watched through binoculars on a tripod from up to a hundred metres distance and directly scored on paper, with timing in minutes. Recordings started one minute after the model had been put up.

On any one place in the colony, only one experiment was made.

Each experiment consisted of: first ten minutes presentation of crow and herring gull at the same time; then 4 alternating five-minute periods in which either was given alone, starting equally often with the crow or the herring gull. The placing of the model on the end of the plank in the 4 five-minute sequences was either left-right-right-left or right-left-left-right. The great number of black-headed gulls attacking the models when they were presented in the colony made counting impossible; therefore all experiments were done about five metres from the colony edge on the beach. Two experiments were carried out in the Sunbiggin Tarn colony in the same way, but only the combined presentation was offered because of the bad accessibility of the habitat.

The simultaneous presentation in this experiment was done with the aim of comparing directly the reactions to the two models without the need for correction for locality differences (e.g., because of different gull-densities) or differences caused by waning effects; the separate presentations came closer to the natural situation in which the gulls are not presented with a choice.

TABLE 3

Number of diving attacks per 10 minutes; stuffed herring gull and carrion crow presented simultaneously

	Experiment number	Attacks on crow	Attacks on herring gull	
Ravenglass (26th & 27th May 1963)	1	38	107	
	2	22	34	
	3	27	62	
	4	42	77	
	5	23	223	
	6	85	200	
Sunbiggin Tarn (17th June 1963)	1	92	172	
	2	87	111	together
Total		416	986	1402

TABLE 4

Number of diving attacks per 5 minutes; stuffed herring gull and carrion crow presented
separately

	Experiment number	Attacks on crow	Attacks on herring gull
Ravenglass (26th & 27th May 1963)	1	40	109
		43	125
	2	24	45
		67	46
	3	55	114
		29	39
	4	39	83
		32	79
	5	123	193
		133	195
	6	133	90
		61	93
		779	1206

Note: See Table 3. With the binomial test, N = 12 x = 2 P < 0.04.

The results are given in Tables 3 and 4; these figures show clearly that
the crow model is attacked less often than the herring gull model—in the
combined presentation the crow only received 30%, in the separate presentation 39% of the total number of attacks (with the binomial test, N = 8,
x = 0, p < 0.008 and N = 12, x = 2, p < 0.04, respectively). The experiments in the Sunbiggin Tarn colony, where herring gulls are hardly ever
seen, were done to establish whether the observed difference could be related
to the frequency of occurrence of the predators. But, as the tables show, the
differentiation seems independent of locality.

Conclusions

The gulls' reactions to crows and herring gulls may be briefly summarised
as follows. In general the behaviour to these predators is very similar, although
some distinct differences do occur. Much of the gulls' behaviour depends on
that of the predator.

Flying crows are more often reacted to than herring gulls, both over the
colony and over the roost. This result could possibly be due to a prior
waning effect. However, although herring gulls are often ignored when flying,
they are always reacted to with attacks when stalling (which is indicative for
hunting).

Crows, more than herring gulls, release fleeing when alighting or flying
over; especially sudden appearance seems to facilitate this. But also many
attacks can be seen especially over the colony.

A stuffed crow in the colony, which has been identified with a crow sitting still, is reacted to with swoops, but less often than a stuffed herring gull—the reverse from what happens to flying birds. This result has been confirmed in the experiments with hens' eggs (II. A. 6.2. 3.2, Table 7), in which attacks on preying crows and herring gulls were counted. The difference in attack-frequency on sitting crows and herring gulls is not related to the frequency of occurrence of these predators in this particular colony.

6. The Effect of the Black-Headed Gulls' Behaviour on the Predators

6.1. Direct and Indirect Effects

In flight the responses of large gulls and crows to the pursuit or diving attacks of the black-headed gull were largely the same and consisted of quick changes in direction or swerving if a gull came very close. In general, both predators had very little difficulty in evading the black-headed gull.

On the ground, however, crows and herring gulls differed considerably in their reactions. Both of them moved quickly to face a dive-attacking black-headed gull, which might cause them great difficulty when several gulls attacked at the same time. As a rule, the large gulls did not move away from the place where they were attacked but turned round, making quick jabs with the bill at the attackers. At the same time, the head might be briefly withdrawn between the shoulders, but sometimes the gull might stretch it or even jump up, trying to grab the attacker. Between attacks they often long-called. Crows reacted much more vigorously and more timidly, some-times jumping several metres to reach the cover of a small hill or a patch of vegetation every time a gull swooped at them. Facing the attacker, it lowered its whole body, drew its head between its shoulders and pointed its bill obliquely upwards. In this posture, a short very low-pitched rattling call was often uttered. No more active defence was ever seen in crows.

Also the indirect effect of the black-headed gulls' behaviour on crows and herring gulls is different. During the whole breeding season, large gulls might be seen drifting in up-drafts over the colony or at the edge of it. There was a regular traffic of them over the colonies and I never saw them alter their course to avoid the colonies. Crows, however, were often seen to make large detours around the colonies when passing; before and after the breed-ing season they frequently scavenged in the colony area but never during the season. Carcasses of gulls were eaten by crows wherever they were, except in and very near the actual colony. The avoidance of black-headed gull colonies by crows is also mentioned by Bergman (1939) and Schinz (1947).

To study what the effect of the gulls' behaviour was on the actual predation, a series of experiments was carried out which will described in the following section.

6.2. The Hens' Eggs Tests

6.2.1. Aims. The principal aim of these tests was not merely to study the effect of the gulls' behaviour on the predatory behaviour of crows, herring gulls and lesser black-backed gulls, but they also provided more precise descriptive details of their hunting mechanisms and the behaviour of the black-headed gulls. In addition, some information was collected about interaction with oystercatchers and finally some observations were made regarding interactions between predators.

6.2.2. Methods. For each experiment a row of ten small hens' eggs was laid out at some places at the inland edge of the colonies. The eggs were ten metres apart, the egg line more or less at right angles with the colony edge which crossed the egg line in about the middle. Thus five eggs were inside the colony and five outside. For each egg line, an area was selected with a more or less even vegetation or else no vegetation. At two metres from each egg, a marker was placed to facilitate instantaneous localisation of a predation incident. The eggs inside the colony were mostly on occupied black-headed gull territories. The black-headed gulls did not take any notice of the eggs or the markers.

Observations were made with field glasses from a hide which was placed on a vantage point 50 to 100 metres away (if possible, at right angles to the egg-line); notes were made with the help of a tape recorder into which a time-base was fed simultaneously. Sometimes eggs were laid out and not watched but checked from time to time.

An experiment started immediately after laying out the eggs and it ended either (a) within two hours if all eggs had been taken by predators; or (b) after at least two hours as soon as six or more eggs had been removed and no predators had been present for at least fifteen minutes; or (c) after three and a half hours. Most of the tests were done in the early morning.

In Ravenglass, these experiments could only be carried out in the early part of the breeding season; after the gulls started laying, predation on the egg line decreased, presumably partly because other food sources became available, but also partly because of an increase in attack-frequency which probably deterred the crows. Therefore, hens' eggs had to be used for the test instead of gulls' eggs. Hens' eggs have the additional advantage that they cannot be eaten by the black-headed gull (although several attempts were made) whereas black-headed gulls' eggs would rapidly disappear in that way.

A series of pilot tests was done in 1962, the results of which we will only quote here if they differ from the main experiments in 1963. In 1963 egg-lines were used in three different parts of the colony.

The reaction behaviour of the black-headed gull in reaction to the predators was the same as in the entirely natural situation—for instance, a predator alighting on an egg in the colony caused a reaction which was, to us, indistinguishable from the one to natural predation.

The figures in the various tables do not necessarily count up to the same totals—because, if things happened fast, it was not possible to collect all the relevant data.

6.2.3. Results. (1) Position preference. Since I often allowed all the eggs to be taken, the total number of eggs taken from different positions cannot be used as an indicator of the predation pressure in those places. Therefore, the order tin which the eggs disappeared was used, and is summarised for all the experiments in Figure 2. The egg which was taken first in a certain test was scored as 1, the egg which was taken second as 2, and so on. If several eggs were left over after the watching session, each was given a median score. Thus each experiment provided ten dots in the figure.

For statistical analysis, the order in which eggs were taken was considered to be a sequence of nine choices. For all first choices, the median of all dots on the abscissa was determined, and the number of first choices left and right

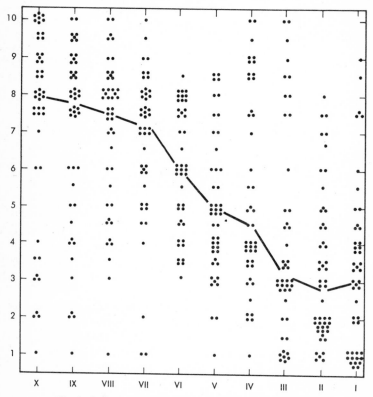

Fig. 1. Order in which the eggs were taken from the egg-lines, by crows and herring gulls. Horizontal is egg-position (X is inside, I is outside the colony), vertical is the order of disappearing of the eggs (e.g., the bottom righthand cluster shows that in 13 tests the egg in position I was taken first, etc.). The solid line connects median preferences.

the median scored. For all second choices, the median of all dots, minus those representing first choices was determined and so on. The scores of nine choices left and right of the median were added and submitted to a χ^2 test with df $= 1$.

From Figure 2, it is clear that the eggs outside the colony are preferred above eggs in the colony. Outside the shifting median, 291, inside of it 95 eggs were taken: $\chi^2 = 99.6$, $p < 0.001$; therefore, these outside eggs run a greater risk. The greatest differences in preference are found at the edge of the colony.

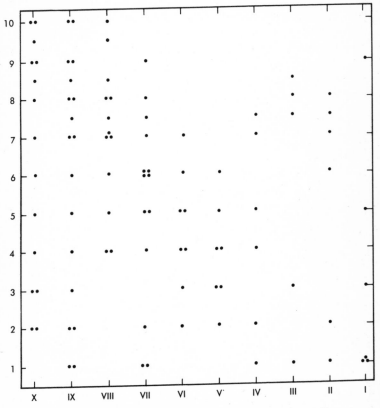

Fig. 2. Order in which the eggs were taken from the egg-lines by herring gulls; for further details see legend of Fig. 2.

What are these preferences if we consider the different predators separately? Figures 3 and 4 summarise the direct observations on herring gulls and crows. The herring gulls took outside the shifting median 52, inside of it 20 eggs; $\chi^2 = 14.9$, $p < 0.001$. The crows took 200 outside, 54 inside of the shifting median; $\chi^2 = 83.9$, $p < 0.001$. Both predators show the same preference

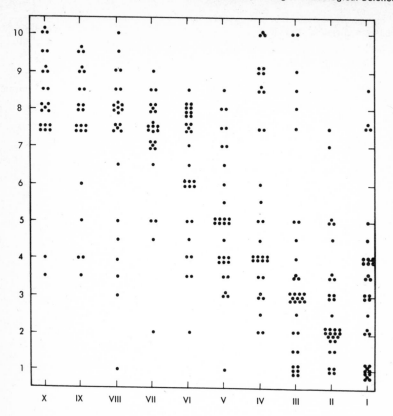

Fig. 3. Order in which the eggs were taken from the egg-lines
by crows; for further details see legend of Fig. 2.

for eggs outside the colony although this tendency is less in herring gulls
(statistically not significantly so, $\chi^2 = 0.9$, df $= 1$, p < 0.5). If this difference
would be consistent, it might be partly caused by an unavoidable place-
conditioning effect: in the beginning the herring gulls often visited the eggs
after the crows had been eating for some time, leaving only eggs inside the
colony for the herring gulls. It is not possible to confirm the impression I had
in the field that herring gulls are less selective than crows.

A few days before the gulls arrived in the colony, a number of control
experiments was done at two of the egg-lines to see whether the differential
predation is indeed due to the presence of the gulls and not, for instance,
to landscape features. In these tests crows were the only predators. From
Figure 5, it becomes clear that in those circumstances the crows fed equally
in the inside and the outside areas (outside the shifting median 29, inside of
it 26 eggs were taken $\chi^2 = 0.2$, $0.5 < p < 0.7$). With the arrival of the gulls
in the colony, the picture changed altogether and there is a highly significant

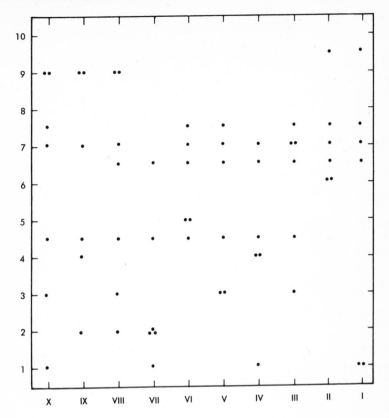

Fig. 4. Order in which the eggs were taken from the egg-lines
by crows, when no black-headed gulls were present in the colony.
For further details see legend of Fig. 2.

difference between the preference expressed in Figures 4 and 5 ($\chi^2 = 14.6$, df $= 1$, p < 0.001). Twice when the crows were present eating eggs in the colony in the absence of the gulls, the black-headed gulls suddenly arrived in large flocks from the roost, circled over the colony and alighted on their territories. The reaction of the crows was remarkable. They disappeared from the colony at once, were pursued over quite a distance, and did not come back until much later, when they proceeded to take "outside eggs" only.

(2) Predation success. If we define a predation attempt as any definite stall in the air above an egg, we see in Table 5 that in our particular situation, about equal numbers of attempts have been made over the whole egg line. However, if we split up these figures for crows and herring gulls, this result appears to be artificial—crows made many more attempts outside the colony whereas herring gulls attempted more often inside. In herring gulls this

TABLE 5

Predation attempts of crows and herring gulls on the egg-line

Egg position :		Outside colony			Inside colony	
		I-II	III-IV	V-VI	VII-VIII	IX-X
Total number of predation attempts	Crow plus herring gull	63	57	52	57	55
	Crow only	46	44	37	16	12
	Herring gull only	17	13	22	43	42
% successful attempts	Crow plus herring gull	81	67	72	53	53
	Crow only	91	66	73	50	42
	Herring gull only	53	69	59	51	53

is at least partly caused by the above mentioned fact that (a) they often arrived later than the crows on the egg line, and (b) subsequently became place conditioned.

We will call a predation-attempt successful if it ends with the predator opening up or taking away the egg; if the egg is immediately dropped again, we only call the attempt successful if this happened directly subsequent to an interaction with birds other than black-headed gulls. Table 5 shows that the success of crows decreased in the direction of the colony but that herring gulls were almost equally sucessful over the whole range.

The over-all success of the herring gulls was 56%, which was greater than but in the same order of magnitude as the success in the natural situation while preying on eggs and chicks (30%, see II. A. 3.).

The success of these predators was related to the number of attacks of the gulls, as is shown in Table 6; both crows and herring gulls had a significantly higher predation success when they were attacked less (for crows $\chi^2 = 53.1$, df = 3, p < 0.001; for herring gulls $\chi^2 = 17.5$, df = 2, p < 0.001).

Since we have often observed the avoidance movements of the predators

TABLE 6

Relation between attack frequency and predation success. Presented is the number of observations

Number of attacks per second	Crow success			Herring gull success		
	+	−	%+	+	−	%+
0	60	2	97	10	0	100
> 0, < 1/6	25	8	76	2	0	100
> 1/6, < 1	20	12	63	17	4	81
> 1	2	15	13	52	59	47

as a reaction to the black-headed gull's attacks, we may conclude from this table that it is actually the increasing number of attacks which caused the decrease in predation success.

In all categories, the herring gulls' success was greater than the crows', although this was significant only in the last category, which is more than 1 attack per second ($\chi^2 = 7.3$, df $= 1$, p < 0.1); there the effect of the gulls' behaviour was about three and a half times as great on crows as on herring gulls.

Crows were more successful outside the colony whereas herring gulls hardly showed this tendency at all. Since success was associated with the number of gulls' attacks, we expect crows to be attacked less outside the colony and herring gulls in about equal amounts inside and outside. This was not quite the case, but the differences in attack-frequency in the different egg positions were smaller for the herring gull (for the crow $\chi^2 = 36.5$, for the herring gull 19.1; for both df $= 4$, p < 0.001), as is shown in Table 7.

This table also shows that herring gulls were attacked more frequently at each particular egg than crows. This was true for all ten egg positions; with a binomial test N $= 10$, x $= 0$, p < 0.001. Since the attack frequency waned rapidly directly after the alighting of the predator, this effect might be caused by the herring gull being just a shorter time on the ground than the crow. This was indeed the case (Table 8; $\chi^2 = 79.3$, df $= 3$, p < 0.001), but it also appeared that the total number of attacks per visit on the herring gulls was greater, both inside and outside the colony (Table 9; $\chi^2 = 22.2$ and 24.5, df $= 3$, p < 0.001). Hence we conclude that in these predation attempts, the herring gull released more attacks in black-headed gulls than the crow.

TABLE 7

Frequency of attacks on crows and herring gulls during predation attempts on different eggs*

No. of attacks per second	Crow					Herring gull				
Egg no.	I-II	III-IV	V-VI	VII-VIII	IX-X	I-II	III-IV	V-VI	VII-VIII	IX-X
0	52	62	49	37	14	6	25	8	2	7
$> 0, \leq 1/6$	35	27	15	11	0	0	8	4	0	0
$> 1/6, \leq 1$	13	19	30	29	36	28	25	31	16	2
> 1	0	2	6	26	50	66	42	57	82	91
	100	100	100	100	100	100	100	100	100	100
Total no. of incidents	46	57	33	19	14	18	12	26	44	44

*The time measured is the period between alighting and either the first peck into the egg, or the flying off, if this happens before the egg is pecked at. In the body of the table, percentages are given of the number incidents at the particular egg position.

For statistical analysis of the figures for the crow, the absolute figures of the first and last two groups of attack frequencies had to be taken together, and of the herring gull data, the first three groups.

TABLE 8

Time spent on the ground during the predation attempts*

	Crow	Herring gull
0 seconds	12	48
< 1 second	1	7
1–10 seconds	24	16
11–50 seconds	55	10
> 50 seconds	55	12

*The time measured is the period between alighting and either the first peck into the egg, or the flying off, if this happens before the egg is pecked at. The total number of observations is presented.

TABLE 9

Total number of attacks per predation attempt*

Total no. of attacks	Outside colony		Inside colony	
	Crow	Herring gull	Crow	Herring gull
0	51	4	12	6
1– 5	41	21	9	8
6–10	18	9	11	8
11–20	7	1	11	11
> 20	5	9	3	5
			13	70

*The data have been split for inside and outside the colony to account for the different numbers of predation attempts in the two sections by the two predators (legends see Table 8).

(3) Interaction between aerial predators. Apart from interactions between predators and black-headed gulls, it was often noticed that aggression between the predators themselves interfered with the taking of eggs and of course this feature is of significance for the black-headed gull. In an attempt to take an egg, a crow or herring gull might suddenly fly (or run) off, being pursued by another predator, or in a few cases fly away in pursuit of another one himself.

The interfering bird might be a con-specific (in crows 50 out of 61, in herring gulls 6 out of 19 interferences). Interferences occurred frequently when more than two predators were present and they were particularly common between pairs of crows. Table 10 shows the protective value for the eggs of the presence of more than two crows; herring gulls were less influenced by the presence of other egg eaters than were crows.

Of the 59 cases of Table 10, in which predation attempts by crows were interfered with, 22 (37%) resulted in the egg not being touched by the predator at all.

For one of the egg-lines near which these interferences were particularly frequent, the time lapse between the taking of two eggs by one or two crows

TABLE 10

Predators interfering with each other*

	Predation attempts with two or less predators present in the experiment area		Predation attempts with more than two predators present	
	Attempts with interference	Attempts without interference	Attempts with interference	Attempts without interference
Predator:				
Crow	8	60	51	16
Herring gull	0	56	1	22

*All figures refer to incidents in which no black-headed gulls interfered.

has been compared with situations in which more crows were present. The average time-lapses were 10 min. 39 sec. (26 observations), and 13 min. 43 sec. (32 observations) respectively, which shows that the presence of more crows delays the taking of eggs. In a median test, the two sets of observations were exactly equal on comparison (median at 5 min. 40 sec.)—thus the increase in numbers of predators did not increase the speed at which the eggs disappeared.

6.2.4. Conclusions. Both herring gulls and crows show obvious avoidance reactions to the attacks of the black-headed gulls; especially when on the ground the reactions of the crow seem much more timid. The breeding areas are mostly avoided by the crows, but not by the herring gulls.

To study these effects more closely, experiments were carried out with hens' eggs outside and inside the colony. The predators learnt quickly where to find these eggs and returned frequently to these places.

Eggs outside the gull-colony were preferred to eggs inside it, both by crows and herrings gulls. At least for crows it was shown that this was due to the presence of the black-headed gulls, and not for instance to landscape features.

Crows made more predation-attempts outside the colony than on eggs inside, but herring gulls attempted more frequently inside. This difference was probably artificial, because herring gulls often came after the crows had been.

Predation-success appeared negatively correlated with the attack-frequency of the black-headed gulls, and this was partly the explanation for the fact that crows were much less successful in the colony, and herring gulls about equally successful over the whole egg-line. The difference in the black-headed gulls' attack-frequency to predators inside the colony and outside was smaller for herring gulls than for crows; in all places, herring gulls were attacked more.

Intraspecific hostility was responsible for many unsuccessful predation-attempts, especially of the crows.

7. Discussion

When extrapolating from the results of the hens' egg tests we have to bear in mind the differences between this arrangement and the natural situation. The hens' eggs were left out exposed, whereas black-headed gull clutches are hardly ever unattended; it is likely that this additional protection will tend to diminish the predation-differences on eggs inside and outside the colony. Therefore, it will not be possible to use the figures so obtained for a quantitative evaluation of the predation pressure and the effects of the gulls' defenses. However, it seems reasonable to assume that the trends established in the artificial situation will also occur in nature, and several times I have indicated circumstantial evidence for this. The qualitative arguments may be usefully applied in the discussion on the functional significance of some of the behavioural and ecological features of the black-headed gull.

In these tests, it is clearly shown that the effect of the gulls' attacks as regards counteracting predation on the brood is beneficial. Crows are much more strongly affected than herring gulls, a conclusion which is supported by observations in the entirely natural situation: their reaction to the gulls' attacks is much more timid, and also they avoid the breeding-area more. Natural crow-predation is much less than that of herring-gulls, although they are capable of much greater destruction if no black-headed gulls are present. It is clear that black-headed gulls are much better able to cope with crow-predation than with that of the herring gull.

The geographical ranges of the carrion crow and the hooded crow together overlay entirely that of the black-headed gull, and they often occur in the same habitat. The large gulls however occur in a much smaller area of the black-headed gulls' range, and generally in a different habitat. The fact that crows are dealt with so much more efficiently may well find its evolutionary origin in this difference in contact between the species involved. At the moment, however, there are many indications that the large gulls are getting increasingly important as predators of the black-headed gulls, through (a) their increase in numbers, (b) expansion of the geographical range of the black-headed gull and (c) change in habitat of the black-headed gull.

Although crow predation is so much better averted than that of herring gulls, yet the adaptations to cope with herring gulls as well as crows are remarkable. The differences in reactions to crows and herring gulls just flying over the colony or the roost show a reverse picture from the differences in reactions to those stalling or sitting on the ground. Crows are attacked almost always when flying over the colony (though not when they fly over the roost), whereas this is only rarely the case with herring gulls. Whether or not the difference in reactions to flying crows and herring gulls is caused by a waning effect is still undecided; however, the distinction is almost certainly very profitable for the black-headed gull. As in other localities (Bergman, 1939; Niethammer, 1942) the great majority of large gulls are quite harmless to the black-headed gulls; only individual specialists prey on the colony. A crow, on the contrary, is probably always a potential predator. It will be argued below . . . that there is a considerable penalty on leaving the nest unguarded; it is only advantageous to attack if the bird overhead is a potential predator. Whether a large gull is a predator or not becomes clear only when it stalls. On the other hand, the fact that they are so rarely attacked when flying over the breeding area may well enable the few specialist gulls to hunt more effectively than they otherwise could have done.

On the ground, a herring gull is attacked more frequently than a crow. It has not been established whether this is in fact due to a larger range of attack around the nest, and therefore to more gulls taking part in the defense, or to greater attack-frequencies of individual gulls. It will be shown below . . . that although one predator may release more attacks in a certain place in the colony than another predator, this may be due to more gulls taking part, whereas individual gulls actually attack this first predator less. Whatever the mechanism is of this distinction between a sitting herring gull and a crow, it seems advantageous to the gull to attack most often the predator which is least sensitive to these attacks.

In flight and when alighting a crow releases some fleeing in the black-headed gulls, especially when it suddenly appears; this hardly ever occurs in reactions to herring gulls. The data presented on predation by crows and herring gulls do not yet provide a clue as to the function of this distinction. Fleeing would seem of direct advantage for the fleeing individual only, not for the brood. Crows are unlikely to prey on adult gulls, although they may occasionally take a sick one (Whitherby et al., 1938), and if anything the large gulls are just as likely to do this (Tinbergen, 1953 and Markgren, 1960). Fleeing of the black-headed gull might be a response which is released by a complex of characteristics of some predators preying on adult gulls some of which are "accidentally" provided by some birds harmless to the adults.

(The above is but a portion of the entire paper by Dr. Kruuk. For the remaining chapters and bibliography, consult *Behaviour* (Supplement) XI: 7–31, 1964.)

4 / The Evolution of Sociality

Descriptions of social behavior abound, and hardly less common are speculations on the origins of sociality. The papers included here are intended to illustrate the possibility of placing such speculations on an empirical footing. A further example is to be found in D. Morris's "Feather Postures of Birds and the Problem of the Origin of Social Signs" (*Behaviour* **9**: 75–113, 1956).

The Evolution of Altruistic Behavior

W. D. Hamilton

It is generally accepted that the behavior characteristic of a species is just as much the product of evolution as the morphology. Yet the kinds of behavior which can be adequately explained by the classical mathematical theory of natural selection are limited. In particular this theory cannot account for any case where an animal behaves in such a way as to promote the advantages of other members of the species not its direct descendants, at the expense of its own. The explanation usually given for such cases, and for all others where selfish behavior seems moderated by concern for the interests of a group, is that they are evolved by natural selection favoring the most stable and co-operative groups. But in view of the inevitable slowness of any evolution based on group selection, compared to the simultaneous trends that can occur by selection of the classical kind based on individual advantage, this explanation must be treated with reserve so long as it remains unsupported by mathematical models. Fisher in the second edition of *The Genetical Theory of Natural Selection* (1958) rejects almost all explanations based on "the benefit of the species" (e.g., p. 49). Sewall Wright (1948) in a summary of population genetics shows explicitly that a general advantage conferred on a group cannot alter the course of intra-group selection. This point is very adverse to the following model of Haldane (1932, p. 208) which seemed to offer a possibility for the evolution of altruism. Haldane supposed an increment to group fitness (and therefore to group rate of increase) proportional to its content of altruistic members and showed that there could be an initial numerical increase of a gene for altruism provided the starting gene frequency was high enough and the individual disadvantage low enough compared to the group advantage conferred. He concluded that genetical altruism could show some advance in populations split into 'tribes' small enough for a single mutant to approximate the critical frequency. He did not, however, sufficiently emphasize that ultimately the gene number must begin to do what the gene frequency tends to do, ex hypothesi, from the very first; namely, to decrease to zero. The only escape from this conclusion (as Haldane hints) would be some kind of periodic reassortment of the tribes such that by chance or otherwise the altruists became re-concentrated in some of them.

There is, however, an extension of the classical theory, generalizing that which serves to cover parental care and still having the generation as the time-unit of progress, which does allow to a limited degree the evolution of kinds of altruism which are not connected with parental care.

As a simple but admittedly crude model we may imagine a pair of genes

Reprinted by permission of the author and the publisher from The American Naturalist **97**: 354–356, 1963.

g and G such that G tends to cause some kind of altruistic behavior while g is null. Despite the principle of 'survival of the fittest' the ultimate criterion which determines whether G will spread is not whether the behavior is to the benefit of the behaver but whether it is to the benefit of the gene G; and this will be the case if the average net result of the behavior is to add to the gene-pool a handful of genes containing G in higher concentration than in the gene-pool itself. With altruism this will happen only if the affected individual is a relative of the altruist, therefore having an increased chance of carrying the gene, and if the advantage conferred is large enough, compared to the personal disadvantage, to offset the regression, or 'dilution,' of the altruist's genotype in the relative in question. The appropriate regression coefficient must be very near to Sewall Wright's Coefficient of Relationship r provided selection is slow. If the gain to a relative of degree r is k-times the loss to the altruist, the criterion for positive selection of the causative gene is

$$k > (1/r).$$

Thus a gene causing altruistic behavior towards brothers and sisters will be selected only if the behavior and the circumstances are generally such that the gain is more than twice the loss; for half-brothers it must be more than four times the loss; and so on. To put the matter more vividly, an animal acting on this principle would sacrifice its life if it could thereby save more than two brothers, but not for less. Some similar illustrations were given by Haldane (1955).

It follows that altruistic behavior which benefits neighbors irrespective of relationship (such as the warning cries of birds) will only arise when (a) the risk or disadvantage involved is very slight, and (b) the average neighbor is not too distantly related.

An altruistic action which adds to the genotype-reproduction (inclusive of the reproduction of identical genes procured in the relative) by one per cent is not so strongly selected as a one per cent advantage in personal reproduction would be; for it involves also an addition of unrelated genes which are in the ratio of the existing gene-pool—an addition which must be larger the more distant the relationship.

A multifactorial model of inheritance, which is doubtless more realistic, does not invalidate the above criterion, and provided fitness is reckoned in terms of 'inclusive' genotype-reproduction, and the dilution due to unrelated genes is allowed for, the classical treatment of dominance and epistasis can be followed closely.

Fisher in 1930 (1958, p. 177 et seq.) offered an explanation of the evolution of aposematic coloring based on the advantage to siblings of the self-sacrifice, by its conspicuousness, of a distasteful larva, and his discussion contains what is probably the earliest precise statement concerning a particular case of the principle presented above: "The selective potency of the avoidance of brothers will of course be only half as great as if the individual itself were protected; against this is to be set the fact that it applies to the whole of a possibly numerous brood." It would appear that he did not credit the possibility that selection could operate through the advantage conferred on more distant relatives, even though these must in fact tend to be still more numerous in rough inverse proportion to the coefficient of relationship.

This discussion by Fisher is one of the few exceptions to his general insistence on individual advantage as the basis of natural selection; the other notable exception from the present point of view is his discussion of putative forces of selection in primitive human societies (p. 261 et seq.).

Literature Cited

Fisher, R. A., 1958, *The Genetical Theory of Natural Selection*. 2nd ed. Dover Publ. Inc., New York. 291 p.

Haldane, J. B. S., 1932, *The Causes of Evolution*. Longmans Green & Co., London. 235 p.

————, 1955, Population genetics. *New Biology* **18**: 34–51.

Wright, S., 1948, Genetics of populations. *Encyclopaedia Britannica* (1961 printing) **10**: 111D–112.

Communication by Insects: Physiology of Dancing

V. G. Dethier

The dances which foraging honey bees perform on their return to the hive and which serve to inform their nest mates of the presence of food, its direction, quality, and distance, constitute a pattern of behavior of considerably greater complexity than was once thought possible in insects. Both aspects of this exercise in behavior, namely, the presentation of information and the effective receipt of information, place equally severe demands upon the integrative capacity of the nervous system. A plausible rationalization of the ability to present information, in terms of the known capabilities of the insect nervous system, and a possible explanation of the origin of this ability are suggested by a series of observations of the responses of flies (*Phormia regina*) following stimulation by sugar (*1*).

Behavior of Flies

The pattern of locomotion which a crawling fly displays on a horizontal surface under uniform lighting varies according to the exteroceptive stimuli encountered. For purposes of the present discussion, three conditions may be recognized: (i) the absence of specific stimuli; (ii) the continuous presence of stimuli; (iii) the withdrawal of stimuli. When it is placed in the first situation, a fly tends to travel in a series of short (approximately 25 centimeters) straight lines connected in a random fashion as far as general direction is concerned. The second situation is exemplified by the actions of a fly which, in the course of its running, suddenly encounters with its tarsi a drop of sugar. The fly immediately halts and turns toward the point source of stimulation so that the mouth parts are brought over the spot. The proboscis is extended, and feeding commences. The fly remains in this position as long as the mouth parts are adequately stimulated. Thus, the characteristic locomotory response to continuous uniform stimulation is complete cessation of movement.

When walking on a paper evenly painted with a sugar solution, the fly adopts an irregular circuitous path (Fig. 1). This situation does not actually constitute continuous stimulation because, although the tarsal receptors are indeed constantly stimulated, the mouth parts are not. The tracks depicted in Fig. 1 represent mouth prints indicating where the fly sucked until stimulation ceased, whereupon locomotion was resumed. Therefore this situation in fact represents typical behavior exhibited upon withdrawal of stimulation. In short, if the source of dominant stimulation is removed before the fly has fed to repletion or is removed as a result of the fly's having consumed it

Reprinted by permission of the author and publisher from Science **125**: 331–336, 1957.

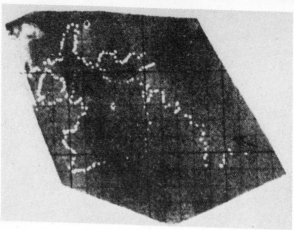

Fig. 1. Pattern of locomotion of a fly on a surface painted with a sucrose solution containing methylene blue. Each white spot represents a point where the labellum was appressed to the surface and the solution was sucked up completely.

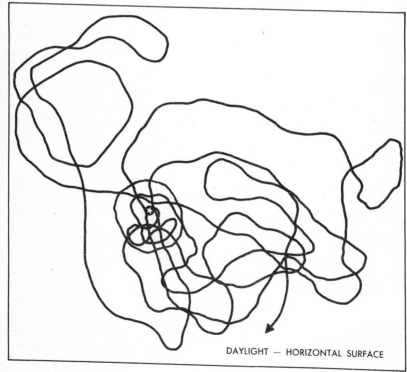

DAYLIGHT — HORIZONTAL SURFACE

Fig. 2. Pattern of locomotion performed in daylight on a horizontal surface by a fly which has been stimulated briefly with sucrose.

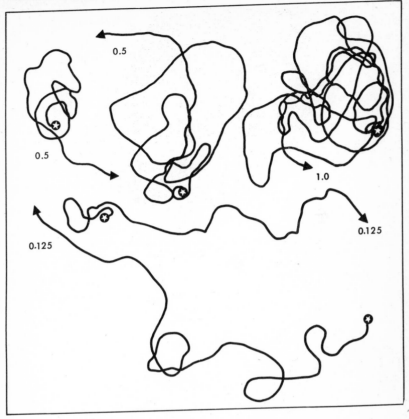

Fig. 3. Variations produced in the pattern of poststimulatory locomotion when the concentration of the stimulus is changed.

completely, the fly begins what, to all intents and purposes, appears as a purposeful searching action.

This action is most clearly seen in the case in which a fly is momentarily presented with a single drop of sugar. The response takes the form of repeated clockwise and counterclockwise turnings in the area of the former drop (Fig. 2). That the action is completely stereotyped, rather than purposeful, is demonstrated by the fact that a fly which is held in the hand and stimulated with sugar, immediately upon being released on a horizontal surface, begins "searching" actions on the spot with no relation to the spatial location of the former stimulus. The action is purely automatic. Two features of this behavior are worthy of particular notice: (i) it takes place *after* the stimulus is removed and continues for some period of time; and (ii) it strikingly resembles a dance.

The intensity and duration of the response is modified by three variables: the concentration of the stimulus; the threshold of the central nervous system of the fly; and the time lapse between the withdrawal of stimulation and the onset of response.

For example, after stimulation with 0.1-molar glucose, there are few turnings, of short duration, before the fly resumes its former random-like mode of running (Fig. 3). After stimulation with 0.5-molar glucose, the fly exhibits a more convoluted action of longer duration. After stimulation with 1.0-molar

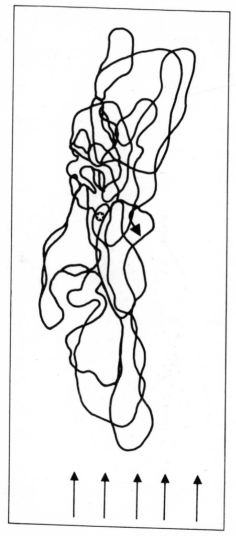

Fig. 4. Pattern of locomotion performed by a fly which is allowed to crawl on a horizontal surface in a beam of light after having been stimulated briefly with sucrose.

glucose, there is still greater convolution and longer persistence of action. These actions differ, not in the acuteness—that is, degrees—of angles of turning, but in the number of turns per unit time and the total duration of action. The concentration with which the fly had been stimulated can clearly be deduced from the pattern of subsequent action.

For any given concentration of stimulus, the intensity and duration of response is related to the threshold of the central nervous system, and any change in the physiological state of the fly which alters this threshold is reflected as a change of response. The nutritional state of the fly thus affects taste acceptance threshold (*2, 3*). A starved fly performs more active gyrations in response to 0.1-molar glucose than a fly which has recently been fed. Flying

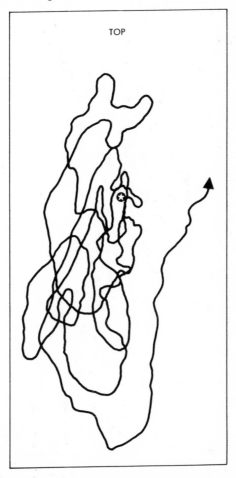

TOP

Fig. 5. Pattern of locomotion performed by a fly on a vertical surface in darkness after brief stimulation with sucrose.

also affects threshold. A fly which has flown for an hour, for example, responds more actively than one which has flown for only 10 minutes.

The importance of the third variable, time, with respect to the intensity of response is related to the decay in intensity. In other words, the rate of turning gradually diminishes as the action proceeds until there is complete cessation and the fly resumes its random movements. Accordingly, any isolated segment of the action characteristically represents the elapsed time between the end of stimulation and the beginning of the particular segment. Since the rate of turning diminishes with time, a diffuse segment of the pattern represents a long time lapse, and a tightly convoluted segment represents a short time lapse. Furthermore, the longer a fly is prevented from responding after stimulation (by being held in the hand, for example), the less intense is the response.

If, at any time during the response, the fly is subjected to the continuing influence of some directional stimulus, such as light, the response acquires a directional component. The pattern of action becomes deformed by being elongated in a plane parallel to the beam of light (Fig. 4). In the dark the pattern is formless. If the fly is permitted to perform its gyrations on a vertical surface in darkness, in which case the continuing directional stimulus is gravity, the action acquires a directional component. The path is elongated parallel to the vertical axis. Light shining on the vertical surface destroys the directional component of the pattern (Fig. 5).

Resemblance to Bee Dances

At this point it is clear that there are some striking parallelisms between the gyrations of the fly and the communicative dances of honey bees. With the fly, the intensity of reaction—that is, the number of turns per unit time—and the duration of the dance are related to the concentration of the initiating stimulus; with the bee, the vigor of the waggle dance and its duration are related to the concentrations of the nectar collected. With the fly, the rate of turning diminishes with time after stimulation so that, with a constant stimulus, any given elapsed time is reflected as circling of given intensity; with the bee, the number of turns per unit time is related to the distance of the food from the hive, that is, flying time (but see subsequent paragraphs)—the greater the distance, the fewer the turns and the more diffuse the dance. With the fly, a continuing stimulus in the form of light or gravity imparts some direction to an otherwise disoriented action; with the bee, the orientation of the dance is related to the direction of light or polarized light when carried out on a horizontal plane and with gravity when conducted on a vertical plane in darkness. If the bee performs its dance on a horizontal comb in darkness, the dance is disoriented; that is, the successive runs point in different directions. The dance also becomes disoriented if light shines on the bee while it is dancing on a vertical comb.

Two major points of dissimilarity in the behavior of the two insects are immediately apparent: the gyrations of the fly possess intensity and direction but lack the clean geometric pattern so characteristic of the bee's waggle dance; the gyrations of the fly lack the precise angular orientation which is one of the main features of the bee's waggle dance. With regard to the first point, there is one important respect in which the circumstances of dancing bees generally differ from those of the circling flies—namely, the crowded conditions under which the bee usually dances. To simulate crowded conditions, a stimulated fly was forced in one experiment to perform in the midst of a crowd of other flies. Under these conditions the action lost some of its diffuse character and acquired a crude geometry of pattern. Furthermore, an insect with short antennae which do not reach the ground makes up for its inability to palpate by crawling in wide, irregular paths. An insect such as the wasp *Polistes*, which palpates the ground with its antennae, can be made to perform a much neater dance than the fly.

With regard to the second point, it must be admitted that the fly cannot be induced to circle at any particular angle with respect to either light or gravity. The difference between the two insects may possibly be accounted for in terms of the highly developed light-compass reaction of the bee and its comparative unimportance in the life of the fly. In its normal relations with the environment, the honey bee relies heavily on a light-compass reaction for orientation at a distance, whereas the fly, although capable of some degree of light-compass response, is largely restricted to positive and negative phototaxis. In each insect, the behavior with respect to light has its counterpart in the effect of light on the orientation of the dance. In this connection it is pertinent to recall that Vowles (4) had postulated one taxis mechanism common to distance orientation to the sun, plane of polarization of light, and gravity and another taxis mechanism operating for orientation to near objects. Vowles regarded the first as the primary mechanism, and Thorpe (5) indicated that the primary mechanism is innate and the other mechanism learned. The observations of the effect of light and gravity in the gyrations of the fly support these conclusions.

The comparison between bee and fly behavior may be carried one step further. When the foraging bee returns to the hive, it regurgitates nectar which is accepted by other bees. The forager then begins dancing, and as it dances its way among the crowd, other bees become excited to the point of following the dancer. When a fly which has recently been fed is placed in a crowd of unfed flies, it cleans its appendages and almost invariably regurgitates some of its crop load. Surrounding flies become greatly excited, follow the fed fly around, attempt to lick sugar from its mouth parts, and even begin gyrations of their own which are indistinguishable from those performed by the first fly. The superficial resemblance of this performance to that of bees dancing in the hive is striking.

Furthermore, if the first fly is fed with a sugar solution containing methylene blue, it is possible, a few minutes later, to detect the dye in the guts of many of the other flies. Clearly, both the fed fly and the foraging honey bee normally regurgitate; the bee disgorges nearly completely the contents of her crop; the fly only a fraction. The comparison suggests that the highly developed trophallaxis, or food-sharing, which goes so far in unifying the bee colony evolved from rather basic and simple individual behavior of the type exhibited by the fly.

It is not possible in the present context to carry the comparison of the two species further. The fly, being solitary rather than social, apparently does not act upon the information contained in the circling performance, beyond being excited enough to follow the circling individual until it flies away. The culminating act of the bee's dance—that is, the departure of stimulated members of the audience for the field—does not follow on the part of the flies. The stimulated flies do not go anywhere, nor would this final step logically be expected.

The circling response of the fly is a facet of adaptive behavior which serves as an effective pattern for food-searching. Since there are contained in it many of the basic components which characterize the waggle dance of honey bees, the possibility exists that the dance of the honey bee might have been derived from a primitive and basic behavior pattern of this sort. The many resemblances suggest this interpretation. This idea is also favored by the fact that there are dance patterns of various degrees of complexity from one species of bee to the next, and within a given species. For example, the Western honey bee, *Apis mellifera*, performs a wide variety of dances, ranging from formless gyrations to the highly stylized waggle dance (*6*, *7*), and bees fed *inside* the hive run about excitedly but fail to perform an organized dance. Other species of bees, as, for example, *Apis florea*, perform dances of lesser degrees of complexity (*8*).

Relation of Dance to Stimulus and Response

The striking manner in which a fly's behavior can be described in terms of stimulus and response suggests the possibility of interpreting the waggle dance of the honey bee in similar terms. Although any attempt at complete interpretation at this time would suffer from gross oversimplification, a working hypothesis can be proposed which may direct further investigation into profitable channels. The hypothesis may be stated in the following terms: the waggle dance is a delayed response to effective taste stimulation and is regulated by a central nervous system threshold. It must be pointed out at the start that, while the hypothesis in its present form can explain many of the characteristics of honey bee dancing, it cannot explain them all.

As von Frisch (*9*) proved, the waggle dance is coded to impart the following information: distance of food source from the hive, direction of food source from hive, and quantity and quality of food. The nature of the food is indicated by the odor of the flower of origin, this odor adhering to the bodies of foragers and being contained in the nectar. This fact need not concern us here. Direction is indicated by the orientation of the dance axis with respect to light or gravity and, likewise, falls outside the scope of the present discussion.

The remaining data are coded principally as intensity of dance—that is, number of turns per unit time. They are also coded as duration of dancing. The code has certain ambiguities in that quantity, concentration, and distance may be signified by the same means, vigor and duration of dancing (*9*, pp. 113, 118). On the basis of this code *alone*, bees should be unable to distinguish between concentrated sugar at a distance and dilute sugar near at hand. That such is actually the case has recently been demonstrated by Boch (*10*). This state of affairs would truly represent an unfit adaptation for survival were it not for the fact that there is a safety factor in the form of a duplicate code. Distance of supply is also indicated by the site of dancing within the hive (*10*). For short distances, the dance is performed near the exit hole; for long distances, at a more remote position in the hive. In addition, the number of bees dancing also indicates distance, quality, and quantity. There may be other factors as yet unknown. The ambiguity strongly suggests that the critical factor or stimulus regulating the dance is identical for the three parameters—distance, quality, and quantity.

A clue to the nature of the controlling stimulus is given by an early observation of von Frisch—namely, that adulteration of the food in the field has a pronounced effect on the character of the dance. This finding points to taste as a controlling stimulus. The foraging honey bee on a round trip from hive to food is stimulated at least three times. Before departure the bee imbibes honey, in the course of which its oral organs of taste are stimulated; while collecting nectar, the bee is intermittently stimulated as it visits successively different blossoms; upon return to the hive, the bee disgorges its load and is stimulated for a third time.

There is one other possibility which cannot be overlooked. The presence of sugar in the fly's fore-gut, or mid-gut, or both has a pronounced effect on the taste threshold, most likely through mediation of receptors in the gut, since the crop seems to play no role (*3*). It is conceivable that a similar situation prevails in the honey bee, in which case stimulation could be effected without the oral organs of taste being stimulated.

If the dance is a delayed response to a taste stimulus, at which of the four moments of stimulation is control over the dance established? It might be argued that the first (fueling) and second (food-gathering) stimuli are too far removed in time to be effective. However, experiments with the fly overcome this objection. For both the bee and the fly the duration of the dance is the same, from a few seconds to 1 minute. For the bee, however, the time elapsed since stimulation at the site of food collection, for example (if this is indeed the moment of stimulation which is critical), is occupied by flying. In other words, another behavior pattern, flying, is interposed between stimulation and dancing. Since bees fly about 14 miles per hour and the maximum extent of foraging is usually 3 miles, the maximum duration of interpolated flight is from 15 to 20 minutes.

Can flying temporarily inhibit dancing? In the case of the fly, it has been demonstrated that a fly which is stimulated with glucose and forced to fly immediately thereafter will, upon the moment of landing, begin the circling which has been delayed by flight. Delays as long as 5 minutes have been recorded. If no flying is interpolated, the maximum delay before extinction of the response is of the order of 1 minute. Thus the possibility of the critical stimulation occurring at the time of fueling or collecting is theoretically tenable.

It is unlikely on other grounds that stimulation at fueling is a factor. Although the quantity of honey taken on as fuel is said to vary according to the distance to be flown (11), the concentration is constant, as compared with the concentration of nectar picked up in the field. Since there is a relation between the tempo of the dance and concentration, the importance of fueling tends to be ruled out. Furthermore, von Frisch's observation that adulteration in the field affects the dance tends to eliminate fueling from consideration.

Evidence that regurgitation may be concerned in releasing the dance is implied by the fact that a forager in the hive disgorges a bit, dances for a few seconds, stops, moves away, disgorges again, then again dances. So it is clear that dancing may occur after several regurgitations. On the other hand, the report that bees sometimes dance on the landing board before regurgitating indicates that regurgitation is not invariably essential for dancing. In any event, there are ample opportunities for a taste stimulus to operate, and the time of stimulation, whether in the field while collecting, in flight through the mediation of internal receptors, or in the hive while disgorging a load, is not crucial to the hypothesis, since any of these eventualities can be accepted.

What is critical is the idea that the *intensity* of the stimulus is limiting. By intensity is meant, not the absolute concentration, but the concentration in relation to threshold. As the behavioral or central nervous system threshold changes, so does the dance of the fly change. Accordingly, for any given concentration of stimulus, if the taste threshold is high, the dance will be slow; if the threshold is low, the dance will be fast. Therefore, any factors which affect threshold may be expected to affect the dance. Two such factors are hunger and flight. Again in the case of the fly, experiments in our laboratory have shown that the taste threshold drops in a regular fashion as flying time increases. The longer the flight, the lower the threshold.

The bee does not differ qualitatively in these respects. Direct measurements of the taste threshold of individual bees have revealed that the tarsal, antennal, and oral thresholds decrease as the bee is starved (3). In our experiments the threshold of the bee had fallen to its lowest level about 60 hours after feeding to repletion with 2-molar sucrose. At this time the crop was nearly empty. The same striking drop in threshold could be brought about by flying the bee continuously for about $1\frac{1}{2}$ hours. In each case renewed feeding was followed by a rise in threshold in excess of 30-fold.

Energy Expended in Flight

There are compelling reasons for believing that the critical variable regulating the intensity of the honey bee dance is energy expenditure (*12*). The work with flies demonstrates convincingly that there is a relation between energy expenditure and threshold. This is indicated by the fact that threshold decreases less rapidly as a fly is flown at low temperatures than when it is flown at high ones. Since wing-beat frequency and energy expenditure are greater at higher temperatures, the drop in threshold is clearly related to this factor rather than duration alone. But just what is meant by energy expenditure and just what relation does exist between this factor and threshold are still unclear. Several possibilities have been eliminated experimentally in the fly's case. Blood sugar level, glycogen level, and crop distention are not concerned (*3*). Present evidence suggests more strongly that some receptor mechanism within the gut is affected by the dynamic relation between the rate of utilization of carbohydrate and the quantity supplied. Similar experiments with the bee give no indication that this insect behaves any differently.

If, as seems to be the case, energy expenditure is the critical determinant for the dance, in which segment of the round-trip flight is the code laid down? Almost all workers agree that the distance which is coded is that of the outgoing flight. Khalifman (*13*) holds the opposite view that the return flight is critical. There is, however, an abundance of evidence to support the first view, and the adaptive value of the dance really requires that the characteristics of the outgoing flight be read from the dance. For example, von Frisch found that bees flying out against a headwind, and home with an assisting tailwind, indicate in their dances the outgoing distance. Heran (*12*) has shown that bees flying uphill on the outgoing flight and downhill on the return flight indicate the conditions of the outgoing flight.

The variables experienced in flight which affect the characteristics of the dance are duration, wind velocity and direction, grade of flight with respect to the horizontal, air temperature, and velocity of flight (*12*). These are reflected in the dance as follows: short distance, short duration, tailwind on outgoing flight, downhill outgoing flight, low temperature, and low velocity all cause the dance to be more intense (faster) and longer; long distance, long duration, headwind going out, uphill going out, high temperature, and high velocity all cause the dance to be less intense (slower). Heran (*12*) has concluded that the indicated distance is coded through energy expended on the outgoing flight.

All attempts to understand the mechanisms of coding have been confounded by the fact that the dance correctly indicates the conditions of the outgoing flight. While Heran (*12*) clearly states that the hypothesis that the indicated distance is coded through expenditure of energy on home flights cannot be maintained, and further points out that the exact meaning and measurement of energy expenditure by the bee is uncritical, the role of the home flight should not yet be completely ruled out of the picture.

The hypothesis of control by taste threshold offers an explanation which merits further exploration. It is possible that the dance is regulated *inversely* by events experienced on the homeward flight. For example, if the bee flies out against a headwind, it will return with a favoring tailwind. The energy expended on the return trip will be comparatively small, the taste threshold will remain high, the nectar collected will not constitute a very intense stimulus. Since the intensity of stimulation is a factor which can regulate dancing, the dance will be slow. Slowness indicates a long flight out, which in this instance is indeed the case. Conversely, if the bee flies out with a favoring tailwind, it must return against a headwind; the expenditure of energy will be greater; the threshold will be correspondingly low; the dance will be fast, which indicates a short flight out and is indeed the case. For headwind and tailwind one may substitute uphill and downhill, high flight velocity and low flight velocity, and the relation of these factors to dancing is similarly explained, since all affect threshold in identical fashion.

As attractive as this hypothesis may be, however, it fails to explain situations in which the outgoing and incoming flights are of equal duration and effort. It is clearly an oversimplification, yet it does contain some features that fit the known facts, and further experimentation on energy threshold relationships might be profitable.

Hypothesis Based on Proprioception

The only other major detailed hypothesis which has been proposed is that of Ribbands (*14*). It envisions the duration and intensity of stimulation of antennal proprioceptors by wind as regulating the dance rhythm. Heran (*12*), in studying the effect of wind velocity on dance characteristics, investigated this idea. Employing fixed bees, he found that the amplitude of wing beat decreased with increased wind velocity unless the antennae were amputated or fastened, in which case the change was smaller. From experiments of this sort he drew the conclusion that wind velocity was perceived by the antennae, that duration and intensity of wind faced provided a measurement of the distance flown, and that the dance shows a distance based on the duration and intensity of the air stream perceived on the outgoing flight.

But while it is true that proprioceptive information of the sort described is perceived through the antennae and that interference with antennal receptors prohibits compensatory regulations of flight, it does not follow that there is a causal relationship between antennal proprioception and dancing. In other words, differences in velocity and the attending differences in flight characteristics mediated through antennal receptors assuredly affect the energy expenditure of the bee and presumably its threshold. Were it possible to remove the antennae without affecting flight, it is doubtful that the absence of proprioceptive input alone would alter the characteristics of the dance. The great difficulty in all conceptions which visualize stimuli experienced on the outgoing flight as having a direct influence on dancing is that the same stimuli experienced on the return flight must be ignored or subordinated.

Importance of the
Physiology of the Individual

No pretense can be made of explaining fully the physiology of the dances of honey bees in terms of the performance of flies. Yet the fact that a type of fly behavior resembling bee dancing can be described in terms of stimulus and response offers a basis for removing the phenomenon of bee dancing from the realm of mysticism and for explaining it in physiological terms. There seems to be adequate reason for believing that the communicative dance of bees represents a highly evolved form of primitive search pattern which is innate and stereotyped. There are many dances of bees, such as some of the transitional dances and dances signifying food close at hand [for example, the "pull dances" described by Hein (6) and the "sickle dances" described by Lindauer (15)], which are less stylized and uniform than the more widely publicized figure-of-eight waggle dances. Thus there appear to be all gradations between excited gyrations and organized dances in the Western honey bee, and from one species of bee to the next. It is not unreasonable to expect that these locomotory responses would be causally related to stimulation by food substances. Since taste threshold is clearly related to energy expended, taste stimulation offers a unique mechanism for a sensory measurement of expenditure.

Because the honey bee is a member of a complexly organized society there is frequently a tendency to regard it as a unit whose actions are subordinated to that needs of the society. Inherent in this view is the danger of considering the insect society as a superorganism (and indeed this view has at times been expressed in the classical literature) and, more dangerous still, of overlooking the physiology of the individuals which constitute the society. The point is well illustrated by the mode of thinking which treats the crop or honey sac of the honey bee as community property which the bee dutifully fills in the field and as dutifully empties in the hive. The fact of the matter is that the crop of the honey bee is as much its own as that of the blowfly is its own. In both insects it is a place of storage, since both insects gorge themselves to repletion upon finding food. Both species use the contents of the crop freely for their own requirements. As postingestion time lengthens, the contents of the crop are directed to the mid-gut for the individual's own metabolism, and as the insects fly the contents are used as fuel. In both species there is a tendency to regurgitate when the crop is full.

In many respects, if the physiology and behavior of the individual are considered, much of colonial life seems to have its basis in stereotyped aspects of behavior which are seen to be fully developed in solitary insects but which have been adapted for the special needs of colonial life and for cohesiveness of the colony. But the physiological requirements and behavior patterns of the individual are not thereby abrogated. The parallelism between the "dancing" of the fly and the dancing of the honey bee is a case in point. The fly and the bee alike are moved to dance by an innate response to a taste stimulus. In both insects the intensity of the taste stimulus is modified by the individual's nutritional state (*16*).

References and Notes

1. This investigation was carried out with the aid of a grant from the Office of Naval Research.
2. V. G. Dethier, D. R. Evans, M. V. Rhoades, *Biol. Bull.* **111**: 204 1956.
3. D. R. Evans and V. G. Dethier, *J. Insect Physiol.*, in press.
4. D. M. Vowles, *J. Exptl. Biol.* **31**, 341 (1954); **31**, 356 (1954).
5. W. H. Thorpe, *Learning and Instinct in Animals* (Harvard Univ. Press, Cambridge, Mass., 1956), pp. 238–248.
6. G. Hein, *Experientia* **6**, 142 (1950).
7. P. Tschumi, *Schweiz. Bienenztg.* **73**, 129 (1950); E. E. Leppik, *Am. Bee J.* **93**, 434, 470 (1953); V. G. Milum, *Am. Bee J.* **95**, 97 (1955).
8. M. Lindauer, *Z. vergleich. Physiol.* **38**, 521 (1956).
9. K. von Frisch, *The Dancing Bees* (Methuen, London, 1953).
10. R. Boch, *Z. vergleich. Physiol.* **38**, 136 (1956).
11. R. Beutler, *Naturwissenschaften* **37**, 102 (1950).
12. H. Heran, *Z. vergleich. Physiol.* **38**, 168 (1956).
13. I. Khalifman, *Bees* (Foreign Languages Publishing House, Moscow, U.S.S.R., 1950).
14. R. Ribbands, *The Behavior and Social Life of Honeybees* (Bee Research Assoc., London, 1953).
15. M. Lindauer, *Z. vergleich. Physiol.* **31**, 348 (1949).
16. For additional information on the behavior of honey bees, the following should be consulted: C. G. Butler, *The World of the Honeybee* (Collins, London, 1954).

On Some New Habits and Their Propagation in Japanese Monkey Groups

Denzaburo Miyadi

Animal behaviors consist of those innate to a species as well as those learned during the individual life. The former (or the instincts) are hereditary and based on some physiological conditions corresponding to certain developmental stages of the animal, though their appearance is not always unconditional. The latter, or learned behavior types, are often acquisitions by trial and error and usually disappear with the death of individuals.

In a higher animal species whose social form is a permanent group, however, an acquired behavior of an individual may be imitated by other members to become a new habit of the group and be preserved independently of the individual life. Such an acquired behavior type is accepted by new-born animals without hesitation as if it were among their innate habits. Thus the behavior is beyond the individual level and may be said to have been socialized or to have reached the cultural level.

It is, however, not always easy to discriminate whether a certain behavior, of which all individuals of a group are possessed, is innate to an individual or encultured to a group. For the distinction, comparative studies of different groups of the same species or the record of the process of habit formation may be useful.

The members of the Research Group on Primates in Kyoto University as well as of Japan Monkey Center have found that there are differences in the habits of Japanese monkeys belonging to different groups. While monkeys of a certain group are indifferent to rice and soya-bean even when they pass through the footpaths between fields, those of other groups cause considerable damage to them. In most groups the mounting of a male on a female is a "taboo" except in their breeding season, but it is not so in all. The looking after of two-year-old babies by leader males is seldom seen in Japanese monkeys except by those of Mt. Takasaki Group, in which it is quite common after the birth of new babies. These differences in habits according to groups can hardly be assumed to be innate.

In recent years, we have succeeded in luring several monkey groups into artificial feeding places. At the begining, we met with resistance by monkeys to new food materials, but they became gradually enough accustomed to them to establish new food habits of the group. Now the new-born babies do not seem to distinguish artificial and natural foods. In this case, it is usually the baby that first tries to feed on the new food and the mother interferes with the adventure of her baby. Meanwhile, however, the mother imitates

Reproduced with permission from Proceedings, XV International Congress of Zoology, pp. 857–860, 1959.

her baby and the behavior propagates itself to other individuals who have intimate relationships with each other, until the whole group acquires a new habit. There are also personal influences on the formation of a new habit. While the first male of Mt. Takasaki Group is reluctant in trying new foods, that of Mt. Minoo Group is quick in learning and he is imitated by other members very soon. There are also differences in the kinds of food which are accepted by groups. For example, only raw monkey nuts are eaten in some groups and only parched ones in others; biscuit is food to none of Mt. Takasaki Group after six years of feeding, in contrast to Mt. Minoo Group where it is accepted by most monkeys. A young monkey of Mt. Takasaki Group, which was isolated from the group by capture, however, began to eat the biscuit within a day.

The established habits are handed down usually from mothers to babies or from elder monkeys to younger ones, but the reverse route is taken in the case of new habits.

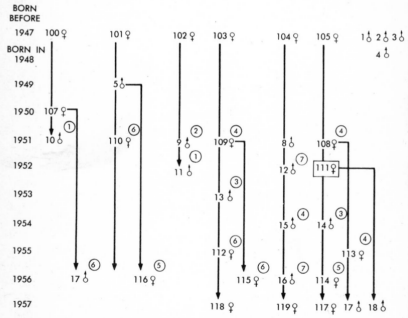

111 ♀ started the washing of sweet potatoes in 1953.
Numbers in circles show the order of propagation.
Solitary males as of January 1958 are shown by the symbol ♂
♀ Indicates death of the monkey.

Fig. 1. Lineage of the Kôsima Monkey Group, showing the propagation of sweet potato washing behavior.

In the Kôsima Island Group, we have discovered another kind of new habit, that is the washing of sweet potatoes before eating them. This processing method was first started in 1953 by a young female and was imitated by other monkeys in the order shown in the figure. It was first learned by her mother and playfellow, and then by her sisters and brothers. At present, many monkeys, especially the younger ones, show the same behavior, which is expected to become a new cultural habit of this group in the future. There seems, however, to be little chance of propagation of new habits from one group to another, except possibly by solitary males, because Japanese monkey societies are well closed to members of other groups.

The benefits of forming a group, for the individual life as well as the welfare of the species, are manifold. Among them may be counted the acquisition of new habits as a culture of the group. A list of vegetable foods in a certain monkey group may amount to more than two hundred, and it will be very difficult to test their edibility by individual experiences instead of by learning from the mother or other members of the group. The cultural acquisition of new habits by a group should be estimated as having an important meaning for the social evolution of higher animals.

Discussion

H. J. Coolidge: I wish to pay tribute to the splendid work now being carried out by the Japan Monkey Center. Since 1953 they have been carrying on studies of behavior in wild macaques. The sweet potato washing described by Dr. Miyadi has spread all over the small island where it was started. It will be interesting to know if, should one of these monkeys be moved to another population, it will teach them this potato washing. Possibly a day will come when this practice is current among all Japanese macaques that are not isolated from each other.

W. M. S. Russell: You have said that *new* habits are in general introduced by *young* monkeys. Do any individuals continue to show this inventiveness all their lives, as can happen in man?

D. Miyadi: I can only say that the inventiveness in monkeys is *more* remarkable in the younger ones than in the older ones.

M. R. A. Chance: How far were the sweet potatoes taken to be washed, and which monkeys started it?

D. Miyadi: Two-year-old females. They took them to sandy pits 50 meters away and to a river bank 30 meters distant.

Sir Solly Zuckerman: Professor Miyadi has discussed the changes in food habits which appear to occur in groups of monkeys living in unrestrained conditions. Since a great deal of control work has been done on food preferences in laboratory animals, and since I believe some of this work has also been done on monkeys, it would be interesting to know whether either he or any of his colleagues in Japan propose extending the naturalistic work he has described into the more experimental field, and particularly, to observe the food habits of monkeys under controlled conditions.

M. R. A. Chance: I am told a rhesus monkey in London had learnt to swim as the result of the lead given by a young animal.

Sir Solly Zuckerman: Did Dr. Chance himself observe the beginning of the swimming habit in the London colony of thesus monkeys?

M. R. A. Chance: No.

Index

Alces, sp. 93
Altmann, M., 93
Altruism, 207

Biston, sp. 169
Black-headed gull, 184
Brower, J. v. Z., 156
Busnel, R–G., 101

Camouflage, 169
Cervus, sp. 93
Cliff nesting, 42, 58
Communication, 210
Communication calls, 101
Corvus, sp. 101
Crows, 101
Cryptic coloration, 169

Dancing insects, 210
Density control, 112
Dethier, V. G., 210
Discrimination learning, 136

Early experience, 2
Elk, 93
Emlen, J. T., 58

Feeding behavior, 136
Frings, H. & M., 101

Galápagos mockingbird, 84
Galápagos swallow-tailed gull, 42
Genetic assimilation, 34
Giban, J., 101
Gramet, P., 101
Gulls, 101

Habitat imprinting, 33
Habitat selection, 1
Hailman, J. P., 42
Hamilton, W. D., 207
Hatch, J. J., 84
Herring gull, 58

Insect dances and communication, 210
Insect survival, 169

Jumber, J., 101
Juvenile ungulates, 93

Kettlewell, H.B.D., 169
Kittiwake, 42, 58
Klopfer, P. H., 136
Kluyver, H. N., 112
Kruuk, H., 184

Larus, sp. 42, 58, 101, 184

MacArthur, R. H., 75
Migrant birds, 75
Mimicry, 156
Miyadi, D., 224
Monkey feeding habits, 224
Moose, 93

Natural selection, 169
Nesominius, sp. 84

Parus, sp. 112
Peromyscus, sp. 2

Prairie deermouse, 2
Predators, 184
Primates, 224

Rissa, sp. 42, 58

Social behavior, 207
Social interactions, 93, 136
Starlings, 156
Sturnus, sp. 156

Territoriality, 84, 112
Tinbergen, L., 112
Titmice, 112
Traditions, 224

Wecker, S. C., 2